CW00734941

ABOUT THE AUTHOR

Michael Howard is author of *Wisdom of the Runes*. He is a well-known writer in the field of folklore and ancient mythologies and contributes regularly to *Prediction* magazine. He in a member of the Folklore Society and an acknowledged expert in the Anglo-Saxon Runes.

TRADITIONAL FOLK REMEDIES

A Comprehensive Herbal

Michael Howard

CENTURY

LONDON MELBOURNE AUCKLAND JOHANNESBURG

© Michael Howard 1987

First published in 1987 by Century Hutchinson Ltd,
Brookmount House, 62–65 Chandos Place, Covent Garden,
London WC2N 4NW

Century Hutchinson Australia Pty Ltd,
PO Box 496, 16–22 Church Street, Hawthorn, Victoria 3122,
Australia

Century Hutchinson New Zealand Ltd,
PO Box 40-086, Glenfield, Auckland 10,
New Zealand

Century Hutchinson South Africa Pty Ltd,
PO Box 337, Bergvlei, 2012 South Africa

Filmset by Deltatype Ltd, Ellesmere Port
Printed and bound in Great Britain by
The Guernsey Press Co. Ltd.,
Guernsey, Channel Islands

British Library Cataloguing in Publication Data

Howard, Michael, 1948–
 Traditional folk remedies: a comprehensive
 herbal.
 1. Herbs——Therapeutic use
 I. Title
 615′.321   RM666.H33

ISBN 0–7126–1731–0

For
LINDA
with love

Contents

Acknowledgements

I would like to thank the following who have been of valuable assistance in the preparation of this book; the staff of the Wellcome Institute for the History of Medicine; the staff of the British Library; the staff of Carmarthen Reference Library; the staff of the Westminster Reference Library; the staff of the Folklore Society Library; the staff of University College, London; the staff of the British Museum; Mrs May Griffiths of Carmarthen, Dyfed; Mrs Kathleen Warner of Halstead, Essex; Mr L.A. Marsh of Thorpe Bay, Essex; Mr L. Percival of Devizes, Wiltshire; A.L. Pickering of Holyhead, Anglesey; Mrs L. Sands of Hastings, East Sussex; Hilda Francis of Oswestry, Shropshire; Mrs S. Montgomery of Didcot, Oxfordshire; John Geddes of Stroud, Gloucestershire; Mrs N. Bate of Littleover, Derbyshire; Mrs S.D. Guyatt of Benfleet, Essex; Christine Webber of Cullompton, Devon; Mrs Morfydd Septima-Douse of Devizes, Wiltshire; J. Newcombe of Wellingborough, Northamptonshire; Tom Richards of Bury St Edmunds, Suffolk; Mrs J.G. Brooks of Chester; Miss J. Park-Robertson of Kirkcaldy, Fife; A. Akroyd of Huddersfield, West Yorkshire; J.R. Green of Abingdon, Oxfordshire; C. Hinton of Wanborough, Wiltshire; Mrs P. Lowe of Hillingdon, Greater London; Miss E.K. Caiger of Wallingford, Oxfordshire; Miss P. Patterson of Huddersfield, West Yorkshire; Sonia Lowrey of Trowbridge, Wiltshire; M. Heathorn of Clacton-on-Sea, Essex; Albert Simmonds of Elmswell, Suffolk; R.E. Newton of Rayleigh, Essex; E.J. Parminter of Aylesbury, Buckinghamshire; Hilda Eldred of Newport, Dyfed; and Mrs W. Stoner of Chippenham, Wiltshire.

Michael Howard
West Wales
1986

Part One

A Short History of Folk Healing

The history of folk medicine dates back many thousands of years; in fact, so closely linked are traditional folk practices and conventional medicine that until comparatively recent times it is difficult to distinguish between them. In the New Stone Age (c. 5000 BCE) early mankind was well aware of the medical use of a wide range of healing plants, and in 1963 archaeologists who opened the prehistoric grave of a man buried in a cave near Shedinar in Iraq uncovered evidence of the extent of this ancient knowledge. Scientific analysis of the dust in which the skeletal remains were found revealed that the corpse had been interred surrounded by flowers, which obviously had a religious significance. The flowers were all discovered to have had medicinal properties; the healing plants in this prehistoric grave included diuretics, emetics, astringents, stimulants and pain relievers.

In addition to traditional folk medicine based on healing plants, archaeological remains offer evidence of primitive types of surgery practised in Neolithic times. Saws made of flint, stone and bone have been unearthed from Neolithic burial places, and some skeletal remains dated from this period display signs of trepanning and the amputation of limbs; evidence of circumcision and ritual tattooing has also been found. Bronze Age (c. 2000 BCE) surgical saws and other medical tools have been identified by archaeologists examining graves of that period in both Europe and the Middle East. The use of naturally narcotic drugs such as opium, mandrake, hemlock and cocaine was also widespread in ancient cultures for medical purposes, and natural antiseptics such as honey, vinegar, salt and alcohol were commonly employed for cleaning open wounds.

This traditional knowledge of folk remedies survives today among traditional peoples, even when they are uprooted from their ancient homelands. In Brazil folk remedies based on herbal ingredients are still used extensively by the slum dwellers who have moved from the jungle to the outskirts of the cities. Dr Celerio Carriconde, an expert in the various different forms of alternative medicine who has spent many years in Uruguay, Chile, Panama and Brazil researching folk remedies, discovered that in rural areas of Panama honey was widely used as an antiseptic, especially during childbirth. Subsequent scientific research has proved that honey contains a bactericidal agent. It is evident from Dr Carriconde's research work that traditional folk medicine as practised by tribal and post-tribal communities produces results comparable to those obtained from the use of more conventional medical products.

The majority of cures achieved with folk medicine and folk remedies were based on natural extracts from well-known plants which the ancient peoples discovered, by trial and error, had the ability to heal various ailments. Before the invention of writing, knowledge about these plants was passed on orally, accompanied by semi-magical rituals within a religious context. This aura of mystery and magic was often deliberately culti-vated by the folk healers in ancient tribal communities; healing and folk medicine became an esoteric art practised by the priest or priestess and regarded as the gift of the gods. As religious consciousness became more sophisticated the healing arts became the specific province of gods and goddesses who ruled over this important aspect of human life; the priesthood who served these deities took the social role of healer and physician within the community by divine right. It was only gradually that this monopoly was breached through the use of simple folk remedies by ordinary people; but despite the spread of knowledge about folk medicine, the *modus operandi* of medical practice retained its atmosphere of religious sanctity, even though in later centuries this degenerated into superstition and half-remembered magical rites.

With the invention of writing, information on herbalism and folk remedies spread to a wider section of the community, although it was still limited to the social élite who could read and write. The first herbals on healing plants are from China, dated *c.* 3000 BCE; the Emperor Shen Nung (2737–2697 BCE) published a medical treatise listing over 260 medical prepa-rations based on herbs, and sixty years later the Emperor Huangh wrote what is now recognized as the first medical treatise listing diseases and their cures. The history of medical herbalism in China is a long one, and by 800 CE it is recorded that Chinese physicians had access to over eleven thousand different prescriptions. Standard medical textbooks were in wide circulation among the healing profession, and a highly organized system of medical practitioners existed.

In India the Hindu sacred book known as the *Rig Veda*, dating from 2000–1500 BCE, contains several references to physicians. At this time they were regarded as an unclean caste and were socially segregated; a possible reason was that their mission as healers brought them into daily contact with the lower levels of Indian society, who were much in need of their expertise. By the second and third centuries BCE medical support establishments similiar to modern hospitals had been set up by Buddhist monks throughout the Indian sub-continent. Chinese travellers in India during this period described them eloquently as 'houses of mercy for the sick', a description which suggests that some may have served as hospices for the terminally ill.

In addition to their herbal wisdom, Buddhist and Hindu physicians could also boast a knowledge of anatomy and surgical procedures which were not even to be achieved by many medieval doctors in Europe. From the ancient Indian medical treatises we know that their physicians divided the supra-orbital nerve for neuralgia, undertook laparotomy for intestinal obstruction and practised suture of the bowels for internal injury. Their knowledge of anatomy seems to have been based on dissection, for which purpose they used the bodies of children under two years of age who had died of natural causes. This age limit was imposed for religious reasons, for by Hindu custom anyone over that age was cremated after death.

It was not only in the ancient Far East that herbalism and folk medicine flourished. In a region of the Middle Eastern country of Mesopotamia which is now part of Syria, the Sumerians had developed sophisticated medical skills. In common with many ancient peoples they believed that disease was the physical manifestation of demonic possession and psychic attack. This is not really so bizarre as it first seems, for modern medical research is slowly proving that many illnesses are related to psychological states of mind and that their physical symptoms are merely a reflection of inner conflicts within the human psyche. The Sumerians believed, however, that these psychically induced complaints would respond to the healing balm of plants which grew prolifically in the area.

The earliest Sumerian medical herbals date from 2500 BCE, but it is possible even older versions exist which have not survived the ravages of time. The Assyrian civilization succeeded that of the Sumerians, in the same region, about a thousand years later. Tablets from the library of Ashurbanipal, King of Assyria between 662 and 626 BCE, reveal that at that period knowledge of herbs with healing abilities was considerable. Over two hundred and fifty natural drugs derived from local plants are described, which suggests that the propagation of medical plants had become a specialized undertaking. The Sumerians also possessed other advanced medical expertise, including surgical skill: they had, for example, some basic idea of urinology (examination of the urine for evidence of infections and diseases); this is shown by the title of one of their physicians – Asu, or 'one who knows water'.

It is difficult to say whether or not a knowledge of herbalism was a natural by-product of civilization in the Middle East, or whether it was imported from outside. In ancient Egypt the first historically recorded physician was Imhotep, allegedly the physician who served the Pharaoh Zoser in the Third Dynasty, c. 2980 BCE. As well as being a court physician, Imhotep was said to have been an astrologer, magician and psychic healer; after his death he was deified and entered the pantheon of Egyptian gods as the patron of medicine.

Several other ancient Egyptian gods and goddesses were also connected with the art of healing. The principal deity of healing was the lion-headed goddess Sekhmet, who in Egyptian mythology represented the creative force of the sun which has healing power. Her powers could, however, be double-edged, for Sekhmet was also credited with causing plagues. By a strange logic, because the goddess was supposed to be the originator of certain diseases it was also within her power to heal those afflicted with these maladies.

Another Egyptian god associated with healing was Set or Seth, the ass-headed brother of Isis and Osiris. His original role seems to have been as a guide to the dead, transporting them to the underworld. He was also the patron of the priests, whose task it was to embalm the dead and perform funeral rites. When Set's followers rebelled against the established priesthood of Isis and Osiris he was transformed into the personification of evil, and his previous divine duties as the helper of the dead were taken over by the jackal-headed god Anubis, son of Isis.

During the days of the Old Kingdom in Egypt the ibis-headed moon god Thoth or Tehuti was recognized as the patron of medicine. This connection lasted into Greco-Roman times, when Thoth's attributes were combined with those of the Greek god of healing, Hermes. According to ancient myth it was Thoth who discovered the medical properties of herbs, and he was said to be the author of the first herbals used by the priesthood.

Medical payri were the closely guarded property of the priesthood, who kept them locked away in the temples which no outsider dared enter. The earliest Egyptian herbal, said to date from 2800 BCE, records various herbs, aromatic gums and spices used for medical purposes; they included frankincense, cinnamon and cassia. It also contains recipes for herbal ointments manufactured by extracting the plant oil from selected herbs or by mixing them with castor oil. It would seem from the available archaeological evidence that around 2000 BCE spices, herbs and aromatics were imported into Egypt in large quantities from southern Arabia and the Far East. During this period the Phoenicians, a seafaring merchant race, regularly transported herbs and spices from the Middle East to barter for salt and tin in Spain and northern Europe.

The so-called Ebers Papyrus, discovered by G.M. Ebers in 1872 and allegedly written around 1500 BCE, contains a list of medical prescriptions with animal, vegetable and mineral ingredients. Each prescription includes details of the symptoms of the disease being treated and provides information on preparing and administering the cure. It is basically a herbal giving recipes and formulae for naturally derived medicines. The papyrus also contained invocations to the gods Ra, Isis and Horus, indicating the magico-religious element so important in Egyptian medicine. The ancient Egyptian healers and physicians were also magicians who were expert at exorcism and ritual; so entwined with healing were magical practices in Egypt during the rule of the Pharaohs that the folk charms and remedies which have survived there today still include prayers to the ancient gods and goddesses. In addition to herbal remedies the Egyptian physicians used charms, votive offerings, incantations, divination and religious ceremonial. In many cases supernatural origins were offered by the priesthood to explain medical conditions with which they were not familiar – rather than admit to their patients that they did not have all the answers the ancient Egyptian physician, like doctors throughout the ages, looked around for a scapegoat.

But Egyptian medicine should not be dismissed as mere superstition supported by a knowledge of medicinal plants. Physicians also carried out surgery, including circumcision. In the event of the death of the patient while being treated by a legitimate doctor, the latter could face the death penalty if found guilty of negligence. This sounds harsh, but the physician was protected: if after four days of the established medical procedure being carried out the patient showed no improvement, the physician was allowed to use alternative treatments. If, after all this, the patient still did not recover, the physician was absolved of all blame if the illness proved fatal.

Although there are numerous references to diseases in the Old Testament there seems little evidence of an organized class of physicians, folk healers or herbalists among the Hebrew tribes. In the New Testament, too, various diseases are mentioned, and one of the disciples who followed Jesus as he travelled the countryside preaching was Luke the physician. It can be surmised that by the time that Jesus began to preach his message to his fellow Jews, who were under Roman occupation, Greek culture, including the arts of the physician, had become widely diffused throughout Judea. Certainly Jesus can be regarded as a folk healer, in the widest possible sense, because he used his healing powers to help the country people. His healing ministry included exorcism to drive out evil spirits, and in that respect he had much in common with many other wandering holy men who preached radical forms of Judaism at the same time.

At the time of Jesus Greek medicine was highly developed. In ancient Greek mythology Aesculapius, or Asklepios, was traditionally the founder of medical practices. He was the god of healing who was taught the wisdom of herbs by the leader of the mythical centaurs, Chiron; in memory of this legend the term 'Chironic medicine' is sometimes given to herbalism and folk healing. In Greek mythology Aesculapius was the son born to the sun god, Apollo, and a mortal woman named Koronis. Apollo himself was said to be a god of healing, because of his solar attributes. His daughter Hygiea carried on the medical tradition, lending her name to the modern practice which is so essential in preventing the spread of infectious diseases. In common with his ancient Egyptian counterpart Imhotep, Aesculapius is said to have been originally a mortal, taught the medical arts from physicians in the Nile valley. He allegedly invented the surgical probe for the exploration of wounds, and introduced bandages and ligatures.

The Greek medical profession was organized into a separate caste or social class. They were paid an annual salary by the state, based on a municipal tax in what resembles a Greek national health service. Each physician was chosen by a public assembly, before which he had to appear and prove that he had the required practical skills to become a member of the profession. All physicians had an office in which they interviewed patients, prepared medicines and carried out operations. They employed medical assistants, who were themselves training to become doctors, and slaves who were only allowed to treat their own class. Religion still played an important role in Greek medicine, and it is recorded that before surgical operations the physician made invocations to the god Apollo.

Herbalism also featured in Greek medicine. The earliest Greek herbal was the *Codex Anicare Julianae*, which is preserved in the National Library of the Vatican. It is a sixth-century edition of a herbal written in the first century by the Greek herbalist Dioscorides. During the fourth century schools of medical science were founded, which attracted botanists and physicians from all over the Middle East. During this period of intense medical activity many new herbals were written and circulated among the healing profession.

Hippocrates, who gave his name to the ethical oath sworn by modern doctors, was one of the first Greek medical practitioners to have an impact on the healing arts. His writings included advice on diet and personal hygiene, and listed over four hundred herbal remedies for a variety of diseases. About a hundred years later another Greek physician, Theophratus, born 370 BCE, wrote his seminal work *The Enquiry into Plants*. This, the first attempt at a scientific method of botany describing common plants, was to prove very useful to medical herbalists who wanted to identify plants in their natural habitat.

It seems probable that the Romans were taught their herbal lore either from the Greeks, or from the Celts whom they conquered as they swept westwards across Europe. Pliny the Elder (*c.* 23–79 CE) was the most important writer on medical plants in ancient Roman times and devoted seven of the thirty-seven volumes of his *Historia Naturalis* to herbal lore. Unfortunately, despite its academic title Pliny's work contained fantastic details of plants and their attributes which were based only on popular superstition and folklore. For this reason it is of little use as a practical herbal, although this fact did not prevent medieval herbalists quoting from it frequently to support the medical claims for their products. Another herbal, written in 200 CE by the Greek Galen, was more accurate. He had travelled extensively and his books became the standard medical texts for Roman healers. Through their military campaigns in western Europe the Romans spread the use of Mediterranean herbs to this part of their empire. Roman officials planted herbs in their gardens which they brought from home, and many of these imported species began to grow in the wild. Fennel, dill, rosemary, savory, garlic, parsley, mustard, mint, thyme, hyssop and sage were all introduced into western and northern Europe during their occupation by the armies of imperial Rome.

Many of the sophisticated techniques employed by pagan medical practitioners were lost at the beginning of the Christian period, especially when the ancient libraries, repositories of pagan wisdom, were burnt to the ground. The collapse of the Roman Empire as a result of internal social disorder and uprisings among its conquered enemies, and the foundation of the Christian Church as the political force which replaced it, ushered in the historical period which we call the Dark Ages. During this time the scientific knowledge of the classical world, along with its major religious and philosophical teachings was rejected by the followers of the new faith.

But despite the Church's opposition to pagan medical practices there are many examples of ancient medicine being used in Teutonic and Anglo-Saxon society. The Roman historian Tacitus recorded in his book *Germania* that after a battle wounded German warriors sought out their wives and mothers, who sucked and licked the wounds. It is well known that human saliva has healing properties. In pagan Germany a special class of priestesses, known as the *Weise Frauen* or wise women, were credited with healing powers. In Scandinavia the established priesthood, known as *godi*, were often assisted by shamans, or *lahki*, who were skilled in the use of medical herbs and possessed supernatural powers to heal the sick. Shepherds, herdsmen and blacksmiths were also generally employed as healers, bonesetters and herbalists; they practised in remote rural areas where no *godi* or *lahki* was available.

Despite their conversion to Christianity, the Anglo-Saxons retained many of their pagan beliefs regarding the causes of disease. For their healing lore, the Saxon doctors drew on many sources of inspiration, including classical Greek medicine, Teutonic magic, Celtic beliefs, Roman herbalism and Byzantine occult philosophies. The combination of these different strands of knowledge comprised the Saxon art of leechcraft which was practised during the Dark Ages.

The folk healer or witch doctor in Saxon times was expected to be capable of treating a complex range of diseases and complaints. Established leech doctors were in fact practitioners of common folk medicine. They held a privileged position in Anglo-Saxon society, but were not easily identifiable because they had no particular distinguishing physical appearance or type of dress. High educational standards were not regarded as very important. Medical textbooks used by the folk doctors had been translated from Latin and Greek into Old English, so, providing they could read, the leech doctors had access to a considerable amount of information on herbs and folk remedies.

Although many of these herbals or leech books were based on early Greek, Roman and Arab treatises there is every indication that the Saxon doctors used indigenous healing practices which owed very little to external influences. The medical expertise gained by the leech doctors was passed on to their apprentices and eventually written down in the reference books consulted by literate folk healers. Evidence of any organized guild or professional body of folk medicine practitioners in Anglo-Saxon society is slim; nor does there seem to have been an established code of practice or ethical system, so obviously that was not one of the positive aspects borrowed from Greek medicine.

The collection of herbs and healing plants was accompanied by the chanting of prayers and magical incantations. Herbs were also gathered in strict accordance with the phases of the moon, a practice which survived into the Middle Ages and far later, when folk healers used occult wisdom in conjunction with herbal remedies. In medieval times the gathering of herbs at the correct astrological aspect was an important stage in folk magic rituals to heal the sick. Another Anglo-Saxon custom which has survived even today is the use of a natural measuring system which uses such phrases as 'a handful of elder flowers' or 'a pinch of caraway seeds' instead of the more scientific units of measurement. The practice of herbalism and folk remedies has always been regarded as an intuitive art – the healer works with nature to treat the mind, body and spirit of the patient.

One of the most famous folk magic charms used by Saxon leech doctors for healing combines occult lore with pagan mythology and herbalism and is known as *The Lay of the Nine Healing Herbs*:

> These nine attack
> against nine venoms
> a worm came creeping
> he tore asunder
> then took Woden
> nine magical twigs
> then smote the serpent
> that he in nine [pieces] dispersed
> Now these nine herbs have power
> against nine outcasts [unclean things]
> against nine venoms [poisons]
> against nine flying things
> [and have might] against the

loathed things
that over land rove
Against the red venom
Against the white venom
Against the blue venom
Against the yellow venom
Against the green venom
Against the dusky venom
Against the brown venom
Against the purple venom
Against the worm blast
Against the water blast
Against the thorn blast
Against the thistle blast
Against the ice blast
Against the venom blast
If only venom came flying from
the east or only from the south
over mankind
I alone know a running river
and the nine serpents behold [it]
All weels must now to herbs give
way
seas dissolve
all sea water
when I this venom
from thee blow.

This incantation contains a specific reference to the Germanic/Nordic Woden or Odin, the shamanic god who hung on the Cosmic World Tree for nine days and nine nights. As a result of this ordeal he received by divine inspiration the wisdom of the magical alphabet known as the Runes. The Saxons believed that Woden had the power to destroy the evil serpent which they believed was the originator of disease. Woden also features on a tenth-century manuscript written in Old High German which was found in Merseburg cathedral, Saxony, in Germany. Although written during a period when Christianity was the official religion, it contains open references to pagan gods indicating that the old ways still survived. The manuscript includes the following magical charm for a sprained ankle:

> Baldur and Woden
> fared to a wood
> there was Baldur's foal's foot
> sprained
> Then charmed Woden
> as well he knew
> for bone sprain
> for blood sprain
> for limb sprain
> bone to bone
> blood to blood
> limb to limb
> as though they were glued.

In Norse mythology Baldur was the beautiful young god of the sun who was killed through the trickery of Loki. In the transitional period between Christianity and paganism Baldur was often identified with Jesus, and this is confirmed by the following (Christianized) version of the magic charm quoted above.

> Our Lord rade [rode]
> his foal's foot slade
> down he lighted
> his foal's foot righted
> bone to bone
> sinew to sinew
> blood to blood
> flesh to flesh
> heal in the name
> of the Father, Son
> and Holy Ghost.

As mentioned earlier, the Anglo-Saxons relied heavily on herbal-based remedies in their medical cures. In addition to their native herbals the leech doctors also had access to translations of classical works, which included the *Herbarium Apuleii Platonici*, an original Latin herbal dating from the fifth century BC. The Saxon translation of this herbal, now preserved in the British Museum, dates from 1000 BC and belonged to the school of Aelfric at Canterbury in Kent.

The most famous native herbal of the period is *The Leech Book of Bald*, allegedly written by a physician named Bald who was closely associated with the court of King Alfred. In the herbal Bald refers to correspondence he has seen between Alfred and the King of Jerusalem on the subject of herbalism. The King sent Alfred a list of Syrian healing plants with their medical properties and prescriptions for their use. The herbal, of 109 leaves, was written in a large bold hand with one or two initial letters displayed in illuminated script. From its contents it can be concluded that Bald was a qualified physician with considerable medical knowledge; he refers to two other doctors, Dun and Oxa, who provided him with folk remedies that they used in their daily consultations. In medieval herbals of the fourteenth and fifteenth centuries the numbers of medically potent plants listed range from 150 to 350, whereas Anglo-Saxon herbals such as Bald's listed over five hundred.

The Saxons thought that many diseases were the work of fairies, elves and hobgoblins, a pagan belief which survived into medieval times when mental illness, for instance, was blamed on demonic possession. In *The Leech Book* the causes of many diseases are credited to the malicious actions of elves, who fired at human beings poisoned arrows – elf shot – which infected them. The concept of elves as understood by the Saxon and Germanic peoples was totally different from the gossamer-winged sprites of nursery fairy tales. The Saxon elves dwelt in the dark solitude of the forest wilderness and resented any intrusion by mankind. They were divided into two separate categories, the shining bright elves and the dark black elves. It was the latter who were held responsible for misfortune and illness; they could be kept under control only by the use of magic spells, charms and herbal remedies as presented in the Saxon medical texts used by the leech doctors.

One typical herbal recipe from *The Leech Book* is a salve to be used to ward off the elven race and nocturnal visions which cause nightmares. It was also allegedly used to help heal women who had been forced to perform sexual acts with the Devil! The recipe given by Bald is as follows:

Take the ewe hop plant, wormwood, Bishop wort, lupin, ashthroat, henbane, harewort, viper's bugloss, heatherberry plants, cropleek, garlic, grains of hedgerife, githrife and fennel. These herbs are to be put into a vessel and placed beneath the altar where nine masses are sung over them. They are then boiled in butter and in mutton fat, holy salt is added, the salve is strained through a cloth and what remains of the worts [herbs] is thrown into running water. The patient's feet, head and eyes are to be smeared with the ointment and he is to be censed with incense and signed over with the sign of the cross.

Today we recognize that nightmares, insomnia and disturbed sleep patterns are the symptoms of psychological disruptions in the human psyche. Within the context of Saxon leech lore the idea that they were caused by externalized spirit forces is just as valid.

Closely allied to elf shot was something called 'flying venom'. The various types of venom are listed in *The Lay of the Nine Herbs*, and were regarded by the Saxons as the agency through which diseases were passed from one person to another. According to Saxon medical opinion these venoms were carried by the wind and could be blown away by a magician or priest using incantations or a mixture of herbs, holy water and salt. This composition was sprinkled over the patient and the sickbed. Today we recognize in this ancient description of flying venom the phenomenon of disease-carrying bacteria.

One herbal folk remedy for the cure of the effects of flying venom reads:

Take a handful of hammerwort and a handful of camomile and a handful of waybroad [plantain] and roots of water dock. Seek which will float and add one eggshell full of honey, then take clean butter. Let him who will help to work up the salve melt it thrice. Let one sing a Mass over the worts [herbs] before they are put together and the salve is wrought up.

Closely interwoven elements of pagan belief and practice existed alongside the influence of Eastern and Christian religious ideas in Anglo-Saxon leech craft. They included the idea mentioned above, that some types of diseases such as mental illness, sexual perversion and epilepsy, were the result of the possession of the patient by demons or evil spirits. In such instances both exorcism by Christian priests and herbal remedies by leech doctors were employed in a joint effort to drive the occupying spirits from the body of the sick person.

In *The Leech Book* periwinkle and mandrake are singled out as plants with special powers to relieve demonic possession. In folk medicine mandrake has always been regarded as a plant with strange powers. According to medieval legends the mandrake screams when it is torn from the ground, and anyone who heard the noise was immediately struck dead. Because of this odd belief medieval herbalists employed specially trained dogs to uproot the mandrake so that they themselves escaped this terrible fate. While this folk tale sounds ludicrous, there may be an element of truth in it which has been sadly obscured by medieval superstition. Mandrakes do possess very long roots, and have been known to make a squeaking noise when they are pulled up. When periwinkle was used to cure possession by evil spirits it had to be gathered using a precise magical formula. It was picked 'when the moon is nine nights old and eleven nights old and thirteen nights and thirty nights and one night old'. Only plants collected in this way would be potent enough to exorcise demons successfully.

The Saxons grew some of the herbs they used in specially prepared herb gardens which they called *wyrtzerd*, but the majority were gathered from the wild. Herbal medicines were prepared by crushing the plants, using a pestle and mortar, and then adding them to ale, milk or vinegar. Potions were manufactured by mixing herbs with honey, and ointments were made by working herbs with butter. Herbal baths for curative purposes were also popular at this period – it was not until later that the medieval Church condemned bathing as a sin. Cosmetic recipes based on herbs were also included in the work books of the leech doctors. For sunburn it was recommended to 'boil in butter tender ivy twigs and smear therewith'. Another cosmetic preparation says 'that the body should be clean and glad and bright hue take oil and dregs of old wine equally, put them into a mortar and mingle well together and smear the body with this in the sun'.

Our Saxon ancestors also used herbs as a protection against the alleged powers of darkness, against being bitten by dogs and for safety from robbers. Herbs could be bound to different parts of the body – such as the forehead to cure head pains – by red threads, cords or wool. In Germanic mythology the colour red was sacred to the thunder god Thor, who was associated with healing and protection against evil. Red was also used in popular folklore to represent sexual energy, vitality and the life force.

In common with later medieval folk belief, the Saxons thought that disease could be transferred from the patient to inanimate objects by the use of simple magical acts. Using this process, for instance, diseases could be deflected into running water (which carried it away), or blood from an infected wound could be thrown across a wagon way or footpath. If a person was bitten by an insect or a rabid animal and the bite became infected, the practitioner of leech craft collected a few drops of blood from the wound. This was placed in a spoon made from green hazel wood. The leech doctor then went to the nearest wagon way and in complete silence threw the blood from the spoon across the path. It was believed that shortly afterwards the infection would vanish and the wound would begin to heal.

In the magic charm which was used when gathering periwinkle the number nine was prominent. It also features in *The Lay of the Nine Herbs* as a significant number with magical properties. Its use in Saxon and Teutonic folk remedies is connected with the fact that nine is a lunar number, representing the three phases of the moon multiplied by itself. In ancient magical rites of pre-Christian origin the moon was strongly featured as a symbol of the pagan Mother Goddess. The worship of this deity was a central act in the pagan Old Religion, which survived into the Middle Ages in a degenerate form under the guise of witchcraft.

The magical and pagan elements which formed such an important aspect of Saxon leech craft were regarded as quite natural by the ordinary country folk, but were not regarded with a similar degree of tolerance by the Church and its officials. Egbert, Archbishop of York, preached a sermon against the use of herbs for magical rituals, and even prohibited the harvesting of herbs if accompanied by the recitation of magical or pagan incantations – although he did add the provision that it was permitted if the end result was for 'Christian purposes', whatever they may have been. As early as 640 St Eligius had preached against herbalism in a general condemnation of the persistent survival of paganism in Saxon England.

> Ye shall observe none of the impious customs of the pagans neither sorceries, nor diviners, nor soothsayers or enchanters nor must you presume for any cause to enquire of them . . . let none regulate the beginning of any piece of work by the day or

the moon. Let none trust in or presume to invoke the names of demons neither Neptune or Orcus, nor Diana nor Minerva nor Geniscus nor any other such follies. Let no Christian place lights at the temples or the stones or at fountains or at trees or at places where three ways meet. Let none to presume to hang amulets on the necks of man or beast. *Let no one* make *lustrations nor enchant herbs* nor to make flocks pass through a willow tree or an aperture in the earth. For by doing so is to consecrate them to the Devil. Let none on the kalends of January join in the wickedness and ridiculous things, the dressing up like old women or like stags or make feasts lasting all night or keep up the practice of gifts or intemperate drinking. Let no one on the festival of St John [24 June] or any of the other festivals join in the dances or leaping or diabolical songs.

One of the many pagan incantations which upset the early Christians who converted the Saxons from their heathen ways was the following prayer to Mother Earth. In common with other pagan peoples the Saxons regarded the Earth as feminine and represented it in their mythology as a goddess. This prayer was commonly used in Anglo-Saxon times by the leech doctor and folk healer as they gathered herbs or prepared remedies.

Hear I beseech thee and be favourable to my prayer. Whatsoever herb thy power dost produce give I pray with goodwill to all nations to save them and grant me this my medicine. Come to me with thy powers and howsoever I may use them may I have good success and to whomsoever I may give them. Whatever thou does grant it may prosper to thee all things return. Those that rightly receive these herbs from me do make them whole. Goddess I beseech thee I pray thee as a supplicant that by thy majesty thou grant this to me. Now I make intercession to you all ye Powers and herbs and to your majesty ye who are Earth, parent of all produced and given as a medicine of health to all nations and hath put majesty upon you be I pray ye the greatest help to the human race. This I pray and beseech from you and be present here with your virtues for She who hath created you [the herb] hath herself promised that I may gather you into the goodwill of him whom the art of medicine was bestowed and grant for health's sake good medicine by grace of thy powers. I pray grant me through your virtues that whatsoever is wrought by me through you may in all its powers have a good and speedy effect and good success and that I may always be permitted with the favour of your majesty to gather you into my hands and to glean your fruits. So shall I give thanks to you in the home of that majesty which ordained your birth.

A similar magical incantation to a pagan goddess, which was evidently used by folk medicine practitioners dates from the twelfth century. A modern translation from Old English reads:

Holy Goddess Earth, parent of Nature, who dost generate all things and regenerate the world which thou alone sharest to the folk on earth. Thou guardian of heavens and sea and the arbiter of all the Gods by whose influence Nature is wrapt in silence and slumber thou art she who restoreth day and putteth the darkness to flight, who governest the shades of night in all security restraining at thy will the mighty Chaos, winds, rains and storms or letting them loose. Thou churnest the deep to foam and putteth the Sun to flight and arouseth the tempests. Or again at thy pleasure thou sendest forth the glad daylight. Thou givest us food in safety by a perpetual covenant and when our soul passeth away it is in thy bosom that we find our haven of rest. Thou too art called by the loving kindness of the Gods, the Great Mother who has conquered the God of mighty name. Thou art the force of nations and Mother of the Gods without whom nothing can be born or come to maturity. Mighty art thou Queen of the Gods! Thee O' goddess I adore in thy Godhead and on thy name do I call, vouchsafe now to fulfil my prayer and I will give thee thanks O' goddess with the faith that thou hast deserved. Hear I beseech thee and favour my prayers. Vouchsafe to me O' goddess that for which I now pray to thee grant freely to all nations upon Earth all herbs that thy majesty bringeth to life now suffer me thus to gather thy medicines. Come to me with thy healing powers. Grant a favourable issue to whatsoever I shall make from these herbs and may those thine to whom I shall administer the same. Prosper thou all thy gifts to us for to thee all things return. Let men take these herbs rightly at my hand. I beseech thee now O' goddess may thy gifts make them whole. I beseech thee that thy majesty may vouchsafe this boon.

The Church's reaction to this incantation can easily be imagined. The words explicitly invoke a pagan deity of feminine origin who is addressed as the creator and controller of the natural world, usurping the role of the Christian God as represented by the medieval clerical establishment. The use of this blatantly pagan prayer addressed to a supreme feminine principle as late as the twelfth century offers ample proof that the old ways were still actively followed and supported by ordinary people.

The knowledge of herbalism was strictly controlled by the Church during the European Dark Ages, but outside its repressive influence there was a considerable trade in its raw materials and in information on their use. Arab doctors, who had studied the great works of the Greek and Muslim physicians, made great advances in the study and practice of medicine during this period. A Persian doctor named Avicenna (980–1037 CE) wrote a treatise called *Canon Medicine* which became a standard medical textbook for Arab physicians. He had studied the properties of medicinal plants and learnt how to distil the essential oils from flowers and herbs.

At Salerno in Italy an advanced medical school was established which taught techniques based on the writings of the Greek medical profession. During the Crusades many wounded soldiers were evacuated from the Holy Land for medical treatment at this hospital. Nobles from all over Europe travelled to Salerno to pay large sums of money to receive the benefits of its medical facilities.

It was through Arab influence that Greek medicine and medical philosophy permeated European culture. In the twelfth century a group of translators became established in Toledo in Spain. They translated Arab medical books founded on Greek ideals into Latin, the universal language of medieval European academics. From Italy other sources of medical knowledge were becoming available through the writings of Constantine the African (1020–87), an Arabic-speaking Christian monk responsible for translating several important Arab medical books into Latin.

During the latter part of the Dark Ages and the early years of the medieval period the Church was gradually increasing in political power and began to persecute unofficial folk healers and herbalists. As mentioned earlier, even in its infancy the Church had felt strong enough to launch verbal attacks on the survival of paganism among the peasant population. In 314 the Synod of Ancyra had forbidden the practice of healing using occult powers. This prohibition was reinforced at the Synod of Laodicaea in 375 and reinforced by other Synods in the fifth, sixth and seventh centuries. The Church condemned all forms of healing the sick as the work of the Devil, and from the fourth to the twelfth centuries reigning popes issued decrees which prevented priests and nuns from studying medicine or administering to the sick except for the performance of the Last Rites. Despite this restriction, many clergy defied their papal leadership. In 1215 Pope Innocent III promulgated a decree which threatened to excommunicate any priest who dared to practise surgery.

This harsh attitude to medical practices gradually softened as the Church became more confident in its campaign to eradicate the surviving remnants of pagan belief in medieval Europe. In an amazing change of opinion the Church began to adopt the role of physician to its flock, using a bizarre mixture of approved magical practices and Christian theology. Pagan charms and prayers for the sick were Christianized, as we have seen, so that they could be used by priests, nuns and monks. The priesthood began to perform the laying on of hands and used exorcism rituals to drive out diseases. Patients were anointed with holy water and sacramental oil, and the cult of holy relics became popular. These were pieces of dirty rags or bones which were allegedly the mortal remains of saints and disciples. Kept locked inside clerical shrines, these relics were only exhibited in public for healing purposes or on special saints' days. Large sums of money were charged for the benefit of touching these objects. Considering the nature of these relics, many of which were blatantly faked, it seems likely that more disease was spread by their use than was ever cured. During the Middle Ages the use of relics to heal the sick became a money-making enterprise and led to many scandals within ecclesiastical circles.

Some positive results of the Church's new interest in healing were seen in the Middle Ages. The use of herbs was adopted on a large scale. Many monastery gardens boasted well-stocked herb plots, and rare plants were imported from the Mediterranean and Middle East to supplement the native varieties. The Benedictine monastic order in particular became renowned for its learning in the field of herbalism and folk medicine; its monks studied both Greek and Roman medical books in an attempt to augment the basic knowledge about medical matters which was then available. Medieval monasteries had attached to them infirmaries for the treatment of local sick people. These were the direct predecessors of modern hospitals such as St Thomas's in London. Each of these monastic infirmaries had an adjacent herb garden which would have contained such well-known plants as mustard, fennel, thyme, sage, rue, mint, parsley and pennyroyal.

Despite the fact that the Church had accepted medical practices it still regarded unorthodox practitioners operating outside its fold with a suspicion bordering on hostility. In the fourteenth century the papal authorities issued edicts against unauthorized healers including midwives, apothecaries and herbalists. In an attempt to curb the influence of rural healers in 1421 the Church prohibited women from practising medicine; if they refused to obey they were sent to prison. Pope Sixtus IV later condemned the practice of medicine by 'Jews and men and women who are not university graduates'. Even the most innocent attempt to help the sick was fraught with potential danger: in 1322 a woman was brought to court in Paris, charged with pretending to cure people of internal complaints, with treating abscesses and open wounds, and with 'examining the urine in the manner of a physician, feeling the pulse and touching the body and limbs'. Several prominent people appeared in her defence to testify that she had cured them of long-standing illnesses and one witness said that the woman had more medical knowledge than all the physicians in Paris.

When the Church began its horrific persecution of alleged witches in the late fifteenth century the position of the folk healer, herbalist and midwife became even more difficult. Anyone outside the Church who used charms or folk remedies to cure sickness became a target for the witch hunters. If found guilty, they faced long imprisonment or even death. The new laws condemning witchcraft had a dramatic effect on the practice of folk medicine: it was driven underground, and during the persecutions a considerable amount of herbal lore was lost.

In the *Mallues Maleficarum*, a guide prepared by two Dominican monks in 1486 for use by the judiciary who persecuted witches, a clear distinction was drawn between wicked and good charms – magical formulae which were the work of the Devil, and those which the Church accepted as legitimate expressions of the Christian faith, the belief in the Holy Trinity and the intercession of the saints. The book in fact recommended only the use of the Pater Noster (or Lord's Prayer) and the Ave Maria as safe charms to heal the sick. When witch hunting became a commercial business in the sixteenth and seventeenth centuries the demonologists who searched out suspects recommended burning herbs to ward off the evil spells of their quarry. Medieval theologians believed in a class of demons known as succubi and incubi, entities which appeared in human form and had sexual relations with their willing or unwilling victims. Church exorcists burnt herbal-based incense in bedrooms at night to prevent the amorous advances of these demons. This incense included such ingredients as sweet flag, ginger root, pepper, clove, cinnamon, mace, nutmeg, benzoin, resin, aloewood and sandalwood. According to one recipe, these raw materials were brewed in three and a half quarts of brandy and water. It is interesting to note that several of the herbs listed have alleged aphrodisiacal properties – a strange choice to ward off sexually aroused demons!

It was widely believed in the Middle Ages that witches had magical powers which enabled them to fly through the air. In some of the early witch trials alleged witches had claimed that they had flown to the Sabbat (the gatherings attended by covens of witches on the dates of old pagan festivals) with the aid of flying ointments made from herbal ingredients. When the Irish noblewoman Lady Alice Kyteler was accused of practising witchcraft in 1324 it was claimed that she possessed a staff 'on which she ambled and galloped through thick and thin when and what manner she listed after having greased it with ointment which was found in her possession'. Another account dates from 1435, when a woman charged as a witch said she rubbed herself with ointment and immediately fell asleep. She then had a dream in which she was flying to the Sabbat to cavort in front of the Devil with other members of her sisterhood.

Such stories led some authorities both within and outside the Church to dismiss the stories of witches flying on broomsticks as delusion. They believed that the narcotic materials in the herbs used for the witches' flying ointment entered the bloodstream of the anointed person, creating hallucinations. In the sixteenth century demonologists had sensationally claimed that the primary ingredient of the flying ointment was the fat of boiled children who had not been baptized. Such a ridiculous claim suggests a desperate attempt by the Church to encourage parents to baptize their offspring into the new faith at an early age, or face the horrific consequences of having them murdered by witches.

Francis Bacon quotes one recipe for flying ointment which contains 'the fat of children dug out of graves'; however he also lists several herbal raw materials, such as wolfbane and cinquefoil, which sound as if they might have been a genuine part of the recipe. Bacon voiced the opinion that the brew 'drugged the witches into delusions of flight'. This experience was, he claimed, caused not by incantations but by anointing themselves with the herbal ointment. Another person with scientific knowledge, Henry More, stated in 1653 that the use of the flying ointment by 'filling the pores keeps out the cold and keeps in the heat' which sounds a sensible conclusion. One active ingredient in the flying ointment was either bear or goose grease, which suggests that the witches used it to keep warm while performing naked outdoor rites.

Several folk recipes for witches' flying ointment have survived. Among the herbs used in their composition are aconite, which changes the rate of the heartbeat, and belladonna (deadly nightshade), which caused delirium. There are three typical recipes: parsley, water of aconite, poplar leaves and soot; water parsnip, sweet flag, cinquefoil, bat's blood, deadly nightshade and oil; baby's fat, juice of water parsnip, aconite, cinquefoil, deadly nightshade and soot. Bat's blood was obviously included because of that animal's ability to fly at high speeds and to sense in the dark. Soot was added presumably because it would make the witch less visible at night.

In 1545 André Lagina, the personal physician to Pope Julius III, was involved in the arrest of a couple accused of witchcraft in the French province of Lorraine. He discovered hidden in the couple's house a jar filled with green liquid, examination of which showed it to be composed of narcotic herbs such as hemlock, deadly nightshade, henbane and mandrake. Lagina tested the liquid on the wife of the local city hangman; on being anointed with the herbal brew, she fell into a deep sleep with her eyes open 'like a boiled hare'. The Pope's physician tried to wake her without any success, and she remained in a comatose condition for thirty-six hours. When she finally regained consciousness she was angry at the physician, for she told him he had taken her away from 'all the pleasures of the world'. Turning to her husband, she said, 'Knavish one, know that I have made you a cuckold, and with a lover younger and better than you.'

Modern authorities on witchcraft have attempted to test the authenticity of these medieval accounts of the flying ointment. In 1902 Karl Kieswetter, a German scholar fascinated by the occult, made a sample of the ointment using a traditional recipe. After rubbing it into his skin he fell asleep and dreamed he was flying through the air in a spiral motion. Another researcher, Gustav Schenk, experimented with henbane by burning the seeds and inhaling the resulting smoke. He reported feeling dizzy, had the feeling that his body was becoming lighter and that parts of his body, including his feet and head, were growing larger. As the intensity of the experience increased Schenk thought that his body was falling apart and felt the sensation of flying at high speed through the air.

One of the most interesting accounts of the witches' ointment was reported by Dr Erich Peuckert, a professor at Göttingen University, in 1960. Dr Peuckert had been studying psychic phenomena and the occult for over forty years and was fascinated by the folk tales of witches flying on broomsticks. In a book called *Magia Naturalis*, or *Natural Magic*, written by Johannes Baptisa Porta in 1568, he discovered a formula for the flying ointment which included thornapple, henbane and deadly nightshade. The original recipe called for baby fat, but the professor substituted ordinary lard from his local grocer. Dr Peuckert decided to experiment on himself and chose a close friend whom he could trust to be his assistant. At six o'clock one evening the two men retired to a private room in the university where they knew they would not be disturbed. They applied the ointment to their wrists and forehead, as suggested in the book. Within a few minutes they had fallen into a deep, trance-like sleep which lasted over twenty hours. When the doctor and his assistant awoke they had the symptoms of a severe alcoholic hangover including violent headaches, sore throats and dry mouths.

Independently, each wrote down a detailed account of his experiences while under the effect of the ointment, and then compared notes. Both men reported sensations of flying through the air, and both had visions of demonic faces. Dr Peuckert reported landing on a hilltop where he indulged in erotic rites with naked women and paid homage to a creature who looked like traditional representations of the Devil.

As a result of his experiment with the flying ointment, Dr Peuckert firmly believed that medieval witches really thought they had flown to the Sabbat and indulged in weird rites. The hallucinogenic nature of the herbs used in the salve, and the ignorance of the peasants, would have prevented them from distinguishing fact from fantasy. The majority of confessions obtained from alleged witches were based on evidence given under torture, which would have increased the sense of unreality.

According to the professor, the secret knowledge of hallucinogenic herbs may have been introduced into medieval Europe by the wandering bands of gypsies who originated in India. This knowledge was disseminated by groups of wise women, who had knowledge of herbs which could both cure and kill, and whose secret societies were the remnants of the matriarchal priestesshoods of the pagan Old Religion. Peuckert also believed that those who used the ointment reported similar experiences because the natural chemicals in the herbs stimulated areas of the brain responsible for creating access to atavistic racial memories of pagan rites.

The witch trials naturally concentrated on the more sensational aspects of the craft. Although the rural herbalists, folk healers and charmers were the targets, along with survivals of pagan customs and practices, at the height of the anti-witchcraft hysteria thousands of innocent people were murdered by the legal authorities. In 1592 a Catholic priest called Father Loos said, 'Wretched creatures are compelled by the severity of torture to confess things they have never done. By cruel butchery innocent lives are taken and by a new alchemy gold and silver are coined from human blood.'

By the early seventeenth century the charge of witchcraft was not only being made against the poorest and uneducated members of society but had extended to include the higher social levels. A canon of Trier cathedral in Germany reported that those burnt at the stake for the alleged practice of witchcraft included a judge, two burgomasters, several councillors and a parish priest. The executioner made so much money out of his bloody work that he rode around like a noble at court on a white horse and clad in gold and silver.

Despite the ferocity of the witch hunt the profession of herbalist and folk healer survived in rural areas of the English countryside. The persecution in England generally did not reach the same peak of hysteria as it had done on the Continent. Even so, during the period 1558 to 1736, when witchcraft ceased to be a major crime, it is estimated that at least 1800 people were executed as alleged witches. The peak period for the witch hunt in England seems to have been, predictably, during the puritanical times of the Commonwealth after the Civil War and, perhaps more surprisingly, during the reign of Queen Elizabeth I.

Each village had its wise man or woman who was skilled in the use of herbs and other forms of folk healing. Often the female wise women were also midwives and laid out the dead. In their role as local midwife they knew which herbs could be safely used as painkillers during childbirth. Ergot, a fungus derived from yeast, was used as a pain reliever at a time when clerics taught that the pain of childbirth was God's punishment on women for the original sin commited by Eve in the Garden of Eden. Wise women also used fresh dung to treat open wounds. Initially our modern reaction to this drastic treatment might be one of horror and disgust, until we consider that both dung and spider's webs, also used to cover wounds, are natural sources of penicillin. They also used willow bark to cure headaches, several hundred years before doctors discovered that it contains the natural source for the ingredients of the modern aspirin. While physicians were still prescribing blood letting and magical charms for curing the sick, the rural wise women had developed an extensive knowledge of herbal remedies and natural drugs which they used to alleviate the misery of many otherwise incurable diseases.

Evidence that the herbal remedies of the country folk healers were not just superstitious mumbo-jumbo is offered by the true story of Dr William Withering (1741–99), who discovered the cardiac stimulant known as digoxin. The doctor found out that the local people in rural Shropshire often preferred to consult wise women who offered folk remedies rather than visit his surgery. One old lady was universally renowned for a herbal tonic she brewed, which had proved successful on many occasions for treating heart conditions. Dr Withering visited the witch and, after lengthy negotiations, purchased the recipe for her miracle cure. When he analyzed the remedy he found that it contained foxgloves or digitalis – the origin of the modern drug digoxin. In his book *An Account of the Foxglove* Withering stated that he had identified twenty different herbs in the potion, but foxglove was the most potent of them all.

The wise women and folk healers also recommended the chewing of raspberry leaves or the drinking of raspberry tea for period pains and childbirth. Modern scientific tests have proved that the leaves of the raspberry plant contain a natural substance which relaxes the uterus. The white witches, as these benign witches were called, also used nettles as a blood purifier. Today it has been discovered that the nettle plant contains a large concentration of vitamin K, which helps to prevent excessive bleeding.

Village wise women were frequently the only people to whom the sick could turn in time of need. In 1552 Bishop Latimer stated: 'When we are in trouble or sickness or lose anything we run hither and thither to witches and sorcerers whom we call wise men seeking aid and comfort at their hands.' Such learned men as Elias Ashmole, founder of the Ashmolean Library at Oxford, and the famous diarist Samuel Pepys believed in the efficaciousness of magical spells to cure illness. Ashmole wore three dried spiders to ward off attacks of the ague, and Pepys always carried a hare's foot around his neck to prevent colic. Most of the popular healing charms used in the sixteenth and seventeenth centuries to cure various diseases were based on Christian prayers, mixed with Hebrew incantations borrowed from the Jewish mystical tradition known as the Cabbala and the grimoires, or grammars, of medieval magic. Other magical charms from this period can be directly traced back to the Anglo-Saxon leech books.

As mentioned earlier, it was still a widely accepted belief among some rural folk healers that many illnesses were caused by the malicious influence of ghosts, black witches and fairies. In some cases the so-called cunningmen were also witchfinders, who would seek out some harmless old woman and accuse her of bewitching their patients. Such anti-social reactions were a direct result of the Church's propaganda relating to the activities of witches in rural communities, accusing them of bewitching livestock and ruining crops with their spells.

Other folk healers actually practised witchcraft as defined in the narrow sense by the Church and the legal officers responsible for justice in country areas. Joan Warden was accused of practising the craft in 1592 merely because she 'not only used charms but doth use ointments and herbes to cure divers diseases'. A Yorkshire woman called Alice Morton was brought to trial for practising witchcraft because she admitted curing cattle with remedies; she denied, however, that she ever cast spells on them to make the animals recover. A woman arraigned before a court in Aldeburgh, Suffolk, in 1597 was said to 'take upon herself to cure diseases by prayer and therefore have recourse of people to far and wide'.

During the sixteenth, seventeenth and eighteenth centuries the wise woman had an important role to play in village society. As well as the folk healers who specialized in herbal remedies, every housewife was expected to have some knowledge of natural treatments for common ailments. An old book dated from the early eighteenth century, when witch hysteria had abated, states that the housekeeper should have 'a competent knowledge of physick that they be able to help their maimed, sick and indigent neighbours for commonly all good and charitable ladies make this a part of their housekeeper's business'.

This social responsibility to act as a healer to the local community was not restricted to servants. Wealthy and aristocratic women were widely expected to learn the use of folk remedies to help those less fortunate than themselves. According to one eighteenth-century writer, a wealthy woman should help her neighbours who are too poor to purchase the assistance of a physician. Those who did not have access to a gentlewoman with healing skills relied on the services of the traditional practitioner of folk medicine. One writer referred to these wise women in the following terms: 'I do not mean to speak of the old woman at [Stoke] Newington beyond St George's Fields unto all the people resort as an oracle, neither will I speak of the woman on the Bankside who is as cunning as the house of cross keys nor yet of the cunning woman in Seacole Lane who have more skill on her cole basket than judgement in urine and knowledge in physic and surgery'.

In the medieval period the practice of medicine, by both orthodox physicians and the village wise men and women, was inextricably linked with magical practices and occultism. Towards the close of the Middle Ages one of the leading proponents of the magico-occult approach to treating disease was Phillipus von Hohenheim (1493–1541), popularly known as Paracelsus. He was not only widely versed in occult lore but was also one of the most enlightened medical exponents of his age. Born at Enseiden in Switzerland, he was the son of an eminent medical student who had become a practising doctor at Villach in Austria. When Paracelsus was a young boy his father often took him on expeditions to the Alps to locate rare herbs which were used for medicinal purposes. The impact of these field trips caused the boy to study medicine as a young man, and in 1515 he received his doctorate in medical science at the famous school for physicians at Ferrara in Italy.

Paracelsus had always been interested in the hidden side of life, and this now led him to study the occult; he pursued his lust for knowledge in that area by adopting a nomadic lifestyle and wandering around Spain, Italy, Greece, Sicily and Russia. In each place he discovered further information about medical practices, with which he complemented the techniques he had learnt at Ferrara. He also studied at many of the leading European universities, published books and exchanged ideas with the most learned men of his time. As well as developing contacts with the highest levels of the academic world Paracelsus delved into the underworld of witches, gypsies, folk healers and herbalists. From these people he discovered the secrets of herbal cures, folk charms, magical rites and such occult arts as palmistry and the tarot.

Paracelsus became convinced that diseases originated in the three substances which the alchemists believed formed the material universe, and which were symbolized on the physical level as salt, sulphur and mercury; in occult terms they represented the mind, body and spirit. If these three aspects of a person are in perfect harmony with each other, then Paracelsus believed that no disharmony or dis-ease could exist. If the three aspects are not balanced, which is frequently the case, then disease manifested itself in the physical body as a direct result of this imbalance. This concept may have seemed far-fetched in the sixteenth century, but today it forms the basis of holistic medicine, including herbalism, which is gradually becoming more acceptable. Even orthodox members of the medical profession have now recognized the link between mental attitudes and common illnesses such as cancer, asthma, heart disease, influenza and stress.

Within the three kingdoms or realms represented by salt, sulphur and mercury Paracelsus identified five causes of disease. He categorized these as, firstly, those from the *Ens Astrale* or created by causes in external nature (environmental factors); secondly, those from the *Ens Veneri* or poisons and impurities (pollution); thirdly, those from the *Ens Naturae* or causes derived from the parents (hereditary diseases and genetic disorders); fourthly, *Ens Spirituale* or those caused by morbid imaginings or evil will (psychological states); and, lastly, *Ens Dei* or those created by the will of God, which could be a legacy from previous existences experienced by the human soul and manifested in this life as a form of divine justice (karmic disease).

One of the most interesting aspects of Paracelsus's definition of disease and its origins is the category known as *Ens Veneri*. He believed that if anything entered the constitution of a human being which was not in harmony with his or her elements 'the one is to another an impurity and can become a poison'. While orthodox medicine tends to deal only with external affects and physical causes, the type of esoteric or occult medicine practised by Paracelsus and many folk healers searched for the fundamental effects which were the cause of the physical symptoms.

As an example of this process at work, according to the theories of Paracelsus promiscuous sexual activity not only increased the risk of sexually transmitted diseases but could also have psychological complications. A person who indulged in physical relations with a sexually deviant man or woman could, according to Paracelsus, be affected with both mental and spiritual malaise. He believed that during the act of sexual intercourse the spirit essence of the partners blended. Any form of sexual act with another person creates a transference of emotional, mental and spiritual energy, which, depending upon the circumstances, can have either a beneficial or a malefic effect on the partners in the act. Sex can therefore be a mystical healing experience or exactly the opposite. It is the difference between established partners making love and the sexual violence between a rapist and his victim.

Paracelsus also believed that changes in the phases of the moon, the influence of the planets and their movements and differences in climatic conditions and atmospheric pressure could have an affect on human wellbeing. He supported the occult doctrine that mankind is a microcosm within a macro-cosm – a tiny replica of the universe. Physical changes in material conditions could therefore have an adverse effect on human health. If he were alive today, Paracelsus would have no difficulty in accepting the modern idea that negative and positive ions in the atmosphere can effect human behaviour; he would also have accepted the recent theory put forward by scientists that comets could be responsible for the outbreak of virus infections on Earth. Paracelsus also taught that thought transference was taking place all the time between people who lived or worked in close proximity. Because of this he claimed that some diseases, especially those of a psychological or psychosomatic nature, could be transmitted from one person to another purely on a mental level.

Controversy naturally surrounded Paracelsus wherever he went. His claim that astrology could be used as a diagnostic tool in medicine was ridiculed by the new breed of physicians who wanted to divorce medical matters from what they regarded as medieval superstition. Paracelsus's friends, the witches, gypsies and folk healers, had taught him the assignation of the zodiac signs to the anatomy of the human body; they had also instructed him in the manner by which various diseases could afflict a person if certain planets were badly aspected in their natal horoscope. To diagnose illness Paracelsus utilized, too, the occult arts of physiognomy (the study of character defects by the features of the face or the form of the body) and cheiromancy (examination of the lines in the palm of the hand). These aspects of occult wisdom were denounced in the sixteenth century as sorcery, but he insisted that by studying lines of illness in the face or discoloured patches of skin he could identify the nature of the illness affecting his patient and prescribe the required course of treatment.

Paracelsus was a pioneer in the field of sixteenth century medicine who sadly was not recognized by his medical contemporaries. He realized that the mentally ill were not sinners possessed by demons but very sick people in desperate need of specialized treatment. He studied the links between disease and the environment of the patient, which had received medical prominence only in recent times. He noted, for instance, that miners often suffered from bronchial problems, and traced this directly back to daily contact with coal dust. He also advocated sunlight, fresh air and frequent baths to speed recovery from long illnesses – this was at a time when sick people were locked away in darkened rooms on the orders of orthodox physicians.

This radical doctor laid down stringent rules which dictated the criteria by which a genuine medical practitioner should be judged – rules designed to cleanse the profession of the many charlatans and quacks who preyed on the gullible, extorting large sums of money from the wealthy for their cranky treatments which were often highly dangerous. In the wise words of Paracelsus, 'A good physician should possess a clear conscience, a gentle heart and cheerful spirit. He should lead a moral life and have a greater regard for honour than for riches. In all matters he should seek to be more useful to the patient than himself.'

Against a background of general ignorance in medical matters in the sixteenth century Paracelsus stands out as a liberal influence seeking to revolutionize the treatment of disease and the relationship between the doctor and his patients. Naturally enough, these enlightened views were not widely accepted, and Paracelsus was criticized by both the orthodox medical community and the fraternity of charlatans who saw in his radical proposals a threat to their income. In desperation at the frequent and savage attacks on his character he once remarked bitterly, 'This pack of mad dogs which attacks me is so large but its understanding is so small.' At one stage the persecution became so concentrated that Paracelsus was forced to walk the streets as a beggar in order to escape physical attack. He clothed himself in rags, slept in ditches and survived on scraps of food donated by charitable passers-by.

While Paracelsus was a compulsive traveller who seldom stayed in one place for more than a few years before moving on, he did manage to find time to write several very important books. His most famous medical works consist of eleven treatises on well-known diseases such as tuberculosis, colic and worms; despite the general opposition to his occult theories, these books became standard reading for sixteenth-century physicians. In addition to medical books he also penned philosophical works including *De Generatione Hominis* or *The Origins of Man*, which dealt with his personal theory of cosmology, and *De Vita Longa*, on hermetic alchemy.

Despite his study of the occult Paracelsus was conventionally a very religious person and remained a practising Catholic throughout his life. He did, however, draw philosophical inspiration from the semi-pagan Gnostics of the early Church, the ancient Greeks and the medieval Jewish Cabbalists. He told his pupils that if they wished to study the inner life of humanity they must learn to examine the foundation of nature as expressed through the teachings of the Cabbalistic mystics. He argued that the Cabbala embraced the ancient occult sciences of astrology, alchemy and mysticism, which the discerning student could use to unravel the spiritual side of reality through their symbolic interpretations. Anticipating Jungian psychology, Paracelsus taught that any disturbance experienced by the inner self created psychic ripples which were the root cause of physical illness.

Because of his investigation into the psychic realms and the occult, Paracelsus was the subject of persecution by the Church despite the fact that he was a dedicated Catholic. He was accused of signing a pact with the Devil in exchange for forbidden knowledge; in the sixteenth and seventeenth centuries this was a common form of slander used against original thinkers who advocated anti-Establishment or anti-clerical ideas which did not meet with the approval of the Pope.

It was hoped that by labelling a person as a devil worshipper he would be made a social outcast by his peers and be unable to propagate his radical ideas. The Church capitalized on the fact that Paracelsus had studied alchemy, the art of transforming lead into gold – which was an occult metaphor for the transformation of matter into spirit – by claiming that he had bargained the so-called elixir of life from the Devil. This elixir had allegedly granted the Swiss physician the gift of immortality, a nonsensical claim disproved when Paracelsus died at Salzburg in 1541. Even after his death the legend of the magical powers which Paracelsus was supposed to have possessed during his lifetime persisted. When bubonic plague swept through Salzburg it was reported that hundreds of people knelt at the doctor's tomb, praying for a cure.

Paracelsus was not alone in seeking advice or inspiration from the rural herbalists and folk healers. Orthodox physicians who had been using herbs for centuries had learnt their craft from the village wise men and women and put it into practice in the cities. During the medieval period the first herbals published since the Anglo-Saxon leech books began to appear in limited editions. The first major work in English on botanical medicine was the *Rosa Medicinae* or *Rosa Anglica*, written in the fourteenth century by a monk called John of Gaddesden. It was based on Greek, Arabic, Jewish and Saxon sources, but also included original data collected by the author.

The invention of printing in the late fifteenth century provided access to a considerable amount of new information on herbalism which boosted its study despite the disapproval of the Church. By the beginning of the sixteenth century many original works were being produced, with printed illustrations of all the plants listed. The first authentic printed herbal is believed to have been written by John Banckes in 1525. In 1550 an English physician named Anthony Askham published an enlarged edition of the Banckes herbal and attributed the actions of herbs to astrological correspondences. The most influential of these early printed herbals was *The New Herball*, written by William Turner and published in 1551; it was based on Turner's travels around Europe studying botany, and the cultivation of herbs in his garden at Kew. John Gerard's three-volume *Herball*, published in 1597, became one of the standard reference works of the period. Born in 1542, Gerard was head gardener to the influential Cecil family during the reign of Elizabeth I. He was also a member of the Company of Barber Surgeons in the City of London; in those days barbers were also surgeons and bloodletters – they gave enemas, performed amputations and extracted teeth. The traditional red and white striped pole which used to be a feature outside old-fashioned barber's shops was a reminder of their original duties.

Gerard's herbal is still in print today, and another reference book on herbalism which has survived the passing of time is the one written by Nicholas Culpeper (1616–54). The son of a clergyman, while still very young Culpeper acquired a considerable knowledge of Latin and Greek. At the age of eighteen he went to Cambridge, and while at the university fell in love with a young heiress. Culpeper persuaded her to elope with him, and they planned to get married in the Sussex town of Lewes. They travelled to their secret destination separately, but the young woman's coach was struck by lightning during a fierce thunderstorm and she was killed instantly. This tragic event completely shattered Culpeper's life. He abandoned his studies at Cambridge and became an apprentice apothecary in St Helens, Bishopsgate in the City of London. After a very short time the brilliant student, still only twenty-four, began his own practice as a medical herbalist in Red Lion Street, Spitalfields. The same year he married Alice Field, a girl of fifteen with a large fortune. His career in Spitalfields was disrupted by the Civil War, during which he fought on the Royalist side and was wounded in the chest by a musket ball. This injury was to lead to tuberculosis, which eventually caused his early death.

As an apothecary and medical herbalist Culpeper was very unorthodox in comparison to other physicians of the period. His strong belief in astrology drew ridicule from his medical contemporaries, who thought that Culpeper was following the example of the rural folk healers. Although he expressed an interest in occult matters, Culpeper made a considerable contribution to the advancement of medical expertise. During his comparatively short career as a physician he had privately printed many tracts on medicine. Although condemned by his critics, they sold well to the general public and helped to dispel some of the ignorance about medical matters which existed in the popular mind. In contrast to the bigoted attitude of his contemporaries, the public recognized in Culpeper a person who was not afraid to be outspoken and who was willing to court unpopularity from his peers for the benefit of the common people.

In 1649 Culpeper translated *The Pharmacopoeia*, the standard reference book in Latin for apothecaries issued by the College of Physicians, and published it, with his critical comments, as *A Physicall Directory*. Culpeper's motive in providing this translation was his personal conviction that medical information should be freely available and not restricted to the upper-class élite. The reaction from his colleagues in the medical profession was swift and predictably virulent: they resented any attempt to remove the aura of mystery which obscured medicine from the masses. The publisher, on the other hand, was very pleased with the venture, for it became a minor bestseller. Culpeper was encouraged to write more books, and the one which gained him the most success was *The English Physician*, published in 1652, two years before his death.

He will always be remembered, however, not for the scholarly textbooks he wrote on conventional medicine but for his famed *Herball*, which in 1986 is still in print in a popular edition. Subtitled 'A compleat physick whereby a man may preserve his body in health and cure himself being sick for three pence charge with such things as grow in England, they being most fit for English bodies', it lists over four hundred different common plants with medicinal uses giving their description, healing actions, astrological correspondences and recipes for their use to cure illness. It is truly a phenomenal work which, although heavily criticized for its superstitious content, has proved invaluable to generations of herbalists and their patients. Orthodox physicians who were incensed by the publication of the *Herball* denounced it as having been produced 'very filthily by two years drunken labour corrupting men's minds with his opinions beside the danger of poisoning men's bodies'. The fact that it is still being consulted today by many herbalists and folk healers offers proof that this statement is untrue.

Originally, apothecaries like Nicholas Culpeper were merely peddlers of drugs which they purchased from others. Gradually, however, the apothecaries became skilled in the preparation and use of natural drugs. The term 'apothecary' comes from a Greek word meaning 'storehouse', and in Roman times an *apotheca* was a place where medicinal herbs were stored. The title of apothecary was given to the keepers of these stores. Many royal palaces and noble households in the Middle Ages had a resident herbalist, who was first known as the spicer or pepperer but later adopted the title of apothecary; his job was to administer the herbs, spices and perfumes used in the household. In fact the office of court apothecary had an unbroken history from early medieval times – the court records of 1313 mention one Odin the Spicer, who was in the pay of King Edward II. He was paid 7½*d* a day to be apothecary to the Queen. Early apothecaries obviously had other royal duties, for in 1329 one was paid to embalm the body of Robert the Bruce. The earliest English reference to an apothecary is in 1180, when one accompanied King Henry II to Ireland. Another apothecary was mayor of York in 1213, and in the same city in 1292 an apothecary was established called Otto the German.

In the fifteenth century the apothecaries became associated with the Grocers' Company in the City of London, which was a medieval guild. The guilds had been set up as early trade unions to protect the legal rights of various types of tradespeople, craftsmen and artisans. Apothecaries were also usually members of the College of Physicians, which had been founded in 1518 by royal charter. The College insisted that no medical practitioner within London and seven miles around could practise unless he had been examined and approved by the Bishop of London or the Dean of St Paul's.

The apothecaries usually purchased their herbal raw materials from the so-called 'Green Men' or 'Green Women', rural folk healers who wandered the countryside collecting herbs for use in remedies. Eventually many apothecaries established their own herb gardens in the towns and cities to grow supplies of medicinal plants. Orthodox physicians disapproved of the contact between apothecaries and the exponents of traditional folk medicine, and in 1540 an Act was passed giving the College of Physicians the legal right to enter an apothecary's shop, examine his wares and, if they considered them unsafe, have them destroyed. By the late sixteenth century the apothecaries had ended their association with the Grocer's Company and formulated plans to establish a separate guild in the City of London which would be responsible for their interests. In 1617 the Worshipful Society of Apothecaries of London was founded, with an initial membership of 114. At the same time an Act of Parliament was passed forbidding grocers and surgeons to prepare or sell medicines. Among established medical practitioners the apothecaries therefore now possessed a monopoly for supplying herbal remedies and medical drugs.

These seventeenth-century apothecaries were the lineal descendants of the old herbalists of the Middle Ages and, through their contact with the rural-based healers, preserved many of the tenets and practices of folk medicine. Their reason for leaving the Grocers' Company was the widespread malpractice which permeated orthodox medical treatments at this time. In the opinion of the new apothecaries' guild,

> unskillful and ignorant men do abide in the City of London which are not well instructed in the art or mystery of Apothecaries but do make and compound many unwholesome, harmful and deceitful, corrupt and dangerous medicines and the same do sell and daily transmit to the great peril and daily hazard of the lives of our subjects. We therefore weighing with ourselves how to prevent the endeavours of such wicked persons thought necessary to disunite and disassociate the apothecaries of the City of London from the freemen of the Mystery of Grocers into one body corporate and politic to whom in all future times the management of these inconveniences might be given in charge and commited after the manner of other companies.

This breakaway movement by the apothecaries was deeply resented by the Grocers, who rejected the charges of misconduct made against them and sought to restrict the new company. However, James I interceded on behalf of the apothecaries and granted their society a royal charter which effectively established them in the City as a respected guild with equal rights to all the others. In response to the granting of the King's charter the apothecaries insisted on strict membership qualifications to deter charlatanism; they even seized dangerous drugs or fraudulent medical products which they saw offered for sale and had them destroyed. It was recorded that one persistent offender was fined the sum of £6 13s 4d for selling 'bad drugs' called 'Methridatic' and 'London Treacle'. Such products were usually burnt in public before the door of the offender.

One of the leading members of the Society of Apothecaries was Thomas Johnson, who was responsible for producing an enlarged edition of Gerard's *Herball* and presented the Society with a copy for its library. Johnson is also said to have been the first person to bring bananas to London. To the amazement of passers-by, he displayed a bunch of these tropical fruits in his shop window on 10 April 1633. Johnson had obtained them from his friend Dr Argent, President of the College of Physicians, who had brought them back from a trip to the West Indies. It was Johnson who introduced the Society to the idea of field trips into the countryside around London to the then rural hamlets of Piccadilly and Islington, to Hampstead Heath and Kent, to gather wild flowers and herbs with healing powers.

From the late 1600s to about 1750 the role of the apothecary as a professional medical practitioner gradually increased. The day book of an unnamed apothecary in Shrewsbury, dated 1706, relates that he sold over the counter to casual customers an assortment of gargles, mixtures, ointments and patent medicines made from herbal ingredients. He also supplied essential oils, gums, spices, resins, chemicals such as saltpetre and borax, soap, brushes, varnish, ink and pencils. In addition to herbal remedies some apothecaries sold coffee, tea, candied oranges and lemons, jam and biscuits, reflecting their earlier membership of the Company of Grocers.

The medical ingredients offered in the *London Pharmacopoeia*, which were available to physicians at this time, make an interesting comparison with the naturally based products sold by the apothecaries. The *Pharmacopoeia* listed nearly two thousand remedies in common use, whose ingredients included dried worms, fox lungs, oil of ants, live frogs, moss from the skull of a murder victim, crabs' claws, saliva from a fasting man, human placenta, snakeskin, swallows' nests, woodlice and the powdered bones of an executed criminal.

In 1673 the Society of Apothecaries had rented from Lord
Cheyne four acres of land by the Thames at Chelsea. A full-time
gardener was employed in the new garden and plants were
transferred from the already well-established Westminster
Herb Garden. The garden in Chelsea was walled, and Lebanon
cedars were planted for the first time in Britain at the gate
nearest the river. During the next two hundred years the
Chelsea Physic Garden, as it came to be known, became famous
as the repository of herbs from the English countryside and
more exotic plants from overseas. The garden created by the
seventeenth-century apothecaries is still in existence, and every
year is visited by over three thousand botanists and herbalists
from all over the world.

During the three hundred years when the apothecaries were
establishing their role as the forerunners of nineteenth and
twentieth-century doctors the country folk still relied on the
skills of the village wise men and women when they fell ill.
Their use of traditional folk remedies brought them into
conflict with those who held orthodox views. Midwives, who
were often also folk healers who used herbal preparations, were
especially singled out. In the sixteenth century the Church had
persuaded Parliament to rule that all midwives had to be
licensed by their local bishop before they could practise. It also
prohibited the use of magical charms, prayers and incantations.
Midwives had traditionally also christened babies, but the
Church ruled that they should only use plain water as opposed
to consecrated water and not indulge in 'profane words'. In the
late seventeenth century several midwives were accused of
witchcraft because, in contradiction of clerical regulations, they
used charms to ease difficult births.

Traditional folk medicine had already been dealt a hard blow
in 1512 by an Act which condemned 'ignorant persons of whom
the great part have no manner of insight or any kind of learning
. . . common artificers as smiths, weavers and women boldly
and continually take upon themselves great cures and things of
great difficulty in which they partly use witchcraft and sorcery'.
Although officially the use of herbal and folk remedies was
outlawed, we know from the profusion of apothecaries and
their support by the highest in the land that such authorized
types of folk medicine were accepted. Henry VIII, for instance,

was very interested in folk remedies and had his court physicians prepare over two hundred ointments, medicines and balms which were based on the herbal recipes of folk healers. Charles II and a number of other monarchs also practised an unorthodox form of healing known as 'the King's touch': he would lay his hands on a sick person and say 'I toucheth thee but God dost healeth thee'. A gold coin was then hung around the person's neck by the king, and he or she was presented with 7s 6d. This royal healing ritual was performed within the sight of a priest, who blessed the proceedings.

The hypocrisy of the double standards in judging medical expertise was obviously noted by Henry VIII's counsellors, for in 1542 the original Act of 1512 was amended to exclude from prosecution a category of folk healers described as 'divers honest persons whom God hath endowed with the knowledge and the nature, kind and operation of certain roots, herbs and waters and the using and ministering of them to such as He provided with disease'. Presumably this amendment was made to prevent apothecaries from facing court appearances for selling remedies based on herbs. It also gave greater freedom to the rural wise men and women who, in theory, could practise their healing craft without fear of prosecution by the law and interference from the Church.

Any euphoria the wise men and women might have felt at this turn of events was quickly dissipated by the passing of the 1563 Witchcraft Act, which reinforced the law prohibiting the use of charms and incantations to heal the sick. Even with this severe restriction in operation the wise men and women still managed to ply their trade, and were consulted by both rich and poor alike – occasionally they only escaped prison because of patronage by wealthy clients. One sixteenth-century wise woman was saved from prosecution because she had treated Sir Francis Walsingham, the head of the 'secret service' and confidant of Elizabeth I.

As the number of trained doctors increased, so the role of the village wise woman began to alter as a result. The first sign of this change was the loss of many of their wealthy patients who abandoned folk remedies for the new methods offered by the apothecaries and physicians. During the eighteenth and early nineteenth centuries the rural wise women and folk healers were increasingly consulted only by poorer members of the community who could not afford to pay for medical attention. Those people who were on a low wage and unable to buy medicines had otherwise to rely on the voluntary support offered by those hospitals that had been set up as charities. This inequality led to a resurgence of interest in herbalism and folk remedies during the nineteenth century. Numerous self-help medical books were published which offered recipes and information for curing a wide variety of common ailments; many of these remedies were based on traditional folk medicine. As late as 1910 an official government report stated that the wise women were still active in country districts where they sold salves, ointments and charms for the treatment of abscesses, sores and burns. It was not until the inauguration of the National Health Service in 1946 that their role began to decline in the face of free medical attention for all and improved facilities for dealing with the sick. However, as can be seen by the recipes collected in this book, traditional folk medicine still played an important part in the lives of many country people until comparatively recently.

Some of the folk remedies practised in the eighteenth and nineteenth centuries seemed to have been based on the worst aspects of medieval superstition. For curing rheumatism country people wore the skin of an eel as a garter, for headaches they wore a snakeskin, and they believed that sore eyes could be cured by washing them with rainwater that fell on 1 June. In the *Sussex County Magazine* of 1939 Dr P.H. Luham reported that even as late as the 1930s local people took their babies to wise women to cure them of diptheria, which was done by tying a hazel twig around the infant's throat; the cost of this treatment was 1s, and if it failed the unfortunate baby had to swallow a piece of stewed mouse, for the price of 2s 6d. *The Brighton Herald* of 1835 records the case of a woman cured of a wen on her hand by the touch of a corpse. For tuberculosis, snails or slugs were boiled up in a broth in milk and eaten before breakfast. An eighteenth-century recipe for 'Snail Water', used in treating various ailments, ran:

> Take a peck of garden snails, shells and all. Wash them in spring water. Bruise them in a stone mortar. Steep in 3 gallons of best ale. Add hartshorn, raspberry, 6 ounces of bruised clover, 2

ounces of liquorice, half a pound of aniseed, 1 ounce of cinnamon, 1 ounce of nutmegs. Let it steep day and night. Distill on a slow fire.

Other strange beliefs in the nineteenth century included wearing a large spider around the neck to cure ague, a superstition which seems to date from the 1600s. For fevers and nosebleeds, country folk wore a toad around their throats. To cure eyestrain, folklore recommended a poultice of crushed snails and bread. In the nineteenth century Sussex folk healers prescribed a live spider boiled in butter to cure jaundice. In Yorkshire a trout laid on the stomach of a sick child was said to cure colic and worms. To avoid cramp, the afflicted person was told to wear an eelskin wrapped around the left leg above the knee. A piece of wood from a gibbet or the paw of a mole carried in a velvet or leather pouch was said to be a sure remedy for toothache. In Shetland a person suffering from ringworm rubbed the affected part of the body with ashes each morning until the condition eased. While rubbing on the ashes the following rhyme was recited:

> Ringworm, ringworm, red
> Never may thou spread or speed
> But aye grow less and less
> And die away among the ashes.

As in Anglo-Saxon times, it was generally believed by country folk that illnesses could be disposed of by transference, the most common example of which is the curing of warts. In one cure, a piece of meat was rubbed on the unsightly wart and then buried in the ground. As the meat rotted away beneath the earth, so it was believed that the wart would gradually fade away.

A snail rubbed on a wart and pierced was also said to make the growth vanish as the creature rotted. In Westmorland old country people counted the number of warts, put into a small bag the same number of pebbles and dropped the bag at a crossroads. Whoever ventured by and was unlucky enough to pick up the bag inherited the warts, which were transferred through the pebbles. An alternative method of wart charming was to tie as many knots in a length of hair as there were warts and then throw it away. Or you could cut an apple in half, rub the warts with it and then tie it together again. The united apple was then buried, and as it rotted away so the warts would disappear.

In another folk remedy people suffering from ague unwound onto a tree a piece of rope which they had coiled around their body. They then ran round the tree singing,

> Ague, ague, I thee defy.
> Ague, ague to this tree I thee tie.

In cases of whooping cough the child was told to handle three live snails; they were then hung up in the chimney, and when they died it was believed the cough would go. Alternatively a spider was held over the head of the child and the following words were recited:

> Spider as you waste away
> So the whooping cough no longer stays.

The spider was then sealed in a bag and hung up over the hearth until it expired. A caterpillar, placed in a bag which was then hung round the child's neck, was used in the same way. In Sunderland the crown of the child's hair was cut and hung on a bush or small tree; birds would carry off the hair to line their nests, taking the cough with them. For a swollen throat a live snake was placed in an airtight jar. As it died and decayed the swelling in the throat would decrease.

Some folk remedies were based on the magical law of correspondences and sympathetic magic. The belief that a mole's paw hung round the neck cured toothache may have arisen because moles have sharp teeth which are good at gnawing. Similarly, babies who were teething could be helped by hanging a rabbit's paw or a dried shrew around their neck. Following the same idea powdered human skulls were used to cure epilepsy, which is a disease of the brain, and marrow or oil extracted from human bones was recommended for treating rheumatism, a disease of the bones. The slimy substance exuded by snails was dropped into the ear as a cure for earache and catarrh, presumably because it resembled nasal mucus; this was also the reason why country folk anointed the chests of children suffering with bronchitis with butter. Children in Dorset were passed through the cleft of an oak tree to cure ruptures, and those suffering from rickets were passed between two straight trees growing close to each other.

Medieval prayers also survived as charms to drive away illness. This one is for healing an inflamed wound caused by a thorn.

> Our Saviour Jesus Christ was of pure virgin born
> And he was crowned with a thorn.
> I hope it may not rage or swell,
> I trust in God it may do well.

It was believed that diseases could be cured merely by reciting words which had special religious significance, or simply by the laying on of hands. These charms and blessings were often passed down through families, preserved on pieces of paper kept in the old family Bible. One example from the Welsh border, recorded in the 1930s, is said to have been an instant cure for toothache:

> Jesus came to Peter as he stood at the gates of Jerusalem and said unto him, 'What does thou here?' and Peter answered, 'Lord my teeth do ache,' and Jesus answered him saying, 'Whosoever do carry these words in memory with them or near them shall never have toothache any more.'

Another folk charm, from nineteenth-century Herefordshire, was said to have the power of curing ague:

> When Jesus saw the cross where he was to be crucified he began to tremble and shake. The Jews asked him, 'Are you afraid or do you have the ague?' Jesus answered them and said, 'I am not afraid, neither do I have the ague. Whoever wears this [the cross] about them shall not be afraid nor have the ague.'

One of the most famous of these Christian folk charms is the following, which is found all over the country as a cure for burns.

> There were three angels came from the west
> One brought fire and the other brought frost
> The third brought the book of Jesus the Christ
> In frost, out fire
> In the Name of the Father, Son and Holy Ghost
> Amen.

Other non-religious folk charms included the curing of bronchitis by wearing a necklace of blue beads. A sore throat, too, could be relieved by wearing a blue stocking around the neck. It is interesting that blue is regarded by spiritual healers as the colour for healing and the life energy. In the 1840s, on the other hand, a shop in London's Fleet Street sold what were called 'Red Tongues' – small pieces of red cloth which were purchased by people as a cure for scarlet fever, presumably because of their colour.

Although today we may laugh at the more bizarre examples of folk remedies, some of the cures were found to have a use in orthodox medicine. One famous example is cod liver oil, officially introduced in 1772 by a Manchester doctor as a treatment for rheumatic pain; it had been widely used by sailors and fishermen for the same purpose for several centuries.

Even as late as the nineteenth century the plant lore used as the basis for herbal remedies was still influenced by the so-called Doctrine of Signatures, devised by Paracelsus in the sixteenth century. According to this Doctrine, if a plant resembled a particular disease or complaint then it was believed to have the power to cure it. If a particular plant resembled a part of the human anatomy in shape, colour or habit, then it was popularly said to be able to heal any disease which affected the organ it resembled. Writing about the general theory of the Doctrine of Signatures, the famous herbalist William Turner said, 'God hath imprinted upon the plants, herbes and flowers as it were in heiroglphicks the very signatures of their virtues.' According to Kircher,

Since one and all the members of the human body under the wise arrangement of Nature agree or differ with the several objects in the world of creation by a certain sympathy or antipathy in Nature it follows there has been implanted in the providence of Nature, both in several members and in natural objects, a reciprocal instinct which impels them to seek only those things which are similar and consequently beneficial to themselves and to avoid and shun those things which are antagonistic and hurtful. Hence has emanated that more recondite part of medicine which compares the signatures or characteristics of natural things with the members of the human body and by magnetically applying like to like produces marvellous effects in the preservation of human health. In this way the occult properties of plants – first of those endowed with life and secondly of those destitute of life – are indicated by resemblances for all exhibit to men, by their signatures and characteristics, both their powers by which they can heal and the diseases in which they are useful. Not only by their parts (as the root, stem, leaf, flower, fruit and seed) but also by their actions and quantities (such as their retaining or shedding leaves, their offspring, number, beauty and deformity, form or colour) they indicate what kind of service they can render to man and what particular members of the human body to which they are specifically appropriate.

Using the Doctrine as a guideline, spotted and scaly plants were believed to be able to cure skin complaints, perforated herbs were recommended for open wounds, plants exuding juices or resins were good for sores, plants that swelled up could be used to treat tumours, and those that shed their bark or skin were ideal for cleansing the skin. Any herb or plant which resembled blood, phlegm or bile was said to be able to cure diseases which create these bodily by-products. Herbs such as lungwort, which is spotted with dark scars, were used to treat tuberculosis and other lung diseases. Liverwort, so named because it resembles the liver in its shape, was used for the treatment of all liver diseases and complaints. Bloodroot was named after the red colour of the roots, and was specifically used for treating bloody discharges and internal bleeding. Canterbury bell or throatwort was, as its common name suggests, recommended for sore throats, possibly because it has a very long stem or neck. Plants which grow between stones and in rockeries – such as saxifrage – are reputed to be able to break up kidney and gall bladder stones. Forget-me-not, whose flower spike is suggestive of a scorpion's tail, is recommended for insect bites. The silky fronds of maidenhair are recommended for curing baldness. According to William Turner,

> Walnuts have the perfect signature of the head. The outer husk or green covering represents the pericranium or outward skin of the skull whereon the hair groweth. Therefore salt made of these husks or barks are exceedingly good for wounds of the head. The inner woody shell hath the signature of the skull and the little yellow skin or peel that covereth the kernal of the hard meniga and piamater are the thin scarfes that envelope the brain. The kernal hath the very figure of the brain and therefore it is very profitable for the brain and resents the poison.

Although some herbalists today regard the Doctrine of Signatures as the outdated product of medieval superstition, it has been found that in practice plants which resemble a certain part of the body are capable of healing disorders which affect that area.

Today the herbal remedies of our ancestors have received a new type of respectability with the interest in alternative therapies and holistic medicine. These new types of medical knowledge, often based on ancient techniques, approach the subject of illness from a different angle from the one taken by orthodox medicine. They are interested in treating the whole person, taking diseases and illnesses as examples of the way in which the mind, body and spirit of the patient manifest disharmony in the total system. Herbalism, which was derived from the old folk remedies, is today a very sophisticated branch of alternative medicine which is increasingly winning scientific recognition and acceptance. In the United Kingdom alone there are an estimated four thousand medically qualified herbalists who have been legally recognized within the provisions of the 1968 Medicines Act.

The importance of the herbal ingredients in folk remedies has been investigated by several scientific research institutes, including Harvard University who amassed a vast collection of data on the subject which revealed totally new information for use by doctors, scientists and botanists. Similar work on folk remedies has been undertaken in West Germany, with the assistance of rural folk healers, in Eastern bloc countries, China, Japan, India, the Netherlands and in other universities in the USA. Research into the efficaciousness of folk remedies and their herbal ingredients has been carried out in the United Kingdom under the auspices of the Herb Society, which has founded a national herb centre with a botanical garden and has begun work on producing a computerized data bank on herbs and their medical properties.

Publication of the research data on folk remedies and herbal-based cures has revealed some interesting facts. Garlic and other plants in the onion family, for instance, have been shown to be able to reduce drastically the amount of cholesterol in the bloodstream. As we now know cholesterol is a steroid alchohol found in body cells and fluids, which has been identified as one of the causes of hardening of the arteries and may lead to fatal heart attacks. An excess of cholesterol can be created by a dependance on rich dairy product-based diets. Other discoveries made by the orthodox medical community indicate that liquorice is more beneficial for the treatment of gastric ulcers than any of the chemically based drugs currently available. Scientists have also isolated an ingredient in cayenne pepper which has proved to be a helpful natural stimulant in the treatment of nervous disorders. Recently a potential anti-cancer agent has been isolated in the common periwinkle, and, since (according to a recent article in the *Guardian*) only an estimated 5 per cent of plants have had their medical properties scientifically investigated, there are probably many more similar revelations to be found in the realm of herbal lore and folk remedy.

Our ancestors may well have shrouded herbal lore in the mist of magical ritual, but this was for a reason. Many of the plants used in folk remedies were highly toxic and their misuse would have been fatal. The legends and myths which grew up around some of the healing plants acted as a protection to prevent their abuse by the ignorant. Today, with our advanced scientific knowledge, we are beginning to realize the full extent of the medical expertise which was possessed by the folk healers, and how we can learn from their approach to healing and the techniques which they employed. In traditional folk remedies we have a legacy of ancient medical knowledge which it would be foolish to ignore or dismiss as mere rural superstition.

For all the tremendous breakthroughs made since the end of the Second World War in the field of drug therapy and medical technology, we are still faced with diseases which afflict large numbers of the human race and for which we have, as yet, no scientifically derived answer. Further research into herbal lore and folk remedies may well be the path to the answers we are searching for in orthodox medicine.

Part Two

Folk Remedies
for Common Ailments

The majority of these remedies are based on herbs, the stock-in-trade of the rural medical practitioner. In contrast to the more dubious items used in folk remedies, which seem as if they belong more to *Macbeth*, the healing plants offer a comparatively safe course of medical treatment if used with care and knowledge or under the guidance of someone well versed in their usage. Before attempting to make up any of these remedies, please read for each plant ingredient the notes on application and use that are given in Part Four. They will tell you which plants should be used with caution.

The oldest remedies given here are derived from old medical literature dating back to the fifteenth century. Some were collected on the Isle of Anglesey in North Wales and date from the eighteenth century. Yet others are contemporary, and have been passed down to their present recipients as a family tradition. They are based on local knowledge, inherited wisdom and folklore, which offers proof that in the British countryside the old lore of healing plants has not been destroyed by the technological pressures of our modern age. Many of the remedies I have collected from country people all over the British Isles, and to those who participated in this two-year research project I am very grateful.

The plants are listed under the specific disease or illness which it was claimed they had the ability to heal. This enables the reader quickly to identify the appropriate remedy for his or her particular condition. Where instructions are given to add a tablespoon or teaspoon of herb this refers to it in its powdered form.

Acidity
Take 2 teaspoons of cider vinegar and mix with 1 teaspoon of lemon juice and 1 teaspoon of potato juice. Add the resulting mixture to ½ cup of warm water. Drink as required.

Acne

Take 2 oz of clover flowers, 2 oz of nettle tops and 2 oz of bonesett [comfrey] flowers. Mix the herbs together with 4 pints of boiling water. Simmer until only 2 pints are left. For the best result take 1 wineglass of the resulting liquid every 3 hours.

Ague (Malarial Fever)

Take an infusion of marigold flowers.

An ointment made with the crushed leaves of elder is also effective.

Anaemia

Dandelion tea is recommended.

Nettle tea (rich in iron) can also be taken, with 1 teaspoon of honey as a natural sweetener.

Alternatively eat raw parsley, or add ½ oz of it to 1 pint of boiling water. Strain, and take the resulting liquid 3 times a day.

Appetite, Lack of

Take a handful of hop and caraway seeds to make a refreshing drink: the seeds should be steeped in boiling water and the resulting liquid taken as required. This mixture is especially recommended after a debilitating illness.

Asthma

Agrimony tea is recommended, prepared as follows. Steep 1 oz of agrimony in 1 pint of boiling water. Strain, and take ½ cup of the resulting liquid as required.

Alternatively, garlic can be used. Macerate 1 lb of sliced garlic into a vessel containing 2 pints of boiling water. Cover, and leave for 12 hours. Add 1 oz of sugar to the strained liquid. Take 1 teaspoon at a time, as required.

Another folk remedy is to boil ¼ oz of caraway seeds and ¼ oz of fennel seeds in a vessel containing ½ pint of vinegar. When this mixture has simmered for a short time add 1½ oz of sliced garlic. Cover the vessel and leave to cool. Strain the resulting liquid and mix with 8 oz of honey. Take 1 teaspoon, as required.

An old country recipe to relieve asthma tells you to drink 1 pint of cold water every morning and to take a cold bath every two weeks.

Arthritis
Make a poultice of fresh young ragwort leaves and apply as hot as you can bear it.

A recipe for a herbal tea which is recommended for arthritic pain requires 2 oz of agrimony, 2 oz of bogbean, 2 oz of burdock, 2 oz of yarrow and ½ oz of raspberry leaves. Place the herbs in 4 pints of boiling water. Simmer slowly until only 2 pints are left. Cool and strain. Drink 1 wineglass of the liquid every 3 hours.

Another recommended folk cure is honeysuckle tea. Loosely fill a teacup with honeysuckle flowers. Add them to 1 pint of boiling water. Steep and strain. Take 1 wineglass of the liquid every 3 hours.

Alternatively take 1 handful of coltsfoot and boil it in milk with oats and butter. Apply as a poultice to the place where the pain is worst.

Backache
Make a poultice from hot aniseed and nettle leaves and apply direct to the afflicted spot.

Baldness
Rub your head with a mixture of onion juice and honey morning and evening.

Bed-wetting
It is well known that bed-wetting has a psychological or emotional cause. However for temporary relief of the unpleasant symptoms the following remedies can be tried.

Add 1 teaspoon of thyme to 3 teaspoons of honey. Take 1 hour before going to bed.

The following recipe is also recommended. Mix together ½ oz of basil, 1 oz of betony, 1 oz of golden rod and ½ oz of tansy. Place in 2 pints of boiling water. Simmer for 15–20 minutes, and cool. Take 1 wineglass every 3 hours.

A tea made from St John's wort and plantain is also suggested by folk healers. Steep 1 teaspoon of each herb in 1 cup of boiling water. Sweeten with honey as required. Take 2–3 cups a day.

Boils
Pick the centres of some blackberry shoots. Boil them, and then add cold water. Leave to soak for 5 minutes. Strain, and take 1 small wineglass of the liquid every morning.

Alternatively, heat the root of dock plant in boiling water. Strain, and drink 1 eggcup of the liquid every morning. This purifies the blood, preventing the outbreak of boils.

See also Skin Complaints.

Bronchitis
Every hour take liquoricc and honey mixed in hot water with lemon juice.

According to rural folklore the following is a sure cure for bronchitis. Take 1 oz of coltsfoot, 1 oz of elderflower, 1 oz of elfwort [Elecampane] and 1 oz of white horehound. Mix the herbs into 2 pints of boiling water. Simmer down to 1 pint. When cool, add ½ teaspoon of cinnamon. Mix well. Strain, and drink 1 wineglass every 3 hours.

Another folk remedy said to produce good results is a mixture of cayenne pepper, honey and warm water. Take morning and night until the symptoms ease.

See also Coughs.

Breasts and Nipples, Soreness of
Take 1 oz each of camomile flowers and bruised marshmallow roots. Boil in 2 pints of water until it has reduced to 1 pint. Place the roots and flowers in fine linen and use as a poultice on the breasts.

Alternatively take equal parts of vervain, betony and agrimony. Pulverize and mix with beer. Strain, and add the resulting liquid to boiling milk. Drink warm to relieve breast and nipple inflammation.

Anoint the breasts with the juice extracted from a mixture of groundsel and daisies.

Take 1 oz of alum, 8 oz of sugar, 2 tablespoons of vinegar and 2 teaspoons of salt. Simmer over a low heat until a salve is created, which should be spread on a linen cloth just large enough to cover the affected breast. Leave this on until the soreness heals, then wash the breast in a mixture of warm water and milk.

If you have persistent soreness or lumps in the breast see your doctor without delay.

Breath, Shortness of
Take 1 oz of caraway seeds, 1 oz of aniseed, ½ oz of liquorice, 1 large nutmeg and 2 oz of sugar. Pulverize finely and take a pinch morning and evening.

Bruises
Make a poultice with vinegar and bran and add oatmeal or breadcrumbs. Apply to sprains and bruises for instant relief of pain and swelling.

Boil some comfrey leaves, set aside to cool, and then strain. Bathe the bruise with the resulting liquid to reduce swelling.

Take equal amounts of feverfew, ribwort, plaintain, garden sage and bugle. Pulverize them and boil in unsalted butter or vegetable oil. Strain, and apply to the bruise.

Boil a handful of hyssop leaves in a little water until tender. Wrap them in a piece of fine linen and apply to the bruise as a poultice.

Gather a handful of mallow leaves. Crush, and mix with butter or vegetable fat. Smear on bruises to stop pain and reduce swelling.

Infuse a handful of rosemary leaves in 1 pint of boiling water. Cool. Add the white of 1 egg and 1 teaspoon of brandy. Apply as a lotion to the bruise.

Burns
To produce a salve take equal parts of the root of yellow dock and dandelion, and add equal amounts of greater celandine and plantain. Extract their juices by steeping the plants in cold water. Strain carefully, and simmer the resulting liquid with a little fresh butter or vegetable fat until the butter or fat has melted. Cool, and place the liquid in containers for future use.

Peppermint oil, elderflower and marigold applied to burns can bring relief.

Take 2 pints of cream or vegetable fat and a handful of fern leaves. Boil the leaves with the cream or fat, and simmer. Allow to cool, strain, and apply to the burn.

Cancer
A tea made from steeping red clover tops in boiling water was used by country people for cancerous growths.

Catarrh
The best cure as recommended by folk healers is to eat a raw onion every morning and evening.

Alternatively, mix equal quantities of elderflowers, peppermint and yarrow. Add 1 oz of the mixed herbs to 1 pint of boiling water.

Take cinnamon and lemon juice in warm water every 3 hours.

Mix the following herbs to make an effective tea: 1 oz of coltsfoot, 1 oz of mullein, 1 oz of sage, 1 oz of thyme and ½ oz of yarrow. Place the herbs in 2 pints of boiling water. Simmer until only 1 pint remains. Take 1 wineglass every hour for the first day, then every 3 hours afterwards until the condition eases.

Chilblains
Mix 1 lb of elderflowers with 1 lb of lard or vegetable fat. Boil together and then simmer gently for 1 hour. Strain and apply the resulting liquid to the chilblains.

Bathe the chilblains in the water drained from boiling potatoes, as hot as you can stand it.

Nettle juice applied directly to chilblains eases their discomfort.

For instant results, boil an onion and apply it directly to the chilblain.

Childbirth
Six months before the birth drink raspberry tea. Add 1 oz of raspberries to 1 pint of boiling water. According to old folk belief this tea enriches the expectant mother's natural milk and prevents a miscarriage.

During pregnancy take linseed tea. Soak 1 tablespoon of linseed in 1 pint of boiling water and add honey to sweeten.

Chills
An eighteenth-century recipe for chills affecting the back and

kidney regions says slice ½ a large nutmeg into a glass of sherry or white wine. Take as required.

Colds

As would be expected, there are numerous folk remedies for treating colds. Here are some of the best ones.

Rub on the chest oil made from rosemary.

Take a handful of yarrow, ½ oz of bruised ginger root and 1 teaspoon of cayenne pepper, and add to 3 pints of water. Boil down to 1 pint. Add honey to sweeten if required. Take a glass at bedtime and repeat each evening until the cold has gone.

Take 5 lb of fresh elderberries. Simmer with 1 lb of brown sugar until it is the consistency of honey. Strain and bottle. Take 1–2 tablespoons in hot water at bedtime.

Wash your feet every evening with hot water. Then mix crushed garlic bulbs and white horehound and smear this mixture on the soles of your feet before going to bed.

Gather some fresh heads of elderflower and a handful of angelica leaves. Steep in boiling water for 10 minutes. Strain off the resulting liquid and add honey to taste.

See also Sore Throats.

Colic

Boil a handful of betony in white wine. Strain, and drink the resulting liquid for relief.

Constipation

Take honey and water every morning.

Mix slippery elm with equal parts of warm water and honey. Take morning and night.

Mix equal parts of buckthorn, rhubarb root and fennel. Boil in hot water, strain and cool. Take 1 wineglass after each meal as a laxative.

Corns

Wash the feet in hot water with some salt added. Squeeze celandine juice on to the corn and leave to dry.

Apply to the corn equal parts of apple and carrot juice plus some salt.

Apply crushed ivy leaves daily, and within a week the corn will drop off.

Coughs

As with colds, there are many folk remedies for treating coughs. Here is a selection.

Take the juice of ½ lemon, 1 teaspoon of glycerine and 1 tablespoon of honey. Fill a glass or cup with hot water, stir in the ingredients and drink as required to ease the cough.

Take 2 handfuls of coltsfoot leaves, 1 oz of garlic and 4 pints of water. Boil down to 3 pints. Strain, and add to the liquid 8 oz of brown sugar. Simmer gently for 10 minutes. Take ½ cup as required.

Take equal parts of white horehound, marshmallow leaves, hyssop, mullein and ground coriander. Infuse 1 teaspoon of mixed herbs in a cup of boiling water for 10 minutes. Sweeten with honey if required. Take 1 cup 3 times a day before meals.

Place 1 large cup of linseeds with a small quantity of liquorice and 4 oz of raisins in 2 pints of water. Simmer slowly until 1 pint remains. Add 4 oz of brown sugar, 1 tablespoon of rum and 1 tablesoon of vinegar or lemon juice. Warm ½ pint of this decoction and sip before going to bed each night.

Take 2 handfuls of coltsfoot leaves and 12 handfuls of plantain leaves. Cut and beat well. Strain the juice and add an equal amount of brown sugar. Boil to a syrup and take 1 teaspoon as required.

Thinly slice 3 garlic bulbs into a ½ pint basin. Add 4 oz of honey and ¼ pint of vinegar. Place the basin in boiling water and leave for 30 minutes. Strain off the liquid, add an equal amount of brandy, and place the resulting liquid in sealed bottles. Mix 2 teaspoons with 1 teaspoon of water and take morning and night.

Pour 2 pints of boiling water on 2 handfuls of coltsfoot leaves. Sweeten with honey. Strain, and take 3 times a day.

Take 4 oz of coltsfoot stalks and soak them in ½ pint of water. Cut the stalks into 1 inch lengths, place them in a saucepan and add some brown sugar. Stir until the sugar dissolves. Bring to the boil and skim, then reboil again until the mixture thickens. Strain the liquid through muslin into sterilized jars. Take 1 teaspoon 3 times a day.

Melt 1 teaspoon of butter or vegetable fat in a saucepan, add 1 tablespoon of honey and stir well. Add 15 drops of vinegar, stirring all the time. Take the resulting mixture 3 times a day.

Mix ½ pint of hyssop, water, ½ ounce of almond oil, 2 oz of sugar and 1 teaspoon of hartshorn. Take 1 tablespoon morning and night.

Take ½ tablespoon of dried sage and ½ tablespoon of ginger. Mix with 1 tablespoon of brown sugar. Add ½ pint of boiling water. Leave for 5–10 minutes, strain, and then sip slowly.

Add 1 tablespoon of dried sage to a saucepan containing 1 pint of boiling water. Simmer for 30 minutes. Strain, then add 1 tablespoon of vinegar and 1 tablespoon of honey. Mix well and allow to cool. Take 1 teaspoon as required.

Mix the juice of 3 leeks with the breast milk of a nursing mother. Drink 3 times daily.

Take 2 oz of caraway seeds. Boil in 2 pints of water until only 1 pint is left. Strain off half the liquid, sweeten with brown sugar and add 1 wineglass of rum or brandy. Take 1 small wineglass of the mixture every night before going to bed.

Cramp
For relief, massage into the cramped muscles clove oil diluted with olive oil.

Alternatively, crush calamint leaves, and massage the aching muscles with them.

Cystitis
Take 1 handful of dried blackberry leaves. Crush, and add them to 1 pint of water. Boil for 5 minutes, then leave to infuse for 10 minutes. Strain, and drink 3–4 cups of the resulting liquid between meals daily.

Diabetes
Mix 1 oz of agrimony, 1 oz of cloves, 1 oz of dandelion root, 1 oz of juniper berries and 1 oz of parsley, then place them in 4 pints of boiling water. Simmer until 2 pints remain. Take a wineglass of the resulting liquid every 2 hours.

Diarrhoea
To 2 pints of blackberry juice add 1 lb of brown sugar, 1 tablespoon of cloves, 1 tablespoon of mixed spice, 1 tablespoon of cinnamon and 1 tablespoon of nutmeg. Boil together for 10 minutes. Add a wineglass of whisky, rum or brandy. Bottle

while hot, cork tightly and seal. Take 1 small wineglass as an adult dose or ½ small wineglass as a child's dose 3 times a day until symptoms ease.

Mix 1 tablespoon of slippery elm and 1 tablespoon of honey with warm water and drink every hour until the condition eases.

Mix 1 oz of mint, 1 oz of queen of the meadow [Meadowsweet] and 1 oz of St John's wort into 4 pints of water, then bring to the boil and simmer until 2 pints remain. Honey, cinnamon or ginger can then be added. Drink 1 wineglass every hour.

Add 1 oz of bearberry, 1 oz of peppermint and 1 oz of raspberry leaves to 2 pints of boiling water. Simmer until 1 pint remains. Strain, and take 1 wineglass every 3 hours.

See also Dysentery.

Dizziness
For curing frequent dizzy spells drink sage tea sweetened with honey.

Alternatively, take 1 lb of fresh cowslip flowers and infuse in 1½ pints of boiling water. Add honey to taste. Simmer and take as a syrup 3 times a day.

Dysentery
Take 2 large nutmegs, 20 white peppercorns, 20 cloves, 1 oz of cinnamon and 1 oz of oak bark. Boil these ingredients in 6 pints of milk. Strain, and divide the resulting liquid into 4 equal parts. Give the patient 1 part every 6 hours for 24 hours.

Earache
Bathe the ears with a strong decoction of camomile.

For fast relief of earache, boil a large onion until it is soft and rub it on the inside of the ear.

Take a branch of young green elder and place it on a grill above a low fire. Collect 1 eggcup of the sap which will exude from the wood. Add to it 1 eggcup of fresh leek juice. Mix together well, and anoint the infected ear 3 times a day.

Eczema
Use marigold tea to alleviate the symptoms. Add 1 oz of

marigold flowers to 1 pint of boiling water. Steep, strain and take as required.

Mix 1 tablespoon of lemon juice and 1 tablespoon of honey with a pinch of cayenne pepper in warm water. Take every morning before breakfast.

Eyestrain

If you are suffering from puffy or tired eyes an old folk remedy is to apply a raw potato to the eyes, which helps to reduce the swelling.

For tired eyes, boil a handful of elderflowers in water. When cool, strain and use the liquid to bathe the eyes.

Take 1 oz of raspberry leaves, 1 oz of marshmallow leaves and 1 oz of groundsel leaves. Mix in 1½ pints of boiling water, and simmer until 1 pint remains. Allow to cool, then strain and use as an eyewash.

Blend some butter or vegetable fat, honey and the white of an egg and anoint the affected eye with it.

Anointing the eyes with the breast milk of two different women is an old folk cure for eyestrain.

Flatulence

Take a handful of feverfew, 1 oz of cumin seeds and 1 oz of ginger. Add to 6 pints of water, bring to the boil and simmer down to 3 pints. Strain and take 3–4 wineglasses a day.

Gallstones

Cut a large handful of leeks. Place them in a saucepan and cover with 4 pints of water. Cover the saucepan and simmer the water down to 2 pints. Strain off the liquid and drink a ⅓ pint of it morning, noon and night. Half the quantity can be used as a child's dose. Make up the leek water freshly every 2 days.

An eighteenth-century recipe needs 4 pints of best white wine, 2 oz of nutmegs and 2 handfuls of hawthorn flowers. Infuse them overnight in a closely covered pot. Next day, distil in a cold still, letting the liquid drop on 1 oz of sugar candy. Drink a tea dish of about 6 large spoonfuls, says the recipe, when the pain begins.

Gout

Steep some rosemary leaves in boiling water. Apply to the afflicted part of body as a poultice.

Take 1 handful of holy thistle and 1 handful of angelica leaves. Infuse, and drink ½ pint of the strained liquid every morning for a month.

Mix goose grass, tansy, sage, columbine and mint. Pound them to a fine powder, mix with beer and drink 3 times a day.

Haemorrhoids

See Piles.

Hayfever

Steep 1 oz of elfwort in 1 pint of boiling water. Strain, and take 1 small wineglass of the liquid every 4 hours until the symptoms ease.

Headache

Bathe the forehead and temples with hot water in which mint and sage has been steeped.

Take 1 small handful each of centaury and feverfew and add 1 oz of camomile flowers. Mix in 4 pints of water. Boil down and simmer to 2 pints. Add 1 oz of rhubarb while the liquid is hot, and stir well. Take 1 wineglass of the resulting liquid 3 times a day.

Take 1 oz of fresh or dried rosemary. Infuse in 1 pint of hot water. Cool and strain. For persistent headaches take 1 wineglass 4 times a day.

A fifteenth-century recipe says make a distillation of vervain, betony and wormwood and wash your head in it 3 times a week to keep away head pains.

Add ½ oz of camomile to 1 pint of boiling water. Strain, and take 1 wineglass 3 times a day.

Add 1 oz of elderflowers to 1 pint of boiling water. Strain, and take 1 wineglass twice a day.

Add 1 oz of limeflowers to 1 pint of boiling water. Strain and take 1 wineglass 3 times per day.

See also Migraine.

Heart Trouble
Add 2 teaspoons of dried hawthorn leaves to 1 pint of boiling water. Steep and strain. Add honey to sweeten if required. Take 1 wineglass 3 times a day.

Take 1 handful of centaury and boil it in beer. Strain the herbs from the beer and pulverize them. Boil again, and strain the liquid through a fine linen cloth. Mix the resulting liquid with twice the amount of honey; boil and cool. Drink 1 wineglass 3 times a day.

An eighteenth-century recipe says take as much of the herb called Dick Tender as will fill a little bag, and add it to a pennyworth of saffron dried and rubbed. Sprinkle it with salt and dry it over a chaffin dish of coals. Lay it on the heat and a warm cloth upon it. Soak the herbs in water and take the liquid 3 times daily.

Hysteria
Mix 1 oz of camomile, 1 oz of valerian, 1 oz of limeflowers and 1 oz of St John's wort and add to 1 pint of boiling water. Steep and strain. Take 1 wineglass 3 times a day.

Take 1 handful each of mugwort, red fennel and red mint. Boil in beer and strain through a fine linen cloth. Drink 1 wineglass warm 3 times a day.

Indigestion
Take 1 oz of greater yellow gentian, 1 oz of bruised columbine roots and 1 oz of camomile flowers. Add to 6 pints of water, boil and simmer down to 3 pints. Strain and cool. Take 1 wineglass 2–3 times a day.

Influenza
Mix 1 oz of boneset, 1 oz of mullein, 1 oz of sage, 1 oz of vervain and 1 oz of yarrow and put them in 4 pints of boiling water. Simmer gently until 2 pints of liquid remain. Strain and cool. Take 1 wineglass every 3 hours until the symptoms ease.

Add ½ oz of elderflowers, ½ oz of peppermint and ½ oz of yarrow to 1½ pints of boiling water. Strain, and leave for 10 minutes. Add honey to sweeten if required and drink.

Take 1 handful of angelica roots and boil gently for 3 hours in 2 pints of water. Strain off the liquid and add sufficient honey to make a syrup. Take 2 teaspoons at night before going to bed.

Insomnia
Take honey in milk with a pinch of nutmeg or cinnamon before going to bed.

Jaundice
Pulverize 1 handful of dandelion flowers, 1 handful of blue cornflowers and 1 handful of parsley in some beer. Take 1 teaspoon with food morning and evening.

Boil 1 oz of agrimony in 1 pint of water. Strain and cool. Take 1 wineglass 3 times a day.

Boil 1 oz of cinquefoil in 1 pint of water. Strain and cool. Take 1 wineglass a day.

Kidney Disorders
Boil 1 handful of nettle leaves in water. Strain through a muslin cloth. Ferment to make nettle beer. Add honey, brown sugar, cloves and ginger root. Drink 1 wineglass 3 times a day.

Mix equal parts of lime water and pearl barley water. Take 1 teaspoon 3 times a day.

Take 1 oz of burdock seeds, 1 oz of dandelion, 1 oz of marshmallow root and 1 oz of tansy. Mix the herbs well and put them in 4 pints of boiling water. Simmer until 2 pints of water remain. Strain and cool. Take 1 wineglass every 2 hours for the first day, then every 3 hours on successive days.

Lactation, Excessive
A poultice of crushed horseradish applied to each breast is an old folk remedy to prevent excessive lactation in nursing mothers.

Lung Disease
Take 1 handful of elderflowers and 1 handful of wood sorrel. Boil in milk. Strain off the liquid and take as required.
See also Tuberculosis

Migraine
Finely crush leaves of basil and feverfew. Mix well and use as snuff.
See also Headaches.

Nausea
Mix 1 handful of rosemary leaves with an equal amount of honey, and eat as required to prevent sickness.

Neuralgia
Add ½ pint of rosewater to 2–3 teaspoons of white vinegar to make lotion. Apply to the afflicted part of the body 3 times a day, using a clean cloth each time.

Nosebleeds
A nettle leaf placed on the tongue or pressed against the roof of the mouth was an old folk remedy for curing nosebleeds (presumably because the shock of the nettle sting in the tender part of the mouth stopped the flow of blood).

Numbness in Hands
Wash numb or trembling hands in a decoction of wormwood and mustard seed.

Piles
Infuse 1 handful of nettles in 2 pints of water. Strain, and take 1 wineglass of the resulting liquid 2–3 times a day.

Pneumonia
Take 1 handful of white horehound and pulverize finely. Add pure spring water. Allow to stand for 3 hours, then strain through a fine cloth. Add an equal amount of honey. Simmer slowly. Take 1 wineglass every 3 hours.

Rheumatism
Boil 1 oz of celery seed in 1 pint of water. Reduce to ½ pint. Strain, bottle and seal. Take 1 teaspoon twice a day in a little water for 2 weeks.

Hot rum laced with nutmeg and pepper is an old folk cure for rheumatic pains.

Sciatica
Boil 1 handful of nettles until they are soft and mushy. Apply in a cloth as a poultice to the painful area.

Scurvy
Steep 2 oz of dandelion roots and 2 oz of daisies in 6 pints of water. Boil down to 4 pints. Take 1 teacup night and morning.

Senile Decay
An old folk remedy to prevent the onset of senile decay was to boil a handful of nettle leaves and eat them morning and night.

Skin Complaints
For itchy skin, says one eighteenth-century recipe, apply hot water and soap using a corncob. Follow this by a treatment with a mixture of lard and sulphur.

Take 1 handful of coltsfoot flowers and soak them in fresh milk for 3 hours. Remove, and wrap in muslin. Use as a compress to remove unsightly blemishes from the skin.

Mix equal amounts of burdock, yarrow and marshmallow. Soak in boiling water, steep and strain. Drink ½ cup of the resulting liquid 3 times a day, or use as a lotion on the affected part of the skin.

Sores
Mix equal amounts of groundsel, kitchen soap and sugar. Apply to the sore to draw out the infection.

Sore Throats
Pour 1 pint of boiling water on a handful of sage leaves. Infuse for 30 minutes. Add enough vinegar to make it acid to the taste. Sweeten with honey if required. Use as a gargle 3–4 times a day.

Add 1 oz of yarrow root to 1 pint of boiling water. Steep, strain and cool. Take 1 tablespoon 3 times a day.

Add 2 handfuls of elderberries to boiling water and stir well. Put in a little honey to sweeten. Cool, and strain through fine cloth or a kitchen sieve. Sip slowly, as required, to ease the soreness.

An eighteenth-century remedy says mix a pennyworth of camphor in a wineglass of brandy. Pour a small quantity on a lump of loaf sugar. Allow to dissolve in the mouth and repeat every hour. After the fourth dose the sore throat will have gone.

Stings
For relief from insect stings or bites rub crushed marigold leaves on the afflicted part of the body.

Stomach Ache
See Nausea *and* Colic.

Toothache
Mix vinegar, tansy, onion and a few peppercorns. Boil, and carefully strain off the liquid. Place 1 teaspoon of this liquid on the inflamed gum or aching tooth.

Apply a crushed garlic bulb to the gum above tooth – it is alleged to deaden the pain.

Tonic
Mix equal parts of greater yellow gentian root, skullcap, burnet root, betony and spearmint. Soak in boiling water. Strain and cool. Take ½ teaspoon 3 times a day as a tonic to relax the body and calm the mind.

Tuberculosis
Boil 1 lb of honey gently in a saucepan. Finely grate two large sticks of horseradish and stir into the honey. Boil for 5 minutes, stirring well to prevent burning. Transfer into jars to cool. Take 2–3 tablespoons daily.

Ulcers (External)
Grate 2 large carrots and make into a poultice. Apply directly to the ulcer.

Warts
Rub any of the following onto the wart: greater celandine juice, marigold juice, juice of dandelion stems, juice of elder stems, juice of heliotrope leaves mixed with salt, juice of hartstongue fern, fig juice, leek juice, milk thistle juice, St John's wort juice, mullein juice, juice of wheat ears mixed with salt, rue juice, thyme juice boiled in wine with pepper, juice of teazel roots boiled in wine, or the burnt ashes of willow bark mixed with vinegar.

Water Retention
Grind 10 broom seeds into a fine powder and take with honey.

Wounds
Bruise a blackberry leaf and apply to open wounds to stop bleeding.

To aid fast healing, wrap bay leaves soaked in brandy around the wound with a bandage.

Part Three

Practical Folk Medicine

The purpose of this part of the book is to offer the reader practical information on the use of folk remedies, with the emphasis on the identification, preparation and use of common herbs for healing purposes. Different herbs for treating specific medical complaints and diseases are named. As with the folk remedies in Part Two, they have been arranged for easy reference under the diseases and illnesses. Following that is a glossary of medical terms with explanations, which will be of particular use when you come on to Part Four. Practical information is then given on the growing, harvesting and preparation of herbs used in medical remedies.

Herbs of Healing for Specific Diseases and Medical Complaints

Alcoholic Poisoning
Feverfew

Allergies
Eyebright

Anaemia
Angelica
Barberry
Comfrey
Dandelion
Fenugreek
Fumitory
Great yellow gentian
Nettle
St John's wort
Sweet flag
Watercress
Vervain

Appetite, for Improving
Angelica
Buckthorn
Camomile
Caraway
Centaury
Chicory
Coriander
Dandelion
Dill
Great yellow gentian

Horseradish
Lady's mantle
Madder
Marjoram
Mint (peppermint and spearmint)
Mugwort
Parsley
Sorrel
Speedwell
Sweet flag
Tarragon
Thyme
Watercress
Wormwood

Arthritis
Buckthorn
Burdock
Centaury
Chickweed
Comfrey
Elder
Meadowsweet
Restharrow
Violet
Wintergreen
Wormwood

Asthma
Burdock

Butterbur
Camomile
Centaury
Coltsfoot
Comfrey
Garlic
Greater celandine
Horseradish
Lovage
Mullein
Nettle
Parsley
Peony
Thyme
Valerian
Watercress
White horehound

Bed-wetting

Bearberry
Fennel
Hollyhock
Lady's mantle
Mallow
Pansy
Restharrow
St John's wort

Blood Pressure, High

Barberry
Chervil
Comfrey
Garlic
Goose grass
Hawthorn
Onion
Parsley
Rue
Skullcap
Vervain
Violet

Blood Pressure, Low

Broom
Heather
Lavender
Motherwort
Rosemary
Shepherd's purse

Bronchitis

Angelica
Bugle
Butterbur
Caraway
Chervil
Chickweed
Coltsfoot
Comfrey
Daisy
Fennel
Fenugreek
Garlic
Ground Ivy
Hedge Mustard
Houndstongue
Knotgrass
Liquorice
Lungwort
Madder
Mallow
Marjoram
Milkwort
Mouse-ear hawkweed
Mullein
Onion
Parsley
Plantain
Primrose
Savory

Soapwort
Speedwell
Sweet violet
Thyme
Watercress
White horehound

Bruises
Agrimony
Buckthorn
Catnip
Celery
Chickweed
Chicory
Comfrey
Fenugreek
Figwort
Herb Robert
Houndstongue
Mugwort
Primrose
Rosemary
St John's wort
Tansy
White horehound
Wintergreen
Witchhazel

Burns
Burdock
Chickweed
Coltsfoot
Comfrey
Houndstongue
Lady's mantle
Plantain
St John's wort
Witchhazel

Catarrh
See Bronchitis

Chilblains
Angelica
Garlic
Hawthorn
Horseradish
Lady's mantle
Mugwort
Onion
Shepherd's purse
Watercress

Childbirth
Columbine
Comfrey
Flax
Groundsel
Lady's mantle
Pansy
Motherwort
Primrose
Raspberry
White horehound

Colds
Angelica
Avens
Burdock
Catnip
Coltsfoot
Elder
Feverfew
Garlic
Hedge mustard
Horseradish
Lungwort
Maidenhair
Marjoram
Meadowsweet
Onion
Plantain

Rose hip
Sage
Spearmint

Constipation
Asparagus
Buckthorn
Chickweed
Chicory
Dandelion
Elder
Elm
Fat hen
Feverfew
Figwort
Flax
Fumitory
Greater celandine
Groundsel
Hedge mustard
Hollyhock
Horseradish
Lily of the valley
Liquorice
Madder
Mallow
Mugwort
Pansy
Raspberry
Rosehip
Rowan
Soapwort
Sorrel
Strawberry

Coughs
See Bronchitis *and* Colds

Cuts, Sores and Insect Bites
Agrimony

Basil
Betony
Borage
Bugle
Burnet
Butterbur
Camomile
Catnip
Chickweed
Chicory
Coltsfoot
Comfrey
Eyebright
Goose grass
Groundsel
Horsetail
Houndstongue
Kidneywort
Lady's bedstraw
Lady's mantle
Marigold
Marshmallow
Plantain
Purple loosestrife
Raspberry
Sage
St John's wort
Thyme
White horehound
Witchhazel

Cystitis
Angelica
Bearberry
Betony
Comfrey
Couch grass
Fennel
Goose grass
Golden rod

Ground ivy
Lady's mantle
Mallow
Pansy
Parsley piert
Watercress
Yarrow

Diarrhoea
Agrimony
Avens
Cinquefoil
Comfrey
Daisy
Herb Robert
Lungwort
Marjoram
Potentil
Purple loosestrife
Raspberry
Sage
Slippery elm
Sorrel

Eye Disorders
Angelica
Borage
Cornflower
Eyebright
Fumitory
Herb Robert
Marigold
Meadowsweet

Fever
Angelica
Betony
Borage
Catnip
Cowslip

Feverfew
Lilac
Limeflowers
Lovage
Meadowsweet
Pink
Poppy
Sage
Viper's bugloss
White horehound
Yarrow

Flatulence
Angelica
Caraway
Catnip
Celery
Coriander
Dill
Fennel
Feverfew
Horseradish
Lavender
Peppermint
Spearmint
Sweet flag
Tansy
Tarragon
Woodruff
See also Indigestion

Gall Bladder Disorders
Betony
Marigold
Peony
Pimpernel
Purple flag
Vervain

Gallstones and Kidney Stones
Barberry
Chicory

Knotgrass
Madder
Parsley piert
Restharrow

Gums, Sore, and Mouth Ulcers
Avens
Cinquefoil
Columbine
Comfrey
Herb Robert
Hollyhock
Marshmallow
Periwinkle
Raspberry
Savory
Self heal
Vervain

Halitosis
Avens
Dill
Peppermint

Headache and Migraine
Angelica
Basil
Betony
Feverfew
Lavender
Limeflowers
Pennyroyal
Peppermint
Primrose
Spearmint
St John's wort
Valerian
Viper's bugloss
Wintergreen

Heart Trouble
Broom
Bugle
Burnet
Figwort
Gipsywort
Great yellow gentian
Hawthorn
Hedge mustard
Lily of the valley
Motherwort
Raspberry
Viper's bugloss
Woodruff

Haemorrhoids
See Piles

Hysteria
Betony
Catnip
Centaury
Lady's bedstraw
Lavender
Lily of the valley
Peppermint
Motherwort
Poppy
Skullcap
St John's wort
Sweet flag
Valerian
Vervain
Viper's bugloss
Watercress

Indigestion
Dill
Fennel
Feverfew

Mugwort
Peppermint
Spearmint
Speedwell
Thyme
See also Flatulence

Influenza
See Colds

Insect Bites
See Cuts.

Insomnia
Catnip
Camomile
Dandelion
Dill
Hawthorn
Heather
Peppermint
Poppy
Primrose
Skullcap
Valerian
Woodruff

Kidney Disorders
Agrimony
Angelica
Bearberry
Betony
Broom
Daisy
Dandelion
Fumitory
Golden rod
Heather
Horsetail
Kidneywort

Parsley
Peony
Restharrow
Shepherd's purse
Strawberry

Kidney Stones
See Gallstones

Lactation, for Improving
Basil
Borage
Caraway
Dill
Fennel
Milkwort
Motherwort
Raspberry

Liver Disorders
Agrimony
Avens
Daisy
Mouse-ear hawkweed
Purple flag
Rosemary

Lung Disease
Comfrey
Knotgrass
Lungwort
Primrose

Menstruation, Inhibited
Marigold
Motherwort
Mugwort
Rue
Shepherd's purse
Southernwood

Tarragon

Menstruation, Excessive
Broom
Bugle
Burnet
Marigold
Moneywort
Mugwort
Periwinkle
Rue
Yarrow

Migraine
See Headache

Mouth Ulcers
See Gums

Nervous Disorders
See Hysteria

Period Pains
Groundsel
Lavender
Motherwort
Pennyroyal
Potentil
Rue
Skullcap

Piles
Figwort
Ground ivy
Horse chestnut
Peony
Pilewort
Potentil
Vervain

Rheumatism
Angelica
Asparagus
Burdock
Celery
Chickweed
Coriander
Daisy
Golden rod
Lilac
Meadow saffron
Meadowsweet
Nettle
St John's wort
Wintergreen

Sciatica
Broom
Ground elder
Ground ivy
Kidneywort
St John's wort
Wintergreen

Sinus Troubles
See Bronchitis

Skin Complaints
Avens
Betony
Borage
Burdock
Burnet
Butterbur
Camomile
Catnip
Chervil
Chickweed
Coltsfoot
Comfrey

Fenugreek
Figwort
Flax
Goose grass
Greater celandine
Groundsel
Heather
Herb Robert
Kidneywort
Lady's bedstraw
Lady's mantle
Lavender
Limeflowers
Madder
Nettle
Pansy
Peppermint
Primrose
Purple flag
Raspberry
Restharrow
Rosemary
Slippery elm
Soapwort
Sorrel
Speedwell
Tansy
White horehound
Witchhazel

Sore Throats
Agrimony
Avens
Caraway
Columbine
Comfrey
Fennel
Fenugreek
Figwort
Ground ivy

Hedge mustard
Herb Robert
Lovage
Lungwort
Mallow
Periwinkle
Plantain
Potentil
Purple loosestrife
Rowan
Sage
Savory
Self heal
Wintergreen

Sores
See Cuts

Stomach Complaints
Angelica
Basil
Caraway
Centaury
Chicory
Cinquefoil
Comfrey
Fennel
Feverfew
Garlic
Great yellow gentian
Greater celandine
Groundsel
Horsetail
Houndstongue
Kidneywort
Knotgrass
Lady's smock
Mallow
Marigold
Marjoram

Marshmallow
Meadowsweet
Milkwort
Moneywort
Rue
Slippery elm
Speedwell
Sweet flag
Tarragon

Toothache
Broom
Clove
Lavender
Marjoram
Wintergreen

Ulcers, Mouth,
See Gums

Water Retention
Agrimony
Asparagus
Bearberry

Broom
Buckthorn
Chervil
Dandelion
Golden rod
Heather
Hedge mustard
Kidneywort
Lady's smock
Lily of the valley
Madder
Maidenhair
Onion
Pansy
Pimpernel
Plantain
Restharrow
Rowan
Shepherd's purse
Sorrel
Speedwell
Watercress
Yarrow

Common Medical Terms

The following terms, used to describe the healing properties of various herbs, are in common use among qualified medical herbalists and practitioners of folk medicine.

Anaesthetic   agent which produces insensibility to pain.
Alterative   agent causing alterations in medical conditions.
Analgesic   agent which deadens pain.
Anthelmintic   agent which expels worms.
Antibiotic   destroys bacteria.
Anticoagulant   prevents blood clotting.
Antiemetic   relieves vomiting.
Antilithic   dissolves gall or kidney stones.
Antiphlogistic   reduces inflammation.
Antipyretic   reduces fever.
Antiseptic   reduces or destroys harmful bacteria.
Antispasmodic   relieves muscular spasms and cramps.
Aperient   mild laxative.
Appetizer   promotes appetite.
Aphrodisiac   stimulates sexual desire.
Asthmatic   agent used to treat asthma.
Astringent   reduces secretions or discharges.
Calmative   mild sedative with calming effect.
Cardiac   stimulates heart.
Carminative   expels stomach gases from intestines.
Cathartic   laxative.
Coagulant   clots blood.
Cholagogue   agent that increases flow of bile to intestines.
Demulcent   soothes irritation.
Depressant   reduces nervousness.
Depurative   purifies blood.
Digestive   promotes digestion.
Diuretic   promotes urinary flow.

Emmenagogue   promotes menstrual flow.

Emollient   softens hard tissues.

Expectorant   promotes discharge of mucus from respiratory passages.

Febrifuge   agent which dispels fever.

Galactagogue   increases secretion of breast milk.

Hydragogue   agent which expels water from the body.

Hydrotic   agent which promotes perspiration.

Laxative   promotes bowel movement.

Narcotic   agent which induces sleep or loss of consciousness.

Nervine   calms nerves.

Stomachic   stimulates stomach.

Tonic   promotes good health and energy.

Vermifuge   agent which expels worms and other parasites from intestines.

Vulnerary   heals wounds.

Preparation of Herbs for Healing

Growing, Drying and Storage

Although herbs can be bought from commercial herb gardens and herb suppliers, if you are to become seriously involved in folk medicine you are recommended to attempt to grow your own raw materials. Herbs are comparatively easy to cultivate. Most of them are hardy plants which do not take up much room in the garden and, once well established, need very little attention. Although herbs usually grow in profusion in the wild, some care is required in first establishing them. The garden should be well drained, and preferably in a sunny, sheltered spot.

One essential requirement for the successful cultivation of herbs is fertile soil. Organic compost or fertilizer can be used, but herbs do not respond well to chemically based fertilizers or pesticides. Nor do they like a soil which is poorly balanced in minerals, and if your projected herb garden has that kind of soil it will need considerable attention before you begin planting.

As you will be growing your herbs not for decorative purposes but for use in medical remedies, arrange your garden so that the plants can be harvested easily. Make a plan of the area you will be using to grow the herbs, so that different kinds of plants can be grown in clumps. A formal herb garden of this type does not need a lot of ground – you will be amazed at how many different varieties of healing plants can be cultivated in a small area. Once the herb garden is established keep weeds under control so that the plants remain healthy.

Harvesting the herbs before using them in folk remedies is a subject which the old herbalists spend many pages of their textbooks describing. We need not go into such detail, but a few simple rules should still be followed. The old herbals recommended that the blossoms and leaves should be collected in spring and early summer; the fruits and berries would be gathered in late summer or early autumn, while the seeds were to be harvested in late autumn or early winter. This sequence of harvesting follows the natural cycle of the seasons and is quite logical. Obviously you pick only those plants which look healthy and disease-free. The ideal time to gather herbs which are not for immediate use and are to be dried and stored is on a sunny morning when the dew has evaporated from the grass. Handle the herbs as carefully as possible so as not to break the stems or bruise the leaves, and take them indoors immediately after picking.

To dry herbs, hang them from the ceiling in small bunches in a dark place. Alternatively lay them out on wooden racks covered with gauze or sheets of white paper. Although the place in which you dry the herbs must be warm, there should also be a free flow of air to prevent must forming on the plants, or premature rotting. Professional herbalists sometimes speed up the drying process by exposing the plants to artificial sources of heat. At home, either use a well ventilated airing cupboard, or put the herbs near a kitchen range such as a Rayburn or Aga. Never expose herbs to direct heat for drying.

Once the herbs have been dried they can be stored in airtight glass containers in a dark cupboard away from direct light. Alternatively they can be stored in plastic bags, although for obvious reasons this can create condensation problems. Remember to label each container with the herb it contains and the date it was harvested.

Making Up Herbal Remedies

Preparing the herbal remedy correctly is one of the most important aspects of the practice of folk medicine. Herbs for healing purposes can be applied in several different ways: ointments, salves and poultices for external use, and infusions and decoctions for internal use. The leaves and flowers of herbs can be soaked in water to distil their essence, but roots and seeds will have to be crushed or powdered. Herbal remedies are best made from fresh ingredients, and if possible they should be used within twelve hours of collection. If medicinal herbs are to be stored longer they should certainly be used within twelve months of harvesting. Seeds and roots can be kept for several years before they become no longer potent enough to work effective cures. Under normal circumstances, especially if you have a herb garden, you will be using fresh raw materials each season and will only need to store a back-up supply for the winter months.

Infusion is the most popular form of utilizing the healing power of herbs where only the leaves, stems and flowers are to be used. A simple process, it involves soaking the herbs in boiling water to create a beverage. The herbs should be boiled in a china, stone or heatproof glass vessel fitted with a tight lid, which helps to prevent the escape of volatile ingredients released from the herbs during distillation. Alternatively, boiling water can be poured over the herbs in the vessel as if you were making tea.

The usual quantity of herbal raw materials used in this distillation method is approximately ½–1 oz added to a pint of boiling water, although exact quantities vary from one herbalist to the next. For best results herbs should be infused for 10–15 minutes. The infused liquid is then strained through a piece of muslin or a fine kitchen sieve into a cup or glass and allowed to cool. If a bitter-tasting herb has been used, a small quantity of brown sugar or honey can be added as a natural sweetener.

The second method used by folk healers and herbalists to prepare herbs for medicinal purposes is called **decoction**; it is suitable for bark, roots and seeds. Approximately 1 oz of herbal raw material is added to 20 fl. oz of cold water in an enamel or glass container and allowed to soak for 10–15 minutes. The temperature is then raised to boiling point and the mixture simmered for 10–15 minutes, after which it is allowed to cool for another 10 minutes. During both processes the container in which the herbal mixture has been placed should be covered. Once the decoction is completed the liquid is strained through a fine cloth or sieve.

The final popular method for using herbs is poultices and ointments. To make a **poultice** you use herbs which have been freshly gathered, bruised and then crushed to a pulp using a pestle and mortar. The resulting pulped material is then mixed with a quantity of hot water. Alternatively dried herbs can be used as a base, and softened by adding cornmeal or flour. When applying the poultice to the patient put the herbal mixture between thin layers of cloth and then apply it direct to the afflicted part of the body.

The simplest method of making **ointments** is to mix 1 part of the powdered plant with 4 parts of lard or vegetable fat. Alternatively the herbs can be distilled, as in the infusion process, and the resulting liquid added to olive oil or any vegetable fat or oil. Add a small quantity of the dried herb left over from the distillation to provide a firm base for the ointment.

A basic **herbal syrup** can be made by dissolving 3 lb of brown sugar in 1 pint of boiling water. Boil the water again until a thick, syrupy substance is created, and then add the herbs.

Herbal teas can be made by infusing approximately 2–3 teaspoons of dried or freshly picked herbs in 1 pint of boiling water. Leave to brew for a few minutes. Always use a pottery or china teapot, never a metal one.

Dried herbs can be powdered using a pestle and mortar and taken in small quantities sprinkled on food or in water, milk or soup. They can also be mixed in hot or cold water, using a ratio of approximately 1 teaspoon to a ¼ glass of water.

Part Four
A Herbal Glossary

What follows is a glossary of the most common herbs in the British Isles which are used for healing in folk medicine. It covers botanical, medical and folklore aspects of herbalism as well as the application of the herbs in remedies. The information is presented in the following sequence for easy reference:

Botanical name
Popular name(s)
Habitat
Flora and general information
Folklore
General medical properties
Specific properties
Application and use

Healing plants with a high toxicity, such as deadly nightshade, have been excluded from the glossary. Although such plants have a long tradition of use in folk medicine they are generally regarded as too poisonous for use by non-professionals. Other plants have toxic capabilities, but can be used under restriction or in small quantities. These plants have been included in the glossary, but with the proviso that they are only used under the direction of a qualified medical herbalist. The majority of herbs are safe in use, but obviously common sense needs to be used in dealing with any botanically derived raw material which is used for medical purposes. If you find you are suffering an unpleasant reaction to any plant material consult a medical herbalist.

AGRIMONY

Botanical name: *Agrimonia eupatoria*.

Popular names: Church steeples, sticklewort.

Habitat: Hedge banks, copses and field borders.

Flora: Perennial, with small yellow flowers July–August.

Folklore: The name agrimony is derived from the Green *argemone*, meaning 'a white speck in the eye'. According to Nicholas Culpeper, this herb was sacred to the planet Jupiter and was ruled astrologically by the zodiac sign of Cancer (21 June to 20 July). Pliny the Elder described agrimony as a 'herb of sovereign power'. In the medieval period agrimony was said to possess magical powers, and was specially recommended as a cure for insomnia. It was said by the old herbalists that if agrimony 'be leyd under a mann's hede he shalt sleep as if he were dede. He shat never waken till from under his hede it be taken.' For this reason the herb was a popular ingredient in herbal pillows. Agrimony was included in a fifteenth-century folk remedy to heal musket wounds, and was also reputed to be able to ward off witchcraft. Its popular folk name of church steeples is derived from the shape of its tall flower spikes. Writing about the medicinal qualities of the plant, Gerard said that the leaves of agrimony are 'good for them that have naughty livers'.

General medical properties: Astringent, tonic, diuretic and expectorant.

Specific properties: This herb has a beneficial effect on the liver, kidneys and bladder. It promotes the flow of urine, prevents diarrhoea, can be used as an expectorant for persistent coughs and as a herbal gargle for sore throats. It should be used with caution for constipation, and can be applied externally on wounds or skin complaints such as acne. A poultice made from the herb will treat insect bites and stings. In the old days agrimony was believed to have the ability to draw out splinters from the flesh.

Application and use: Infuse the herb by pouring approximately ¼ pint of boiling water onto ½ teaspoon of dried agrimony. Leave for 15 minutes and then take 3 times daily.

ANGELICA

Botanical name: *Angelica archangelica.*

Popular names: Holy Ghost, archangel, masterwort.

Habitat: River Banks, damp fields and meadows.

Flora: Biennial or perennial, with greenish-white flowers May–August.

Folklore: Angelica derives its religious-sounding name from the fact that it is usually in flower on the Christian festival of St Michael on 8 May. Despite these orthodox religious associations, angelica was a plant widely prized by the pagans. With the coming of the new religion its pagan overtones were reversed, and it became a magical plant which had the power to protect its user from the powers of darkness. This was because in Hebrew mythology St Michael was the guardian of the gates of the underworld and waged war against the rebel archangel Lucifer. In the Middle Ages it is recorded that angelica grew freely in many London fields; it was collected by the old herbalists and folk healers as it had many medicinal and culinary uses. Because of its fragrance, angelica was widely used in crystallized form as a cake decoration. Its seeds are used in the making of vermouth. In his famous *Herbal*, Gerard states that the flowers of angelica baked with sugar or distilled water extracted from them 'makes the heart merry' and 'makes good the colour of the face and refreshes the vital spirits'. During the Great Plague of 1665 Londoners chewed pieces of angelica root in the belief that it would save them from catching the disease.

General medical properties: Appetizer, carminative, expectorant, stimulant, stomachic, tonic and diuretic.

Specific properties: Angelica will stimulate the appetite after long illnesses and is also recommended in cases of anorexia nervosa. It is used for treating anaemia, migraine, vertigo and general dizziness for whatever cause. The candied roots can be eaten to ward off infection and warm the stomach. As an expectorant the herb helps coughs, influenza, colds, sore throats and bronchitis. It helps to calm fevers, and eases flatulence and indigestion. Angelica can also be used to cure cystitis and as a urinary antiseptic. Good results have been achieved with this herb for treating muscular cramps, stimulating kidney action, and preventing nervous headaches and rheumatic pain. Angelica tea is good for improving bad eyesight and relieving deafness. Externally the plant can be used for chilblains.

Application and use: Infuse 1 teaspoon of crushed seeds in ½ cup of boiling water. Take 1 cup before each meal.

ASPARAGUS

Botanical name: *Asparagus officinalis*.

Popular names: Garden asparagus, sparrow grass.

Habitat: Cultivated.
Flora: Perennial, with whitish-green flowers in May and June.

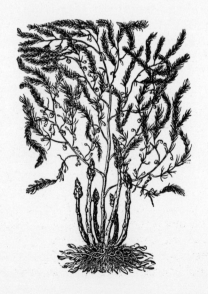

Folklore: The name of this plant is derived from a Greek word which means 'to sprout', referring to the fleshy shoots which are used in cookery. This plant has been cultivated for over two thousand years. It was used by the old herbalists both as a cure for constipation and for its alleged power to revive the sexual abilities of the impotent!

General medical properties: Diuretic and laxative.

Specific properties: Asparagus is recommended for the treatment of kidney disorders, water retention, gout and rheumatic pains.

Application and use: Infuse 1 teaspoon of the root stock in 1 cup of boiling water for 15 minutes. Take 1 cup a day.

AVENS

Botanical name: *Geum urbanum*.

Popular names: Colewort, herb bennet, St Benedict's herb.

Habitat: Woodland, hedgerows and ditches.

Flora: Perennial, with yellow flowers May – July.

Folklore: This plant gained its popular name of St Benedict's herb from the medieval *herba benedicta*, meaning the blessed herb. Because of its strong aromatic properties it allegedly had the magical power to drive away evil spirits. It was also believed that anyone who carried a sprig of this herb would not be bitten by rabid dogs or poisonous snakes. The leaves grow in threes, so the herb became associated with the Holy Trinity of the Father, Son and Holy Ghost; in addition, in Christian flower lore its five-petalled flowers symbolized the wounds suffered by Jesus on the cross. According to Culpeper, this plant was governed by the planet Jupiter; both he and Gerard recommended its use as an antidote to poison and animal bites. Paracelsus suggested that avens should be used to treat catarrh, stomach upsets and liver disease. In folk belief it was said that if you dug up the root of this plant before sunrise and hung it in a linen bag around your neck it would cure piles and strengthen the eyesight.

General medical properties: Astringent, stomachic and cardiac.

Specific properties: Avens is recommended for the cure of diarrhoea; it prevents vomiting and catarrh and can be used to ease the symptoms of the common cold. It can also be prescribed for heart disease, obstructions of the liver and the prevention of colic. It is used as a throat gargle and for the treatment of halitosis and mouth ulcers. Externally, it removes spots and blemishes from the skin.

Application and use: Boil 1 teaspoon of the root in ¼ pint of water and simmer for 5–10 minutes. Take 1 cup a day.

BALM

Botanical name: *Melissa officinalis*.

Popular names: Garden balm, sweet balm, lemon balm.

Habitat:
Cultivated, or on roadsides and in hedgerows.

Flora:
Perennial, with yellowish-white flowers in July.

Folklore:
This plant has the fragrance of lemons, hence its folk name of lemon balm. Its name in fact derives from a Greek word meaning 'bee', because large numbers of bees are attracted to the flowers. In southern Europe, where the plant originated, it is widely used for culinary purposes to flavour soups and salads.

General medical properties: Stimulant and carminative.

Specific properties: Balm is recommended for treating headaches, coughs and influenza, and for breaking fevers.

Application and use: Infuse 1–2 teaspoon of the dried herb in 1 cup of boiling water. Take one cup daily.

BARBERRY

Botanical name: *Berberis vulgaris.*

Popular names: Common barberry, sow berry.

Habitat: Woodland and hedgerows.

Flora: Perennial shrub, with yellow flowers May–June.

Folklore: This medicinal plant with its distinctive purple berries is much loved by pigs, hence one of its common names. It was introduced into Europe by medieval monks who cultivated it in their gardens; they ate the ripe fruits as a preserve and used the yellow dye which can be extracted from the roots for dyeing cloth. In ancient Egypt the barberry was used with fennel seeds as a cure for plague. The old herbals recommended the use of this plant as a gargle for sore throats and as a purgative for which it is renowned. Barberry is becoming rarer, as it is the host plant of the black rust fungi which attacks wheat, and for this reason is regarded as an enemy by farmers.

General medical properties: Cholagogue and astringent.

Specific properties: Barberry contains an alkaloid known as berberine which has astringent qualities. It is recommended as a mouthwash and throat gargle, also for use in remedies for curing dysentery, lowering blood pressure, dissolving kidney stones and as a purgative. The herb is also useful in cases of vitamin C deficiency as it has a high content of that vitamin.

Application and use: Infuse 1 teaspoon of the plant in 1 cup of boiling water. Infuse for 15 minutes. Take 1 cup daily.

BASIL

Botanical name: *Ocimum basilicum.*

Popular names: Sweet basil, garden basil, St Joseph's wort.

Habitat: Cultivated as culinary herb.

Flora: Perennial, with white to red flowers blooming June–September.

Folklore: Basil has been grown for centuries in kitchen gardens for use in cooking, and is recommended for use in sauces, dressings, soups and as a garnish. The herb is believed to have been introduced into the British Isles from Asia as late as the sixteenth century. In India it is recorded that basil was regarded as the sacred herb of the pantheon of Hindu gods and goddesses. To the ancient Cretans and Romans it was a symbol of love, a tradition which survived in popular English folklore – country people said that anyone who grew basil in their garden would never be short of admirers of the opposite sex. In the Middle Ages basil was used to alleviate the labour pains of expectant mothers and was said to be able to draw out the poison of scorpion stings. The latter attribute may come from the similarity of the Latin *Basilicum* to *Basilisk*, a mythical reptile hatched by a serpent from a hen's egg; anyone who came under the gaze of this creature was immediately struck down dead. In fact the common name of the herb is an abbreviation of the Greek *basilikon phuton*, meaning 'kingly herb'. Because of its strong smell basil was often used as a room freshener in medieval times.

General medical properties: Mild sedative, antispasmodic, digestive, appetizer, carminative and galactagogue.

Specific properties: Basil is recommended as a sedative, for stopping stomach cramps, vomiting, constipation and headaches, and in the treatment of whooping cough. It also helps relieve insomnia, migraine, dizziness and vertigo. The soothing oil of basil is recommended for treating insect stings, bites and minor scratches or cuts. Finally, the herb is reputed to be able to increase the flow of breast milk in nursing mothers.

Application and use: Infuse 1 teaspoon of the dried herb in ¼ pint of boiling water. Take 1 tablespoon 3 times a day. Mixed with sage it makes an excellent herbal tea.

BEARBERRY

Botanical name: *Arctostaphylos uva-ursi.*

Popular names: Bear's grape, whortberry, mountain box, red box.

Habitat: Woodland, heathland and hills.

Flora: Evergreen shrub, with white or pink flowers May–June.

Folklore: The scientific and popular names of this plant originate in the Greek *arkton staphyle* meaning 'bear's grapes'; in past times the glossy red berries of the shrub were regarded as a delicacy by the native European bear. The plant was used by rural folk healers in thirteenth-century Wales as an antiseptic but was not officially recognized until the eighteenth century.

General medical properties: Diuretic and antiseptic.

Specific properties: The active ingredients of bearberry leaves are hydroquionone and arbutin, both of which have an astringent effect which is useful for treating inflamed urinary tracts, especially in cystitis. A harmless side-effect of its use is that the patient's urine turns bright green. The leaves also contain a substance called allantoin which soothes and heals irritated body tissue. Today, bearberry is used principally for kidney disorders and water retention.

Application and use: Infuse 1 teaspoon of dried leaves in 1 cup of hot water. Cool, and take 2–3 cups a day. *Over-use can cause constipation.*

BETONY

Botanical name: *Stachys officinalis.*

Popular names: Wood betony, lousewort, common betony.

Habitat: Woodland and meadows.

Flora: Perennial, with reddish-purple flowers June–August.

Folklore: Allegedly the common name of this herb derives from an old Celtic word *bewton,* meaning 'good for the head', but this may be only speculative. Betony does have a long history as a magical plant with occult powers. Antonius Musa, physician to the Roman Emperor Augustus Caesar, wrote a book on the virtues of this herb, claiming that it was a good protection against evil and sorcery. An old superstition claimed that if two snakes were placed within a ring of betony they would fight to the death; possibly because of this belief the herb was regarded as a cure for snakebites and attacks by rabid dogs. In the old days betony was planted in churchyards, allegedly to stop the spirits of the dead from walking at night. If gathered without the use of an iron implement, betony was said to cure drunkenness. In his *Herbal* Culpeper assigned this herb to the rulership of the planet Jupiter and the zodiac sign of Aries, the ram (21 March–20 April).

General medical properties: Nervine, sedative, tonic, expectorant and asthmatic.

Specific properties: Betony is recommended for treating gallstones, heartburn and high blood pressure. It also prevents excessive sweating and the spitting of blood. Because it works on the central nervous system it is ideal for treating migraine, nervousness and neuralgia. It also acts as a mild sedative and tonic and is recommended for treating kidney infections. Externally, it can be used in an ointment for the treatment of boils, sores and cuts.

Application and use: Infuse ½ teaspoon in 1 cup of boiling water. Take once or twice a day.

BLACKBERRY

Botanical name: *Rubus fruticosus.*

Popular name: Bramble.

Habitat: Hedgerows and cultivated.

Flora: Shrub, with whitish-pink flowers June–September. Blackish-red berries September–October.

Folklore: The common name, bramble, is derived from the word *brom*, meaning 'thorny shrub'. In Germany the plant is still known as *Brombeere*. Culpeper assigned this plant to the ancient goddess of love, Venus; he also said, however, that it was ruled by the astrological sign of Aries, which comes under Mars – this was because the shrub has soft fruit but prickly thorns. Gerard recommended that blackberry leaves should be boiled in water with honey and white wine as a mouthwash for gum ulcers or as a lotion for sores on 'the privie parts'.

General medical properties: Astringent, tonic and diuretic.

Specific properties: Blackberry is recommended as a gargle for sore throats, for water retention and as a general tonic. The berries are rich in vitamin C and therefore good for preventing colds and influenza.

Application and use: Infuse 1 handful of berries in 1 pint of hot water. Take as a gargle for a sore throat or drink as a general tonic.

BORAGE

Botanical name: *Borago officinalis.*

Popular names: Bugloss, cool tankard, burrage.

Habitat: Culinary herb cultivated in gardens but also found wild.

Flora: Annual, with blue-purple star-shaped flowers June–August.

Folklore: Borage is a well-known cultivated herb widely used in cordials and cooling drinks. The name borage is said to derive from Arabic *abou rach*, meaning 'father of all sweat', a reference to the herb's alleged properties of promoting perspiration, for which reason it was recommended for treating fevers. The ancients believed that borage could cure melancholy by creating a state of euphoria: if drunk in moderate quantities, an infusion of borage allegedly had the effect of lowering the inhibitions and made the drinker talk profusely. Because the herb attracts bees it was always planted near hives. Its candied flowers were used for cake decorations, and its roots for flavouring wine.

General medical properties: Demulcent, diuretic, hydrotic and stimulant.

Specific properties: Borage promotes the flow of urine and perspiration and can therefore be used to treat fevers, chills and influenza. Externally, it can be made into a poultice for cooling inflammation.

Application and use: Infuse 1 teaspoon of fresh flowers or 2–3 teaspoons of dried flowers with ½ cup of water. Steep for 5 minutes and then strain. Alternatively, fresh borage leaves can be crushed with watercress or dandelion leaves to make a herbal juice.

BROOM

Botanical name: *Cytisus scoparius*.

Popular names: Common broom, he broom (without flowers), she broom (with flowers).

Habitat: Heathland, woodland and sandy places.

Flora: Perennial, with yellow flowers throughout summer.

Folklore: Traditionally, in popular folklore this plant has a sinister image. According to an old rhyme which originates in Sussex,

> If you sweep the house with blossomed broom in May
> You will sweep the head of the household away.

Despite this grim warning, country weddings always featured a bundle of green broom tied with multi-coloured ribbons as a good luck charm. Broom has always been associated with witchcraft. In heraldry it was the plant of the Plantagenet kings, who some historians believe may have been the secret leaders of the medieval witch cult. Their family name of Plantagenet is derived from one of the Latin names for broom, *Planta genista*. Medieval herbalists mixed the burnt ashes of broom with white wine to cure dropsy (water retention). Its pungent smell was said to have the power to calm wild horses and rabid dogs. It has a very strong, unpleasant taste.

General medical properties: Cardiac, diuretic, emetic and anticoagulant.

Specific properties: Broom is used to treat heart disease and kidney disorders and to increase urinary flow. It also treats low blood pressure and reduces excessive menstrual flow. It has been used to cure toothache, sciatica and gout. *Use with caution.*

Application and use: *Only under the direction of a medical herbalist.*

BRYONY
See White Bryony.

BUCKTHORN

Botanical name: *Rhamnus catharticus.*

Popular names: Purging buckthorn, waythorn, hart's horn, herb ivy, wortcress, black alder, alder buckthorn.

Habitat: Woodland and hedgerows.

Flora: Perennial, with greenish flowers May–June. Black berries ripen in September.

Folklore: Buckthorn, first recorded in Anglo-Saxon times, is renowned in folk medicine for its purgative qualities. Its straight, flexible branches are used to make wickerwork furniture. The pigment known as sap green is derived from the juice of the berries mixed with limewater and gum arabic. The woody parts were used in the old days to produce a charcoal that was employed in the manufacture of gunpowder.

General medical properties: Laxative and diuretic.

Specific properties: The general use of buckthorn in folk remedies is as a purgative to relieve constipation and increase urine flow in cases of water retention. Externally, it can be used to treat bruises.

Application and use: Infuse 1 teaspoon of *matured* dried bark in 1½ pints of boiling water in a covered container for approximately 30 minutes. Cool, and take 1 tablespoon morning and evening. *Use with caution. Do not use fresh bark and do not overdose, which produces vomiting and stomach pains as side-effects. If in any doubt about its use consult a medical herbalist.*

BUGLE

Botanical name: *Ajuga reptans.*

Popular names: Common bugle, creeping bugle, carpenter's bugle, bugle weed.

Habitat: Woodland and fields.

Flora: Perennial, with white or pink flowers May–July.

Folklore: One of the common names, carpenter's herb, indicates its use in folk medicine – it was said to be able to stem the flow of blood from cuts. As well as preventing bleeding, bugle contains an unknown ingredient, similiar to digitalis, which acts as a heart tonic.

General medical properties: Astringent, cardiac stimulant, expectorant and anti-haemorrhagic.

Specific properties: Principally used as an agent to stop bleeding from open wounds. Also inhibits menstrual flow, relieves bronchitis and acts as a tonic for the heart.

Application and use: Infuse 1 teaspoon of the herb in a cup of boiling water for 15 minutes. Take 1 cup a day.

BURDOCK

Botanical name: *Arctium lappa*.

Popular names: Cockle buttons, cat's bur, gypsy rhubarb, beggar's buttons, thorny burr.

Habitat: Ditches, watersides, hedges and wasteland.

Flora: Biennial, with purple flowers July–September.

Folklore: Burdock is popular with children because of its tiny burs, which cling to clothes; it is mentioned in Shakespeare's play *King Lear* on this account. In various parts of Europe and the Far East this herb is actively cultivated for culinary purposes: its young leaves are eaten in salads and the root can be boiled and served with butter to make a pleasant vegetable. It resembles rhubarb, hence one of its popular names which indicates that it was highly regarded by gypsies. Gerard said that the juice of the burdock leaf mixed with honey 'procureth urine and taketh away the pains of the bladder'.

General medical properties: Alterative, diuretic and tonic.

Specific properties: Burdock is recommended externally to treat skin complaints including boils, eczema and psoriasis. It is also said to be useful in the treatment of arthritis, rheumatic pains, bronchitis and asthma. It is an excellent blood purifier and can be used to heal burns.

Application and use: Infuse 3 teaspoons of finely chopped leaves in 1 pint of boiling water for 10 minutes. For bruises or external inflammation, apply a poultice of fresh leaves boiled for 5 minutes in lightly salted water. A hair lotion to prevent premature baldness can be made up by macerating 4 oz of fresh root and 2 oz of fresh nettle root for 8 days in a pint of rum. Massage the scalp daily with this mixture.

BURNET

Botanical name: *Sanguisorba officinalis*.

Popular name: Meadow pimpernel.

Habitat: Cultivated in gardens and growing wild in dry, grassy places.

Flora: Perennial, with purple flowers June–July.

Folklore: According to Culpeper, this plant used to grow wild in the fields next to St Pancras church in London and by a causeway in a field near Piccadilly. He assigned burnet astrologically to the sun, and described it as a 'precious herb', claiming that its frequent use 'preserves the body in health and the spirit in vigour'.

General medical properties: Tonic, astringent, cardiac and vulnerary.

Specific properties: Burnet is generally used as a tonic. It is also recommended for heart disease, for inhibiting menstrual flow and for healing open wounds and running sores.

Application and use: Burnet can be made into an ointment for external use, and the leaves can be infused for internal use.

BUTTERBUR

Botanical name: *Petasites hybridus*.

Popular names: Bog rhubarb, devil's hat.

Habitat: Wet places near rivers and ditches.

Flora: Perennial, with blue or red flowers in February–March.

Folklore: The botanical name is derived from the Greek *petasos*, a large hat – a reference to the shape and size of the leaves. The French herbalists called it devil's hat, but the reason is obscure. Its commonest name may derive from the fact that butter was once wrapped in its leaves. Culpeper described butterbur as 'a great preserver of the heart and cheerer of the vital spirits'. He also recommended its use to promote perspiration, for which reason it was used to treat the bubonic plague in the Middle Ages, and suggested that 'it were well if gentlewomen would keep this root preserved to help their poor neighbours' for 'it is fit the rich should help the poor for the poor cannot help themselves'. Among butterbur's other attributes was the power to kill tapeworms, a common problem in the days when inadequate hygiene was combined with a poor diet.

General medical properties: Antispasmodic, expectorant, astringent, febrifuge, vulnerary and diueretic.

Specific properties: Butterbur has a great many uses in folk medicine – for treating coughs, reducing fever, healing open wounds, curing stammering, and relieving stomach cramps and period pains. Because it is a muscle relaxant it can be recommended for general stress, headaches and asthma. Externally, as well as healing open wounds and cuts it can be applied as a poultice, using the leaves to reduce the swelling in bruises and to treat skin diseases. It is also used in cases of water retention as a diuretic.

Application and use: Infuse 1 teaspoon of the root in 1 cup of boiling water. Simmer for 15 minutes. Cool, and drink 1 cup of the infused liquid 3 times a day.

CAMOMILE

Botanical name: *Anthemis nobilis.*

Popular name: Chamomile.

Habitat: Cultivated and wild, in grass and heathland.

Flora: Perennial, with yellow-white flowers June–July.

Folklore: The use of this herb dates back to ancient Egypt, and camomile lotion is still widely used for treating skin disorders. In the Middle Ages herbalists used camomile flowers soaked in white wine as a cure for dropsy (water retention) and jaundice. In the past, because of its ground-covering ability, this plant was used to create lawns, hence the old saying: 'A camomile bed, the more it is trod the more it will spread.' Camomile was also very popular in cottage gardens because it was believed to have the almost mystical power of reviving wilting plants next to it. For cosmetic purposes, essence of camomile was used as a skin cleanser, and a dye was made from the flowers to lighten the hair.

General medical properties: Antispasmodic, sedative, appetizer, diuretic and demulcent.

Specific properties: Camomile is recommended for the treatment of fevers, insomnia and joint pains, for increasing appetite after long illnesses, for relieving period pains, for controlling bad coughs (as an antispasmodic) and for asthma. Externally, it can be applied as a lotion to heal rashes, inflammation, sores and bruises.

Application and use: Infuse 1 handful of camomile flowers in 1 pint of boiling water for 10–15 minutes.

CARAWAY

Botanical name: *Carum carvi.*

Popular name: Caraway seed.

Habitat: Cultivated as culinary herb, and wild in grassy places.

Flora: Biennial, with white flowers June–July.

Folklore: The name derives from Arabic *karawiya.* It is known that this herb was cultivated by the ancient Egyptians, and its actual use by mankind may date back as far as 3000 BC. The cultivation of caraway seeds for medicinal purposes is mentioned in the Bible. In the seventeenth century caraway seeds were a popular confection, eaten dipped in sugar candy. In Shakespeare's day the roots of the plant were eaten as a vegetable, and Culpeper compared it favourably with parsnips, indicating that it was good for the digestion. Shakespeare in fact mentions the root in *The Merry Wives of Windsor* when a character says, 'In an arbour we will eat a last year's pippin of my own graffing with a dish of Caraway and so forth.' Caraway was often included in the wedding feast, or the seeds were thrown at the bride and groom as a good luck charm. As an aromatic plant it was also used to flavour liqueurs.

General medical properties: Antispasmodic, appetizer, carminative, stomachic and expectorant.

Specific properties: Caraway seeds contain an oil which has a beneficial effect on the gastric juices and prevents excessive flatulence; it is therefore recommended as a digestive and for treating lack of appetite. In addition the plant can be used to treat uterine cramps, and it promotes the flow of breast milk in nursing mothers. As a gargle it can be used to sooth the symptoms of laryngitis and sore throats in general.

Application and use: Infuse 3 teaspoons of crushed leaves in ½ cup of boiling water, or infuse 1 teaspoon of freshly crushed seeds in 1 cup of boiling water. Leave for 10–15 minutes. Cool, and drink a cup of the infusion 3 times a day.

CATNIP

Botanical name: *Nepeta cataria.*

Popular name: Catmint.

Habitat: Cultivated.

Flora: Perennial, with purple-white flowers June – September.

Folklore: Commonly called *Herba cateria* by the old folk healers, this plant has the uncanny power of attracting cats because of its distinctive smell. Whenever you see a patch of catnip in a country garden you will also see a cat sitting near it. So attracted by this herb are some cats that they will even eat the young shoots when they first appear in the early spring. Frequently catnip is used to stuff toy mice as playthings for cats. According to an old saying, the only sure way to grow catnip is to sow seeds; otherwise

> Set it, you won't get it.
> Sow it, they won't know it.

Today catnip is rarely used by herbalists for its medical properties, but it has always been highly regarded by practitioners of folk medicine.

General medical properties: Carminative, antispasmodic, sedative, astringent, stomachic and emmenagogue.

Specific properties: The use of this herb for medicinal purposes includes the treatment of infantile colic, anaemia, inhibited menstruation, diarrhoea, gastric upsets, insomnia, fevers, influenza, flatulence and nervousness. It contains an oil whose major ingredient is thymol, which has an antispasmodic effect useful for treating bronchitis. Externally, it can be applied to cuts, bruises and sores.

Application and use: Infuse 1 teaspoon of the herb in 1 cup of boiling water. Take 1–2 cups a day.

CAT'S FOOT

Botanical name: *Antennaria dioica*.

Popular names: Mountain everlasting, life everlasting, cudweed, cotton weed.

Habitat: Woodland and meadows.

Flora: Perennial, with white and pink flowers May–August.

Folklore: The botanical name refers to its resemblance in shape to antennae. One of its popular names, cotton weed derives from the downy appearance of the leaves. The old herbalists used cat's foot as a remedy for mouth ulcers and to treat coughs.

General medical properties: Astringent, expectorant and mild diuretic.

Specific properties: Cat's foot can be used in cases of water retention and bronchitis, for treating mouth ulcers and as a gargle.

Application and use: Infuse 1 teaspoon of dried flowers in 1 cup of boiling water for 10–15 minutes. Take half a cup 3 times a day or as a gargle.

CAYENNE

Botanical name: *Capsicum annum*.

Popular names: Red pepper, chilli pepper.

Habitat: Cultivated.

Flora: Annual or biennial, with white flowers and distinctive red fruit.

Folklore: Cayenne peppers were introduced from North America in the fifteenth century, allegedly by the physician who sailed with Christopher Columbus to discover the New World. Because the plants are used to warm climates they have to be cultivated in greenhouses in the British Isles. The general name *Capsicum* derives from a Greek word meaning 'to bite', referring to its hot and pungent nature. The seventeenth- and eighteenth-century herbalists used cayenne pepper as a remedy for drunkenness.

General medical properties: Stimulant, tonic and digestive.

Specific properties: Tests with cayenne have indicated that it promotes the flow of gastric juices and saliva, and it is therefore both an appetizer and a digestive. It has also been recommended for treating nausea and as a cure for sore throats. Externally, it can be applied as a poultice to relieve sore or cramped muscles. It has the effect of mildly irritating the surface of the skin, which causes increased blood flow to the area and reduces inflammation. *Use with caution, since in concentrated form cayenne can cause irritation, especially on exposed skin.*

Application and use: ¾ teaspoon infused in 1 cup of boiling water.

CELERY

Botanical name: *Apium graveolens.*

Popular names: Common celery, wild celery.

Habitat: Cultivated and wild, in damp places near the sea.

Flora: Biennial, with white flowers July–November.

Folklore: Celery has been a popular vegetable since Roman times, even though in its wild form it tastes bitter. The cultivated celery eaten today was introduced by Italian gardeners in the Middle Ages. As well as being a popular salad plant, celery has also proved useful in folk remedies. It has been used as a cure for arthritis, rheumatism and gout, and was recommended for loss of appetite.

General medical properties: Antirheumatic, diuretic, carminative, sedative, appetizer and tonic.

Specific properties: In addition to its use in treating rheumatic pain, celery can also alleviate the state of depression which often accompanies this disease. It also acts as a urinary antiseptic, inhibits flatulence, promotes a good appetite and reduces obesity. Externally, it can be used to treat bruises.

Application and use: Infuse 1 teaspoon of seeds in ½ cup of boiling water, bring back to the boil and strain before use. Fresh celery juice extracted from the stems is also recommended. Take ½ cup 3 times daily.

CENTAURY

Botanical name: *Centaurium erythraea.*

Popular names: Feverwort, birthwort, common centaury.

Habitat: Woodland, fields and hedgerows.

Flora: Biennial or annual, with red flowers July–August.

Folklore: The name derives from the myth that Chiron the centaur used this herb to heal Hercules of an arrow wound. It was considered a sacred plant by the ancient Celtic druids, and preserved its magical aura into the Middle Ages. According to the medieval occultist Albertus Magnus, 'Magicians assured us that this herb has a singular virtue for if mixed with the blood of a female hoopoe and put in a lamp with oil all those present will

see themselves upside down with their feet in the air.'
Culpeper, with more inhibition than Albertus Magnus,
assigned centaury to the astrological rulership of the sun,
because 'their flowers open and shut as the Sun either showeth
or hideth its face'. Today centaury is one of the herbal
ingredients of vermouth.

General medical properties: Tonic, nervine, stomachic and
appetizer.

Specific properties: Centaury is primarily used as a gastric
stimulant, since its bitter ingredients have a stimulating effect
on the stomach and gastro-intestinal system: it encourages
appetite, and counteracts indigestion. It is also widely used as a
tonic and for treating nervous conditions.

Application and use: Infuse 1 teaspoon of the dried herb in 1
cup of boiling water. Leave for 10 minutes. Take 1 cup before
each meal.

CHERVIL

Botanical name: *Anthriscus cerefolium*.

Popular name: Garden chervil.

Habitat: Cultivated as a culinary herb.

Flora: Annual, with white flowers May–June.

Folklore: Chervil is a well-known culinary herb which was
introduced from France, according to some botanists; however, others say it was brought to the British Isles by the
Romans. It is used in sauces and soups, and as a garnish to fresh
vegetables and salads. In the Middle Ages pregnant women
were bathed in an infusion of this herb, which was believed to
make them feel well. A lotion made from chervil juice was used
by country-dwelling gentlewomen as a skin cleanser. Medically, it was used in folk remedies as a blood purifier.

General medical properties: Digestive, diuretic, depurative, tonic and expectorant.

Specific properties: Chervil juice can be used to treat skin disorders, gallstones, abscesses and sores, water retention, bronchitis and high blood pressure.

Application and use: Infuse 1 teaspoon of the fresh herb in ½ cup of boiling water. Take ½ cup a day. Alternatively, sprinkle the finely chopped herb over food.

CHICKWEED

Botanical name: *Stellaria media.*

Popular names: Starwort, adder's mouth, stitchwort, hen bite.

Habitat: Gardens, fields, hedgerows and wasteland.

Flora: Annual or biennial, with white flowers all year.

Folklore: As the list of possible habitats indicates, this is a prolific 'weed'. The botanical name, *Stellaria*, and the common name starwort, refer to the star-shaped flower. The name chickweed derives from the fact that traditionally this plant was used to feed chickens; it is also liked by rabbits, hamsters and gerbils. In the kitchen it can be prepared as a salad or cooked as a vegetable.

General medical properties: Vulnerary, antirheumatic, laxative, expectorant and emollient.

Specific properties: Chickweed is recommended for the treatment of skin diseases (especially where there is excessive itching), bronchitis, rheumatic pains, arthritis and period pains. Externally, the crushed stems and leaves can be used to heal open wounds, cuts, bruises and burns.

Application and use: Boil 1 teaspoon of the herb in 2 pints of water until only 1 pint remains. Take ½–1 cup a day. The crushed leaves can be made into a poultice or ointment for external application.

CHICORY

Botanical name: *Cichorium intybus.*

Popular name: Endive.

Habitat: Cultivated, and wild in grassy and waste places.

Flora: Perennial, with blue-violet flowers July–September

Folklore: Chicory is a well-known culinary herb which has recently received some popularity as a substitute for caffeine in coffee, especially in health food products. The common name endive comes from the Arabic *hendibeh*. The plant has a long history and is recorded in ancient Egypt, where its blanched leaves were used in salad, as they are often still used today. According to folk belief a sprig of chicory worn on the person had the magical power to unlock doors and to make the wearer invisible. The old herbalists used chicory principally as a tonic, and it was renowned by them for its stimulatory qualities.

General medical properties: Appetizer, tonic, digestive, laxative and diuretic.

Specific properties: The main use of the herb today is still as a tonic and mild stimulant, but it is also utilized to promote the appetite, especially after long illnesses, and to treat jaundice, gallstones, gastro-enteritis and sinus problems. Externally, it can be applied to cuts and bruises.

Application and use: Steep 1 teaspoon of the root or leaves in ½ cup of boiling water. Strain, and take 1–1½ cups of the resulting liquid a day. The boiled leaves or flowers can be applied externally as a poultice. *Use with caution, as prolonged dosage can affect the eyesight. If uncertain, consult a medical herbalist.*

CINQUEFOIL

Botanical name: *Potentilla anserina.*

Popular names: Wild tansy, silverweed, gooseweed, cramp-weed.

Habitat: Roadsides, marshy ground and pastures.

Flora: Perennial, with yellow flowers May–September.

Folklore: The early name of this plant was *Argentina*, meaning 'silver'; it belongs to a genus of plants with over three hundred different species, one of which, *Potentilla argentea*, retains the idea of the silver colour. The botanical name of the genus comes from Latin *potens*, 'powerful', a reference to the plant family's general astringent qualities; *anserina*, the specific name, means 'pertaining to geese' – it was thought that geese were attracted to the leaves as food. In the Middle Ages frogs were also recorded as being frequently found near cinquefoil, although no sensible reason has been offered to explain their liking for it. The name cinquefoil refers to its five distinct leaves; cramp-weed indicates that it was used in folk remedies to relieve the agony of muscular cramps. The medieval herbalists boiled the roots in milk as a cure-all, and the resulting juice was used to treat epilepsy. In magical lore this herb was said to have the power to ward off witches and evil spirits.

General medical properties: Astringent, antispasmodic, tonic and stomachic.

Specific properties: Cinquefoil can be used to treat piles, uterine and general muscular spasms, stomach pains and period discomfort, and as a gargle for mouth ulcers and sore throats. Externally, it can be used on cuts and wounds.

Application and use: Infuse 2 teaspoons of the root, or of the dried leaves or flowers, in 1 cup of boiling water. Take 1 cup 3 times daily.

CLOVE

Botanical name: *Eugenia caryophyllata*.

Popular name: Clove.

Habitat: Imported from tropical countries.

Flora: Evergreen, with yellow flowers.

Folklore: Cloves were introduced into Europe as early as the sixth century as a culinary spice. Highly scented, they are still used as a flavouring in apple pies; in the sixteenth century they were included in body powders for their deodorant effect. Medically they have been used particularly in the relief of toothache because of their numbing nature.

General medical properties: Antiseptic and anaesthetic.

Specific properties: For the treatment of painful teeth.

Application and use: Apply oil of clove direct to the gum above or below the tooth.

COLTSFOOT

Botanical name: *Tussilago farfara*.

Popular names: Billsfoot, horsehoof, foalfoot, coughwort, bullsfoot, son-before-father.

Habitat: Wasteland and wet places.

Flora: Perennial, with yellowish flowers in early spring.

Folklore: Named after the shape of its leaves, coltsfoot has been recognized as a folk remedy for coughs since earliest times. The Greeks called it *bechion*, and the Romans knew it as *tussilago*, which can both be translated as 'cough plant'. When the Romans occupied Britain they sent back to Rome cough mixtures made of coltsfoot and flavoured with honey. Coltsfoot leaves are unusual because they appear after the flowers, which is why medieval herbalists nicknamed the herb *filius ante patrem* or 'the son before the father'. Coltsfoot was also a principal ingredient in herbal smoking mixtures, possibly because it had a soothing effect on the chest.

General medical properties: Emollient, demulcent, antispasmodic, diuretic and expectorant.

Specific properties: The primary use is for treating coughs, colds and bronchial disorders. It has a general calming action on inflamed respiratory tracts and can be used on asthmatic conditions. Externally, it can be applied in poultice form on sores and burns.

Application and use: Infuse 2 teaspoons of the dried flowers in 1 cup of boiling water. Drink warm 3 times a day. Freshly crushed leaves or flowers can be made into a poultice with honey and applied externally.

COLUMBINE

Botanical name: *Aquilegia vulgaris*.

Popular name: Common columbine.

Habitat: Woodland and scrub, and culivated as a garden flower.

Flora: Perennial, with blue and white flowers August–September.

Folklore: In the old herbals columbine was considered sacred to the planet Venus and the goddess of love; if you carried a posy of columbine, it was believed to elicit sincere affection from the person you loved. Culpeper said that a potion made from columbine seeds taken in wine made childbirth easier.

General medical properties: Astringent and diuretic.

Specific properties: Generally columbine is restricted to mouthwashes for sore gums and mouth ulcers, but it can also be used to ease childbirth and promotes urinary flow in cases of water retention.

Application and use: Steep 1 teaspoon in 1 cup of cold water. Bring to the boil and strain. Take 1 tablespoon 3 times a day.

COMFREY

Botanical name: *Symphytum officinale*.

Popular names: Knitbone, gumplant, healing herb, slippery root.

Habitat: Meadows and gardens.

Flora: Perennial, with whitish-purple flowers May–August.

Folklore: The common name of comfrey is derived from Latin *confirma* meaning 'joined together'. It was widely believed in ancient times that comfrey could help broken bones heal more quickly, hence its popular name of knitbone. The medical profession laughed at this claim until it was discovered that comfrey contains silica and albition, both substances which aid the fast healing of bone matter. Comfrey is an important animal feedstuff in many parts of the Third World and is also used as raw material for organic compost. Recent scientific tests have revealed that it is a natural source of vitamin B12 and is rich in protein – it is estimated that comfrey contains the same percentage of protein as soya beans and 10 per cent more than cheddar cheese. To date, attempts to extract this protein for human consumption have not proved successful.

General medical properties: Astringent, demulcent, vulnerary, expectorant and sedative.

Specific properties: Comfrey can be used as a cough remedy, for treating asthma, as a gargle for sore throats, and to treat tuberculosis and dysentery. Externally, a poultice of the leaves can be applied to cuts, wounds, bruises and varicose veins.

Application and use: Infuse 1 teaspoon of the rootstock in 1 cup of boiling water. Take 1 wineglass twice a day. A poultice made from the fresh leaves can be applied externally to sore breasts.

CORIANDER

Botanical name: *Coriandrum sativum.*

Popular name: Coriander.

Habitat: On bare ground, and cultivated.

Flora: Annual, with white and reddish flowers June–September.

Folklore: This plant, cultivated for over three thousand years, is mentioned in ancient Hindu scripts, in the medical texts of the Greek physicians, in the Bible, in the Ebers Papyrus of ancient Egypt and in almost every medieval herbal. Its name originated from Greek *koris*, 'bed bug', a reference to the similarly unpleasant smell of the unripe fruit. The fresh leaves are widely used for flavouring in various types of cookery, while the root can be cooked as a vegetable. The gastric juices are stimulated by chewing the seeds which are also used in making liqueurs, in curries and in baking.

General medical properties: Carminative, stimulant and appetizer.

Specific properties: Coriander is generally used to stimulate the appetite and cure flatulence. Applied externally, the bruised seeds offer relief from rheumatic pain.

Application and use: Infuse 1 teaspoon of the dried leaves or seeds in 1 cup of boiling water for 15 minutes. Take 1 cup daily.

CORNFLOWER

Botanical name: *Centaurea cyanus*.

Popular names: Bachelor's buttons, blue knapweed, blue burnet, bluebottle.

Habitat: Wild in cornfields and cultivated in gardens.

Flora: Annual, with blue flowers June–August.

Folklore: The cornflower gained its popular name of bachelor's buttons because it was often worn by young men in love; if the flower faded too quickly it was taken as an omen that the lady in question did not return that love. According to Greek myth the cornflower was originally a handsome boy who fell madly in love with the goddess Flora, whose festival was celebrated in the spring. The goddess changed the boy into a cornflower so that she would always have him by her side. Traditionally cornflowers are luck flowers. In folklore the cornflower was said to have the power to heal diseases of those with blue eyes. Although it was once a common sight in English cornfields, the herbicides of modern agriculture are fast making it a rarity in its natural environment.

General medical properties: Diuretic, tonic and astringent.

Specific properties: Cornflowers are recommended for treating eye irritations, conjunctivitis and weak eyesight. They can also be used in cases of water retention and as a general tonic.

Application and use: Infuse 1 oz of dried flowers in 2 pints of boiling water. Strain, cool, and take 1 cup before meals.

COUCH GRASS

Botanical name: *Elymus repens.*

Popular names: Twitchgrass, witch grass.

Habitat: Wasteland.

Flora: Perennial, with purple flowers June–October.

Folklore: Although hated by gardeners because it is very difficult to eradicate, couch grass has a long history as a medicinal plant dating back to ancient Greece and Rome. Sick dogs are known to seek out the plant and eat it to cause vomiting. In the past the roasted root has been used as a substitute for coffee and as a replacement for bread during periods of famine. The medieval herbalists used couch grass to treat inflamed bladders, painful urination and water retention; recent scientific tests have indicated that it does possess a strong diuretic action. Other tests have proved that it has antibiotic qualities, too.

General medical properties: Antiseptic, antibacterial and diuretic.

Specific properties: Recommended for the treatment of water retention, in cystitis and as a urinary antiseptic.

Application and use: Infuse 1 teaspoon of the root in 1 cup of boiling water. Cool and strain. Take 1 cup a day.

COWSLIP

Botanical name: *Primula veris.*

Popular names: Palsy wort, St Peter's herb, herb Peter.

Habitat: Meadows and marshy land.

Flora: Perennial, with yellow flowers May–June.

Folklore: Cowslips derive their common name from the Old English *cusloppe* or cowslop, because they grew in fields where domesticated animals were grazed. Its generic name comes from Latin *primus*, first, referring to the fact that it flowers in the early spring. The popular name of herb Peter or St Peter's herb originated in the myth that the flower sprang up on the ground where the saint dropped the keys to Heaven. The medieval herbalists regarded the cowslip as a safe sedative for those suffering from insomnia. It was also said to cure the palsy, a form of paralysis with involuntary tremors – hence another of its names. Although once widely used in folk remedies, by the 1870s its popularity had declined. In the nineteenth century cowslips were used to garland maypoles and were scattered on the village green for country dances. Cowslip was also a major ingredient in country wines, fermented with sugar, honey and lemon juice. The roots were also used in the brewing of orthodox wines and beers to improve the flavour of the finished product. The candied flowers were used for cake decorations and were popular as confectionery. In folklore the cowslip was regarded as the home of elves and fairies, hence Puck's lines in Shakespeare's *A Midsummer Night's Dream:*

> Where the bee sucks there suck I,
> In a Cowslip's bell I lie: There I couch when owls do cry.

General medical properties: Sedative, nervine, anti-spasmodic, expectorant and narcotic.

Specific properties: Cowslip is used to cure insomnia, ease bronchial coughs and act as a general nerve sedative.

Application and use: *Use with caution, as cowslips have irritant qualities to which allergy sufferers may prove sensitive.* Infuse ½ oz of leaves or flowers in 1 pint of water. Drink 1–2 cups a day.

DAISY

Botanical name: *Bellis perennis*.

Popular name: Eye-of-the-day.

Habitat: Wild in pastures, and cultivated.

Flora: Perennial, with yellow and white flowers March–October.

Folklore: The humble daisy is held in high regard by horti-culturists because it manufactures lime and so enriches the soil. Chaucer called it the eye-of-the-day because it opens its flower when the sun shines and closes it at sunset. The childhood custom of making daisy chains is of great antiquity: it may date from sacrificial offerings of flowers made to the old pagan gods.

General medical properties: Expectorant, astringent and diuretic.

Specific properties: Daisies are recommended to help alleviate kidney disorders, rheumatism, arthritis, bronchitis and diarrhoea.

Application and use: Infuse 1 teaspoon of the dried herb for 10 minutes in a cup of boiling water. Drink 1 cup 2–3 times a day.

DANDELION

Botanical name: *Taraxacum officinale*.

Popular names: Lion's tooth, priest's crown, puffball.

Habitat: Wasteland.

Flora: Perennial, with yellow flowers in early summer followed by distinctive puffball of seeds.

Folklore: The common name of dandelion is derived from the French dent de lion or lion's teeth, which the leaves were said to resemble. The Tudors gave it the rather cruder nickname of piss-in-the-bed, a reference to its ability to increase the flow of urine. Children have always blown the seeds from its puffball to tell the time; however, it is said that if all the seeds are blown away the unfortunate child will be rejected by its mother. In country lore, to see the seeds blown free of the puffball by the wind is claimed to be a sign of rain coming. The plant was also used in a popular rustic love charm: a single girl plucked a fresh dandelion and blew the fluffy head; the number of blows it took to disperse all the seeds indicated the number of years she would have to wait before getting married. To dream of a dandelion is a portent of difficult times ahead. Ideally, dandelions should be gathered on Midsummer's Eve (23 June) when they were supposed to have the power to ward off the evil spirits believed to be abroad on that night.

Apart from being a medical plant the dandelion has also been used for food. Its blanched leaves are used in salads, and the roots provide a coffee substitute as sold in health food shops. There is very little mention of the herb in the classical world, but it is known that the Arabs used it in the eleventh century. A Russian variety of the plant was grown during the Second World War because its roots exuded a latex material from which rubber was made; the British plant provides only small quantities of this product, insufficient for commercial use. In scientific tests dandelion roots have been proved to increase bile secretion, which might prove useful in the treatment of hepatitis.

General medical properties: Diuretic, laxative, tonic, anti-rheumatic, expectorant and appetizer.

Specific properties: The dandelion is mainly recommended for use as a diuretic to cure water retention. It can also be used in the treatment of chest congestion, jaundice, rheumatic pain, gout, constipation, diabetes, circulatory disorders, insomnia, anaemia and as an anticholesterol agent.

Application and use: Steep 2 teaspoons of the herb in 1 cup of cold water. Boil, cool and strain. Take ½ cup a day, lukewarm or cold.

DILL

Botanical name: Anethum graveolens.

Popular names: Dilly, dillweed, common dill, garden dill.

Habitat: On wasteland, and cultivated as a culinary herb.

Flora: Annual, with yellow flowers in June.

Folklore: The common name of dill originates in a word in the Indo-European group of languages meaning 'to blossom', and is said to have originated in Asia. It has been used as a medical plant for centuries and is mentioned in the Bible. In folklore dill has traditionally been regarded as an antidote to witchcraft: according to the old country rhyme, 'Vervain and Dill hinderith witches of their will.' It was also regarded as a plant with aphrodisiac properties, and was a favoured ingredient in medieval love potions. Dill water is still included in recipes for gripe water to be administered to children. In the kitchen dill can be a flavouring or garnish in soup and sauces, with fish and in cakes and pastries. It is also used as a perfume in cosmetic soaps.

General medical properties: Carminative, appetizer, antispasmodic, nervine, stomachic, stimulant and galactagogue.

Specific properties: Dill is said to cure flatulence, insomnia, colic and indigestion, and to increase the appetite. It also promotes breast milk in nursing mothers. The seeds, chewed, are recommended for halitosis.

Application and use: Steep 2 teaspoons of the seeds in 1 cup of boiling water for 10–15 minutes. Take ½ cup 2–4 times per day.

DOCK

Botanical name: *Rumex obtusifolius*.

Popular names: Broad-leaved dock, herb Patience.

Habitat: Wasteland.

Flora: Perennial, with greenish flowers June–September.

Folklore: Dock leaves are an old country cure for nettle stings, and the plant is often found in the vicinity of a nettle bed. The general use of the dock family in folk remedies is as a laxative and for jaundice.

General medical properties: Astringent, tonic, purgative and cathartic.

Specific properties: This plant can be used as an all-purpose purging agent, especially in cases of liver disorder. Externally, it can be used to treat skin diseases such as ringworm and scabies. In small doses it is regarded as a tonic.

Application and use: *Only on the advice of a medical herbalist, as contact for long periods can create skin allergy and overdosing causes nausea.*

DOG ROSE

Botanical name: *Rosa canina*.

Popular names: Briar rose, queen of flowers.

Habitat: Woodland and hedgerows.

Flora: Perennial shrub, with white or pale pink flowers June–August.

Folklore: This flowering shrub gained its popular name of dog rose because medieval herbalists of the seventeenth and eighteenth centuries used it to treat the bites of rabid dogs. Pliny the Elder said that the ancient name for Britain – Albion – was derived from Latin *alba*, meaning 'white', because the island was covered with wild white roses. Rosehips, a natural source of vitamin C, were used in folk remedies to treat colds and influenza; rosehip syrup was manufactured in large quantities during the Second World War when other sources of vitamin C, such as oranges, were unavailable.

General medical properties: Laxative, diuretic, astringent and tonic.

Specific properties: Rosehip syrup is recommended for the prevention and treatment of colds, influenza and bronchitis. It can also be used as a general tonic, for constipation and infections of the gall bladder.

Application and use: Infuse 2½ teaspoons of rosehips in a cup of boiling water. Simmer for ten minutes. Strain and take 1 cup daily.

ELDER

Botanical name: *Sambucus nigra*.

Popular name: Black elder.

Habitat: Woods and gardens.

Flora: Perennial shrub or tree, with yellow-white flowers July–September.

Folklore: The elder was known to the ancient Egyptians and has a long history in folk medicine. Elderflower water is still used in modern cosmetic preparations, and is recommended as a skin cleanser and a treatment for sunburn. Medieval herbalists and folk healers used elderberries to bring on menstruation. Until comparatively recently elderflower and peppermint were widely used in a rural folk remedy for coughs and colds. Elderflowers and elderberries both produce a very light, enjoyable wine popular among country people. The fruit can also be used in conserves, jams and pies.

For various reasons the elder was regarded with awe by country folk, who thought it was an unlucky tree to have in the garden despite its many advantages. If a tree was cut down it was believed that the Elder Mother who lived inside it would wreak havoc in the lives of those responsible. This folk belief dates back to the pagan worship of the Moon Goddess, who had the elder as her sacred tree. If you gathered elder branches on May Day, it was believed that pieces of it could be used to cure the bite of a rabid dog. However, the tree could only be cut safely by repeating the following charm before touching it with your saw: 'Old girl give me of thy wood and I will give you some of mine when I grow into a tree.' This simple trick was said to save the cutter from a dire fate for daring to interfere with the Elder Mother.

General medical properties: Diuretic, purgative, antispasmodic and laxative.

Specific properties: Elder's berries, flowers, leaves and bark can be used to treat constipation, arthritis, influenza, hay fever, sinus trouble, fevers and catarrh. Externally, they are helpful for bruises, chilblains and sprains.

Application and use: Infuse 2 tablespoon of flowers in 1 cup of boiling water. Take 3 cups a day, hot. Infuse fresh berries in boiling water for 2–3 minutes and extract the juice. Take 1 wineglass, diluted with water, a day. *Use with caution.*

ELECAMPANE

Botanical name: *Inula helenium.*

Popular name: Elfwort, scabwort.

Habitat: Damp places, woodland and hedgerows.

Flora: Perennial, with yellow flowers June–September.

Folklore: The specific name, *helenium*, derives from Helen who was carried off to Troy by Paris in classical mythology; where her tears fell on the ground this flower is said to have sprung up. A sacred plant to the ancient Celts, it was known to the Anglo-Saxons and used by the medieval Welsh herbalists. Its other popular names of elfwort and scabwort may indicate respectively a connection with the fairies and its use in curing skin diseases. Gerard recommended its use for 'the shortness of breath' and dealing with persistent coughs; he claimed that the plant purged the chest of phlegm and mucus. In medieval times the flowers were candied and eaten as a confection, and elecampane is still used in the flavouring of some European wines and liqueurs.

General medical properties: Expectorant, tonic and antibiotic.

Specific properties: The chief use of elecampane is as an expectorant for dealing with bronchial coughs. It is also used in cases of water retention and as an antiseptic. In addition it promotes menstruation and is a tonic and appetizer, although these are only minor uses.

Application and use: Infuse 1 teaspoon of the root in 1½ pints of boiling water for 15 minutes. Drink 1–2 cups a day as required.

EYEBRIGHT

Botanical name: *Euphrasia officinalis*.

Popular name: Meadow eyebright.

Habitat: Meadows and pastures.

Flora: Annual, with white flowers June–September.

Folklore: The generic name originates in a Greek word meaning 'gladness'. It seems to have been unknown to European herbalists until it was introduced in a herbal dated 1305, although it was known in the classical world. Culpeper assigned this herb to the zodiac sign of Leo (21 July–21 August) and said that it strengthened the brain. Gerard recommended it for 'feeble eyes' and, as its common name suggests, this was its principal use in folk medicine. In ancient Iceland the plant's juice was used to treat serious eye disorders; in medieval Scotland folk healers mixed its juice with milk and applied it as a lotion to the eyes, using a feather. Folk herbalists also used eyebright to restore a bad memory and in cases of vertigo.

General medical properties: Astringent, anti-catarrhal and anti-inflammatory.

Specific properties: Eyebright can be used to cure eye problems, sinus disorders, catarrh, allergies and inflammation.

Application and use: Infuse 1 teaspoon of the dried herb in 1 cup of boiling water for 10 minutes. Cool, strain and take 1 cup 3 times a day or use as an eyebath.

FAT HEN

Botanical name: *Chenopodium album.*

Popular names: White goosefeet, pigweed.

Habitat: Wasteland.

Flora: Annual, with greenish-white flowers June–September.

Folklore: The generic name derives from Greek *khenopodion*, meaning 'goosefoot', a reference to the shape of its leaves. Fat hen is related to spinach and is an edible vegetable which was included in the human diet from Stone Age times to the nineteenth century. The seeds can be crushed to make flour, and the leaves can be cooked like spinach or eaten raw in salads. The plant has also been widely used as animal feed.

General medical properties: Purgative.

Specific properties: Fat hen plant is rich in iron, calcium and vitamins B1 and C. It can therefore be used in cases of anaemia and vitamin C deficiency, and as a laxative to cure constipation.

Application and use: Infuse 1 teaspoon of the dried herb in 1 cup of boiling water. Take 1 cup a day.

FENNEL

Botanical name: *Foeniculum vulgare*.

Popular names: Common fennel, sweet fennel.

Habitat: Wild on wasteland, and cultivated as a culinary herb.

Flora: Perennial or biennial (occasionally annual), with yellow flowers July–October.

Folklore: The plant's generic name comes from Latin *foeniculum*, which means 'little hay' and refers to the appearance of the dried leaves. Fennel was introduced into northern and western Europe by the occupying Roman armies. The ancient Egyptians, Greeks, Chinese and Hindus used it for both its culinary qualities and medicinal properties. Pliny the Elder cites over twenty herbal remedies containing fennel, and the Greek physicians said that it increased milk flow in nursing mothers. It is one of the nine sacred herbs mentioned in the famous Anglo-Saxon charm. According to a country saying, fennel should never be cultivated but only gathered from the wild: 'Sow Fennel, sow trouble' was the rustic advice. Despite this, fennel has been a popular feature of kitchen herb gardens for centuries. It is used in soups and sauces, and as a garnish for fish. The roots and stems may be eaten as a vegetable, and the seeds are used in liqueur manufacture. In folk belief, a few fennel seeds placed in the keyhole of a haunted house kept ghosts away. In magical lore fennel was believed to be able to restore libido to the impotent and frigid, and for this reason it was often included in medieval love charms and potions.

General medical properties: Antispasmodic, carminative, diuretic, stomachic, stimulant, expectorant and galactagogue.

Specific properties: Fennel has a strong smell of aniseed. It can be recommended for colic, flatulence, indigestion, bronchitis, obesity, jaundice, sore throats, bed-wetting, gall bladder disorders, colic, earache and toothache. It also has uses in veterinary medicine. The seeds, boiled in barley water, are said to increase the flow of breast milk.

Application and use: *Use with caution, as overdosing can affect the nervous system and the fresh leaves are an irritant.* Infuse 2 teaspoons of the crushed leaves or seeds in 1 cup of boiling water for 10 minutes. Take 3 times a day.

FENUGREEK

Botanical name: *Trigonella foenum-graecum.*

Popular name: Greek hay.

Habitat: Wasteland, and cultivated.

Flora: Annual, with pink flowers June–July.

Folklore: Originally fenugreek was extensively cultivated in the ancient world as an animal feedstuff, hence its common and specific names, Greek hay and *foenum-graecum.* It is believed that the herb was introduced into medieval Europe by the Benedictine order of monks, but it was not mentioned in any English herbal until the sixteenth century. Fenugreek was used by the famous Arab physicians, but the Egyptians and Hindus cultivated it for food. In the Middle Ages it is recorded that fenugreek was added to inferior hay because of its pleasant smell. Culpeper assigned rulership of the herb to the planet Mercury, which rules Gemini (21 May–20 June) and Virgo (22 August–22 September). He claimed that the bruised leaves, placed on top of the head, cured vertigo. Seventeenth-century apothecaries recommended that after giving birth women should sit over the fumes from a decoction of this herb, with their legs open, to help expel the placenta. Today fenugreek is widely used in veterinary medicine, in chutney and curries, and as a substitute for coffee.

General medical properties: Emollient, vulnerary, tonic, expectorant and demulcent.

Specific properties: Fenugreek has always been renowned for expelling poisons and unwanted waste materials from the human body. It can also be used as a cure for bronchitis, a gargle for sore throats and a general tonic. Externally, it is recommended for treating wounds, sores and boils.

Application and use: Infuse 1 teaspoon of the seeds in 1 cup of boiling water for 10 minutes. Use one cup 3 times daily.

FEVERFEW

Botanical name: *Tanacetum parthenium.*

Popular names: Flirtwort, feverwort, featherfoil.

Habitat: Farmland.

Flora: Perennial, with yellow flowers June–July.

Folklore: The common name of feverfew is derived from Latin *febrifugia*, which means a plant which has the ability to drive out fevers. According to the old herbalists and folk healers, feverfew was used to bring on menstruation and for expelling the placenta after childbirth; it was also used in cases of stillbirth. Culpeper stated that this herb was ruled by the goddess Venus and had been provided by her to aid womankind. When its leaves are crushed it gives off an unpleasant smell which repels insects.

General medical properties: Tonic, sedative, mild laxative and emmenagogue.

Specific properties: Recent research has indicated that feverfew is very efficacious in the treatment of headaches and migraine. It can also be used in cases of colic, flatulence, indigestion, colds, influenza, alcoholic poisoning and inhibited menstrual flow.

Application and use: Infuse 1 teaspoon of the dried leaves or flowers in 1 cup of boiling water, and take 1 cup daily.

FIGWORT

Botanical name: *Scrophularia nodosa.*

Popular name: Pilewort, throat-wort, heal all.

Habitat: Wet places, ditches and woodland.

Flora: Perennial, with greenish-brown flowers June–July.

Folklore: It is believed that the name figwort is a corruption of Latin *ficus*, 'fig'. In the classical world it was used as a herbal cure for piles, which resemble figs! Culpeper states that figwort is ruled by the planet Venus and the zodiac sign of Taurus (21 April–20 May). He recommended its use to cure the skin disease known as the King's Evil in his day but now known as scrofula. Folk healers believed that the beneficial action of this plant on the liver would cure any skin disorder.

General medical properties: Diuretic, mild laxative, cardiac stimulant.

Specific properties: Figwort can be used to cure sore throats, ease constipation and stimulate the heart, and to alleviate water retention. Externally, it can be used to treat all skin diseases and helps reduce the swellings of bruises.

Application and use: Infuse 1 teaspoon of the dried root stock or flowers in 1 cup of boiling water. Take 1–2 cups a day.

FLAG
See Purple Flag, Sweet Flag.

FLAX

Botanical name: *Linum usitatissimum.*

Popular name: Linseed.

Habitat: Grassland, and cultivated.

Flora: Annual, with blue flowers June–July.

Folklore: It is estimated that flax has been cultivated for use in making linen for at least three thousand years. The ancient Egyptians used flax-derived linen to wrap their mummies, and it was imported into northern and western Europe by the Romans. The first recorded use of flax in western Europe was in Ireland *c*. AD 500. To ensure a good crop of flax, farmers used to ring the local church bells on Ascension Day. Flax oil has many uses in modern industry, including the manufacture of paints and varnish.

General medical properties: Demulcent, emollient and laxative.

Specific properties: Medically, the linseed oil derived from the flax seeds has emollient properties, both internally and externally, and is effective on burns. The plant is used to treat bronchitis and lung disorders, and for easing childbirth and constipation.

Application and use: Infuse 1 teaspoon of ripe seeds in 2 pints of water. Boil until only 1 pint remains. Sip occasionally during the day. For external use mix crushed seeds with hot water and apply as a poultice.

FUMITORY

Botanical name: *Fumaria officinalis*.

Popular name: Earth smoke.

Habitat: Wasteland, fields and gardens.

Flora: Annual, with reddish-purple flowers May–September.

Folklore: Expert opinion differs considerably on the origin of this plant's name. According to some, the classical writers thought that it grew from 'the vapours of the Earth'. Other sources say that its grey leaves look like wisps of smoke rising from the ground. Alternatively, it was claimed that the smoke derived from burning its leaves had magical powers and could drive away evil spirits. Folk healers believed that its use to improve the eyesight had the side-effect of causing the eyes to water, as if they had been exposed to smoke. In the Middle Ages young women washed themselves with a decoction of fumitory to make skin blemishes vanish.

General medical properties: Diuretic, laxative, alterative and stomachic.

Specific properties: Used for serious skin diseases, cleansing the kidneys and to treat conjunctivitis.

Application and use: *Toxic. Use only under the direction of a medical herbalist.*

GARLIC

Botanical name: *Allium ursinum.*

Popular name: Wild garlic, ramsons.

Habitat: Wild in hedgerows and woodland, and cultivated.

Flora: Perennial, with white flowers in summer.

Folklore: The common name originates in the Anglo-Saxon *gar*, meaning 'lance', and *leac*, meaning 'pot herb'. In common folklore garlic bulbs hung around the neck traditionally ward off vampires. Country people often grew a patch of garlic in their gardens as a protection against the spells of black witches. Garlic has always been recognized as one of the most important natural folk remedies. The ancient Egyptians valued garlic bulbs so highly that they ordered a daily ration of them to be fed to the builders of the pyramids to give them strength. In ancient China the plant was used by physicians as a cure for leprosy. During the plague outbreaks in the Middle Ages, garlic was widely used as an antiseptic. This use persisted as late as the First World War, when troops in the trenches were treated with garlic to prevent their wounds from becoming septic. The garlic plant belongs to the same botanical genus as the onion, and is widely used in cooking, especially in European countries.

General medical properties: Expectorant, diuretic, nervine and antibacterial.

Specific properties: Scientists at New York State University have recently discovered that garlic contains a chemical substance called ajeone, which acts as a blood thinner; they believe that it can be used to treat circulatory complaints such as arteriosclerosis and blood clots which cause strokes. Garlic is also recommended for treating colds, sinus disorders, bronchitis, asthma and colic. It lowers blood pressure, purifies the blood and acts as a nerve sedative. Externally, it can be used to treat chilblains.

Application and use: For general use, take ½ teaspoon of garlic juice pressed from fresh bulbs 2–3 times a day. For coughs, eat grated bulbs mixed with honey. To treat asthma, boil a large quantity of bulbs in water until they are soft, then add as much vinegar as there is water left over. Add some sugar, and boil again until a syrup is formed. Take 2–3 teaspoons a day, as required.

GENTIAN
See Great Yellow Gentian.

GOLDEN ROD

Botanical name: *Solidago virgaurea.*

Popular names: Aaron's rod, woundwort.

Habitat: Wild in woodland and heathland, and cultivated in gardens.

Flora: Perennial, with yellow flowers July–October.

Folklore: Golden rod was cultivated by the Arabs, who recognized its important medical uses. Its popular name of Aaron's rod suggests that it may have been known to the Hebrews for similar reasons. In the fifteenth and sixteenth centuries herbalists used golden rod to heal wounds, hence another popular name.

General medical properties: Astringent, diuretic, anti-catarrhal, antispasmodic and antiseptic.

Specific properties: Golden rod is used for treating catarrh, dissolving kidney stones, cleansing wounds and curing water retention.

Application and use: Infuse 2 teaspoons of the dried flowers in 1 cup of boiling water for 15 minutes. Take 3 times a day.

GOOSE GRASS

Botanical name: *Galium aparine.*

Popular name: Cleavers.

Habitat: Fields and hedgerows.

Flora: Annual, with white or whitish-green flowers in summer.

Folklore: The popular name refers to the clinging action of the stems, which are covered in tiny prickles. In folk medicine the herb was used to treat skin diseases. The dried plant can be used to make a herbal tea, and is also recommended as a coffee substitute.

General medical properties: Vulnerary and diuretic.

Specific properties: This plant is recommended for lowering blood pressure and reducing the temperature in fevers. It is also used for treating water retention and cystitis. Externally, it can be used to heal wounds and skin diseases.

Application and use: Infuse 1 teaspoon of the dried flowers in 1 cup of boiling water for 15 minutes. Take 1 cup a day.

GREATER CELANDINE

Botanical name: *Chelidonium majus.*

Popular names: Jewel weed, snap weed, touch-me-not, felon-wort, swallow wort.

Habitat: Wasteland and hedgerows.

Flora: Although a member of the poppy family, with which it shares narcotic properties, this wild flower is sometimes confused with the buttercup, probably because lesser celandine (*Ranunculus ficaria*), to which greater celandine is not related, somewhat resembles the buttercup in appearance. Greater celandine's botanical name comes from the Greek *khelidon*, meaning 'swallow', a reference to the popular belief that the herb flowers when the swallows arrive from North Africa in the summer. Pliny the Elder, the Roman writer on herbalism who was renowned for his speculative stories, claimed that it was so named because 'swallows cured their young ones' eyes that were hurt by bringing this herb and putting it on them'. As greater celandine is frequently found growing on waste ground near human habitation, some authorities have taken this as a sign that it was cultivated for medical purposes. In magical lore during the Middle Ages it was believed that anyone who carried a bunch of greater celandine flowers and the heart of a mole could conquer his enemies and win law suits with ease. On a more mundane level, it was utilized by gypsies as a foot refresher.

General medical properties: Narcotic, purgative and stomachic.

Specific properties: The use of this herb is restricted to its purgative qualities and for treating skin diseases. *As it is very toxic it should be used with extreme caution.*

Application and use: *Strictly only on the advice, and under the direction, of a qualified medical herbalist.*

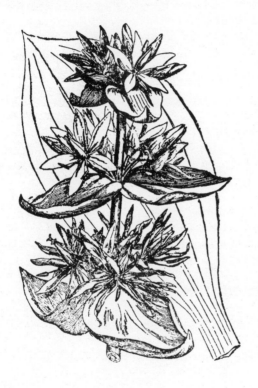

GREAT YELLOW GENTIAN

Botanical name: *Gentiana lutea.*

Popular names: Felwort, bitter root, bald Mary.

Habitat: Hilly pastures and woodland.

Flora: Perennial, with yellow flowers in August.

Folklore: This plant, legendary in folk medicine, was named after the ancient King Gentius, who lived in what is now Yugoslavia in the first century BC; he was allegedly the first person to discover its medical uses. It was widely used for medical purposes by both the Greeks and Arabs, probably on account of its renowned bitterness. Medieval herbalists regarded Gentian as a cure-all; they mixed it with honey to disguise its taste and used it as an antidote to poison. Today it is used as a bittering agent in some alcoholic drinks. The plant is long-lived, and some have been known to survive for nearly fifty years.

General medical properties: Gastric stimulant, digestive and appetizer.

Specific properties: Because of its bitter quality this herb is recommended for use as an appetite improver and to stimulate the gastric juices.

Application and use: *Use with caution, as overdosing can cause nausea.* Infuse 1 teaspoon of the dried root in 1 cup of boiling water for 10 minutes. Drink 1 cup before meals 3 times a day.

GROUND ELDER

Botanical name: *Aegopodium podagraria.*

Popular names: Herb Gerard, bishopweed, gout weed, goat-weed.

Habatit: Hedgerows and roadsides.

Flora: Perennial, with white flowers in summer.

Folklore: The botanical name is derived from Greek *aigos*, 'goat, and *podos*, 'foot', and Latin *podagra*, 'gout'. In the Middle Ages folk healers recommended this persistent weed, which is the bane of gardeners, as a herbal remedy for gout. Its young leaves can be cooked as a vegetable or eaten raw in salads.

General medical properties: Diuretic, sedative and pain reliever.

Specific properties: It is mainly used for treating gout and sciatic pain and also rheumatism, also in cases of water retention to promote urine.

Application and use: As a diuretic, infuse 1 teaspoon of the fresh leaves in 1 cup of boiling water for 15 minutes. Take 1 cup a day. For external use, apply fresh leaves as a poultice to painful areas.

GROUND IVY

Botanical name: *Glechoma hederacea*.

Popular names: Cat's foot, alehoof, Jack-in-the-hedge, Gill-creep-by-the-ground.

Habitat: Hedgerows.

Flora: Perennial, with blue-purple flowers in late spring and early summer.

Folklore: Despite its common name, this plant is not a member of the ivy family. It was used in Saxon times as an additive in beer, and was recommended by medieval practitioners of folk medicine for the cure of urinary infections and persistent coughs.

General medical properties: Astringent, expectorant, anti-catarrhal and diuretic.

Specific properties: Used for treating catarrh, bronchitis and cystitis, for easing sciatic pain and as a gargle for sore throats.

Application and use: Infuse 1 teaspoon of the dried leaves in 1 cup of boiling water for 15 minutes. Take 3 times a day.

GROUNDSEL

Botanical name: *Senecio vulgaris.*

Popular names: Birdseed, ragwort.

Habitat: Fields and gardens.

Flora: Annual, with yellow flowers in summer.

Folklore: This plant is disliked by gardeners because it spreads quickly and is difficult to eradicate from cultivated land; its common name comes from an Old English word translated as 'ground swallower'. Pliny the Elder recommended groundsel for the treatment of toothache: he suggested that the afflicted person rubbed the tooth with the plant and then replaced it in the ground; if the plant rerooted itself, the tooth would cease to hurt. In folk medicine this plant was widely used to treat female disorders, especially painful periods; the medieval herbalists used it to help young girls who were going through the trauma of their first period at the onset of puberty. It was once used as birdseed, hence another of its popular names.

General medical properties: Stomachic, purgative, laxative and astringent.

Specific properties: In addition to the relief of period pains groundsel also acts as a laxative and for stomach ache. Externally, it can be used as an antiseptic lotion for cleansing wounds and to treat bleeding gums.

Application and use: *Large doses can cause liver problems. Use only as directed by a medical herbalist.*

GYPSYWORT

Botanical name: *Lycopus europaeus.*

Popular Name: Gypsyweed.

Habitat: Marshes and ditches.

Flora: Perennial, with white and purple flowers in July–September.

Folklore: Gypsywort is so named because the Romany tribes extracted from the plant a black dye which has been used for centuries to colour linen.

General medical properties: Cardiac, sedative and anti-haemorrhagic.

Specific properties: In folk medicine this herb has been used to prevent blood clotting, as a sedative in heart conditions and high blood pressure, and for reducing the pulse rate in over-active thyroid conditions.

Application and use: Infuse 1 teaspoon of the dried flowers in 1 cup of boiling water for 10 minutes. Take one cup three times a day.

HAWTHORN

Botanical name: *Crataegus monogyna*.

Popular names: May, whitethorn.

Habitat: Woodland and hedgerows.

Flora: Perennial tree, with white flowers in May.

Folklore: The hawthorn was once highly regarded as a magical tree sacred to the fairies and the pagan fertility goddesses of pre-Christian times. The Church also looked on the tree with respect, as it was supposed to have been the origin of the crown of thorns worn by Jesus on the cross. It was said to be unlucky to bring hawthorn blossom into a house before May Day. Laid above the lintels of doors, hawthorn branches warded off witches, evil spirits and lightning. As Sir John Mandeville said in 1350, 'The white thorn hath many virtues for he that bearest it on him none manner of tempest shall harm him. [If it] be in the house where you are in then none evil ghost shall enter.' The virtue of the hawthorn to protect from thunderstorms is recorded in this old saying:

> Beware of the oak
> It draws the stroke.
> Around the ash
> It courts the flash.
> Creep under the thorn
> It will save you from harm.

In the Middle Ages peasant girls bathed in hawthorn dew on May Morning to improve their complexions. The strange smell of the hawthorn blossom made some country people say that it carried the Great Plague, while others claim that the odour has aphrodisiac qualities.

General medical properties: Tonic, nervine and cardiac stimulant.

Specific properties: Hawthorn berries are used in folk medicine as a general tonic and heart stimulant. The tree is also recommended for the treatment of hypertension, sore throats and chilblains.

Application and use: Infuse 2 teaspoons of berries in 1 cup of boiling water for 15 minutes. Take 3 times a day.

HEATHER

Botanical name: *Calluna vulgaris.*

Popular name: Ling.

Habitat: Heaths and moorland.

Flora: Evergreen shrub, with pink flowers August–October.
Folklore: The generic name comes from a Greek word meaning 'to sweep': in the old days besom heads were often made from

the stiff branches. In folk belief heather has always been regarded as a lucky plant to grow in the garden; its use as a good luck charm by the gypsies is well known, and continues to this day.

General medical properties: Astringent, antiseptic, sedative and diuretic.

Specific properties: It is used as a sedative in cases of insomnia, as an antiseptic for cleansing wounds, and for urinary infections. Externally, it can be used to treat skin diseases.

Application and use: Infuse 1 teaspoon of the dried flowers in 1 cup of boiling water for 15 minutes. Take 1 cup a day.

HEDGE MUSTARD

Botanical name: *Sisymbrium officinale.*

Popular names: Wiry Jack, singer's plant.

Habitat: Fields, wasteland and hedgerows.

Flora: Perennial, with yellow flowers April–November.

Folklore: The Greeks used this plant for medical purposes, believing that an infusion of it mixed with honey was an antidote for all known poisons. In folk medicine hedge mustard was recommended for its ability to soothe sore throats, and was therefore used by public speakers and professional singers. It was once used in sauces, but its strong flavour makes it an acquired taste.

General medical properties: Diuretic, expectorant, tonic, stomachic and laxative.

Specific properties: The juice and flowers are recommended for use in bronchitis, water retention, constipation and stomach upsets, and as a general tonic and revitalizer.

Application and use: *Use with caution. Overdosing can affect the heart. It must not be used to treat old people or children.* Steep 1 teaspoon of the dried flowers in ½ cup of boiling water for 5 minutes. Take 1–2 cups a day.

HERB ROBERT

Botanical name: *Geranium robertianum.*

Popular names: Red robin, St Robert's herb.

Habitat: Woodland and wasteland.

Flora: Annual or biennial, with pink or red flowers June–September.

Folklore: In the Middle Ages this plant was regarded as sacred to St Robert. It was also believed to be the special herb of the fairies, and was associated with hobgoblins. Herb Robert was widely used in medieval folk medicine.

General medical properties: Astringent, diuretic and sedative.

Specific properties: Used to treat sensitive skin complaints, as a lotion for eye trouble, for stopping diarrhoea, as a gargle for mouth ulcers and sore throats, and externally to reduce swellings and bruises.

Application and use: Infuse 1 teaspoon of the dried flowers in 1 cup of boiling water for 15 minutes. Take 1 cup a day.

HOLLYHOCK

Botanical name: *Althaea rosea.*

Popular names: Garden hollyhock, common hollyhock.

Habitat: Cultivated.

Flora: Perennial, with mainly pink, yellow or red flowers August–October.

Folklore: The hollyhock was imported into Europe from China in the sixteenth century and soon became well established in English country gardens. Its medical uses were also quickly recognized by folk healers. The sixteenth-century herbalist William Turner, called it the holyoke (from which its common name derives), meaning 'holy plant', and it was also known popularly as beyond-the-sea, referring to its origins in the Far East. Hollyhocks have been used to produce a natural colourant for use in winemaking.

General medical properties: Antiphlogistic, emollient and laxative.

Specific properties: The hollyhock can be used to reduce internal and external inflammation, to stop bed-wetting and as a mouthwash for sore or bleeding gums.

Application and use: Infuse 1 teaspoon of the dried flowers in 1 cup of boiling water for 15 minutes. Take 1 cup a day, or use as a mouthwash as required.

HOP

Botanical name: *Humulus lupulus*.

Popular names: Hop bine, willow wolf.

Habitat: Wild in hedges, and cultivated.

Flora: Perennial, with green flowers in late summer.

Folklore: The common name is said to originate in the Old English *hopen* or *hoppan*, meaning 'to climb'. It derived its name of willow wolf from the habit of its leaves, which twined around willow trees in the wild. The hop is famous for its use in brewing beer; though it was known in the classical world for other attributes, in the medieval period it seems to have been cultivated only for this particular purpose. The oil from hops is used in perfume manufacture and its stem are used for basketwork. It is also a popular ingredient for herbal pillows, used in the Middle Ages as a sure cure for insomnia; scientific analysis of the hop has indicated that it does indeed contain certain effective sedatives. In the kitchen, the blanched leaves and buds can be eaten after boiling or steaming. Gerard recommended that the excess water from boiling hops should be added to the dough in breadmaking, to get rid of the lumps. Hop tea, widely used in folk medicine as a general tonic, was said to aid the digestion. A brown dye can be distilled from the leaves and flowers.

General medical properties: Sedative, tonic, diuretic, nervine and antibiotic.

Specific properties: Hops are generally recommended for treating insomnia and nervous disorders because they are a sedative. They also have a limited effect in cases of water retention.

Application and use: Infuse ½ oz of hops in 1 pint of boiling water. Cool, and take as required.

HOREHOUND
See White Horehound.

WHITE HOREHOUND

Botanical name: *Marrubium vulgare.*

Popular name: Hoarhound.

Habitat: Hedgerows and woodland.

Flora: Perennial, with white flowers June–July.

Folklore: Horehound is a bitter plant related to the various mints. Its common name comes from Old English *harhune*, meaning 'downy plant', and has nothing to do with dogs. Its botanical name is said to originate from a Hebrew word, *marob*, which means 'bitter juice'. It was one of the five bitter herbs which Jehova commanded the Israelites to eat during the Passover feast which celebrated their flight from Egyptian tyranny. Horehound has been used as a folk remedy for coughs for thousands of years and was known for this purpose in ancient Egypt. It is still included in some popular cough medicines sold over the chemist's counter in many European countries. Culpeper claims that horehound leaves made into an ointment, would stop skin growing over the nails. In the eighteenth century horehound was powdered and made into a snuff which, if mixed with salt, was said to be a cure for the bite of a mad dog.

General medical properties: Anti-catarrhal, expectorant, tonic, laxative and emmenagogue.

Specific properties: Horehound is principally used as an expectorant in the treatment of bronchitis, catarrh and persistent coughs. It can also be used to treat asthma, constipation, lung diseases and inhibited menstrual flow, and for easing childbirth. Externally, it can be applied to cuts, bruises and minor skin conditions.

Application and use:
Make a decoction of the dried flowers, seeds or juice as a remedy for poor breathing, coughs and lungs complaints: Infuse 1 oz of the leaves in boiling water, and sweeten with brown sugar or honey to conceal the bitter taste. Use also as a winter drink for sore throats. A syrup can be made by boiling 1 lb of brown sugar with 1 lb of leaves.

HORSE CHESTNUT

Botanical name: *Aesculus hippocastanum*.

Popular name: Conker tree.

Habitat: Woodland and roadsides.

Flora: Deciduous tree with white flowers in May and shiny brown fruit in green outer case September–October.

Folklore: In classical times the word *Aesculus* was used to denote oak trees, but the specific part of the horse chestnut's botanical name may derive from the fact that the fruit was used as cattle and horse feed. The tree was first imported into Europe from Asia as late as the sixteenth century. Its medical properties for easing the discomfort of piles soon became apparent to herbalists and folk healers. The nut-like fruits were carried as a charm against rheumatism by country people, but were said to be effective only if they had been stolen or obtained by begging.

General medical properties: Astringent, tonic, antirheumatic and antiphlogistic.

Specific properties: Horse chestnut fruits, or conkers as schoolchildren call them, are used in folk medicine as a tonic, to treat rheumatic pain, to thin the blood and to cure piles. The active ingredient is escin, medically recognized as an anti-inflammatory agent.

Application and use: *Use with caution, as large doses can be toxic, and only under the direction of a medical herbalist.*

HORSERADISH

Botanical name: *Armoracia rusticana.*

Popular names: Common or garden horseradish, red cole.

Habitat: Damp places and waysides, and cultivated.

Flora: Perennial, with white flowers June–September.

Folklore: Botanists believe that the botanical name is derived from an obscure Latin word meaning 'spoon' – a reference to the shape of the leaves – and a word meaning 'wild radish'. Gerard was responsible for its present name, although before his time it was called red cole. The plant does not seem to have been widely used for culinary purposes until the seventeenth century, after which, because of its popularity as a salad vegetable, its medical qualities too became well known.

General medical properties: Stimulant, diuretic, laxative and appetizer.

Specific properties: Horseradish is used in folk remedies to relieve the symptoms of colds, influenza, flatulence, fevers and urinary infection, and to increase the appetite. Externally, it can be used to treat chilblains and boils.

Application and use: Infuse 1 teaspoon of the powdered root in a cup of boiling water for 15 minutes. Take 1 cup a day. For chilblains and boils, apply slices of root direct to the painful area.

HORSETAIL

Botanical name: *Equisetum arvense.*

Popular names: Sharegrass, bottlebrush, pewterwort, shavegrass.

Habitat: Wet places and wasteland.

Flora: Perennial.

Folklore: Horsetail is a prolific plant, which once established on cultivated land is difficult to eradicate. One of the oldest species of plants, it first evolved in the earliest prehistoric period. Fossil remains suggest that the original horsetail was the size of a small tree. The Romans called it 'the herb of the earth' and ate it in salads. In the Middle Ages it was used for cleaning metal utensils and polishing wood and pewter, hence one of its popular names. It was also employed in cosmetics for strengthening fingernails.

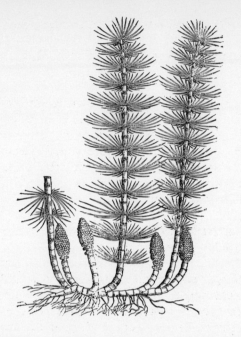

General medical properties: Diuretic, astringent, vulnerary and tonic.

Specific properties: Horsetail is used to treat kidney and bladder disorders, gastro-enteritis, the prostate gland and urinary infections. Externally it is applied to chilblains and open wounds.

Application and use: *Use with caution as it can cause internal irritation.* Steep 1 teaspoon of the leaves or whole plant in 1 cup of boiling water for 30 minutes. Take 1–3 cups a day. Apply the leaves externally as a poultice.

HOUNDSTONGUE

Botanical name: *Cynoglossum officinale*.

Popular names: Dog's tongue, gypsy flower, rats and mice.

Habitat: Wet places, wasteland and hedgerows.

Flora: Annual or biennial, with red-purple flowers May–September.

Folklore: As its common and popular names suggest, houndstongue was supposed to offer protection against attacks by savage dogs. The procedure was to wear a leaf from the plant in your shoe, and dogs would avoid you. Its leaves do in fact resemble a canine tongue. However, the plant also has an unpleasant smell reminiscent of mice, so in some country districts it was called rats and mice.

General medical properties: Demulcent, anti-inflammatory, anti-catarrhal and narcotic.

Specific properties: Houndstongue is recommended for soothing persistent coughs, treating lung diseases and for piles. The bruised leaves can be applied to relieve the discomfort of insect bites and stings. An ointment made from the leaves is said to cure baldness and will heal sores and ulcers.

Application and use: Steep 1 teaspoon of the dried root or leaves in 1 cup of boiling water. Take a sip at a time during the day.

KIDNEYWORT

Botanical name: *Anemone hepatica.*

Popular names: Liverwort, pennywort.

Habitat: Woodland, rocks and stone walls.

Flora: Perennial, with blue flowers in May.

Folklore: This plant derives its botanical name from Greek *hepataros*, 'liver', medieval herbalists used it to cure diseases of that organ. Culpeper assigned it to the planet Venus and the zodiac sign of Libra (23 September–22 October). According to him, the juice is favourable for 'unnatural heats' and curing 'St Anthony's fire' [sciatica]. Folk healers also recommended it for soothing the pain of gout.

General medical properties: Anti-inflammatory, diuretic, demulcent, tonic and expectorant.

Specific properties: Kidneywort can be used for water retention, bronchitis and kidney disorders. Externally it can be used to treat pimples, blemishes, boils, sores, sciatica, gout and swollen testicles.

Application and use: *Toxic if taken in large doses. Use only as directed by a medical herbalist.*

KNOTGRASS

Botanical name: *Polygonum aviculare.*

Popular Names: Birdweed, lowgrass, pigweed.

Habitat: Wasteland and fields.

Flora: Annual, with white flowers June–October.

Folklore: In his famous *Herbal* Culpeper says this plant is ruled by Saturn and comes under the zodiac sign of Capricorn (21 December–19 January). He recommended its use to stop blood flowing. The old herbalists regarded knotweed as a sure cure for the spitting of blood.

General medical properties: Astringent, coagulant, diuretic and expectorant.

Specific properties: Knotweed is suggested for treating dysentery, prolific menstrual flow, bronchitis, jaundice and lung disease. It is used particularly for dealing with internal bleeding, and can also dissolve kidney and gall bladder stones.

Application and use: Steep 3 teaspoons of the flowers in 1 cup of boiling water for 10 minutes. Take 1 cup a day.

LADY'S BEDSTRAW

Botanical name: *Galium verum.*

Popular names: Cheese rennet, yellow bedstraw, wild rosemary, maiden's hair.

Habitat: Meadows and hedgerows.

Flora: Perennial, with yellow and white flowers June–September.

Folklore: Lady's Bedstraw is very common all over the British Isles. Because of its pleasant, honey-like scent it was once used to stuff mattresses and as an insect repellent. Its popular name of cheese rennet indicates its use for curdling milk until the early nineteenth century; milkmaids also used the flowers to colour the milk used in cheese. In Gloucestershire it was used in making the distinctive deep yellow Double Gloucester cheese. In traditional folk remedies it is used as a nerve tonic and sedative.

General medical properties: Nervine, sedative, tonic, diuretic and insecticide.

Specific properties: Lady's bedstraw is used to treat hysteria, epilepsy and extreme nervousness. It also has limited use for skin diseases.

Application and use: Infuse 1 teaspoon of the flowers in 1 cup of boiling water for 15 minutes. Take 1 cup a day.

LADY'S MANTLE

Botanical name: *Alchemilla vulgaris.*

Popular name: Lion foot.

Habitat: Woodland and meadows.

Flora: Perennial, with greenish-yellow flowers May–June.

Folklore: The generic name means 'little magical one', and refers to the medieval belief that the plant had magical powers because of the fact that dew, an important ingredient in many medieval magical and alchemical rituals, gathers in its leaves overnight. Country people gathered this dew and used it as a beauty lotion. Culpeper claimed that women with sagging breasts could make them firm and rounded by smearing them with the juice of this plant. A pillow filled with the flowers was said to induce a good night's rest.

General medical properties: Sedative, anti-inflammatory, appetizer, astringent and tonic.

Specific properties: Lady's mantle was recommended by folk healers for treating inflammation, and it prevents excessive bleeding. It was much used in the past for what were called 'women's troubles' as it relieved the discomfort of the menopause and inhibited excessive menstruation. Externally, it heals sores and ulcers.

Application and use: Steep 1 teaspoon of the dried leaves in 1 cup of boiling water for 10 minutes. Take 1 cup a day.

LADY'S SMOCK

Botanical name: *Cardamine pratensis.*

Popular names: Cuckoo flower, bittercress.

Habitat: Fields, woodland and wet places.

Flora: Perennial with white flowers April–May.

Folklore: This plant, which is rich in vitamins, was once cultivated for use in salads as a substitute for watercress.

According to popular folk belief lady's smock was sacred to the fairies, and so it was considered very unlucky to bring it into the house because the fairies would be offended and seek revenge on the household. If the plant was included in May Day garlands the person carrying it would fall sick for the same reason.

General medical properties: Diuretic, appetizer, digestive and stomachic.

Specific properties: Lady's smock can be used to treat loss of appetite, indigestion, water retention and stomach upsets.

Application and use: Infuse 1 teaspoon of the fresh leaves or flowers in 1 cup of boiling water for 15 minutes. Take 1 cup a day.

LAVENDER

Botanical name: *Lavandula officinalis*.

Popular names: English lavender, garden lavender.

Habitat: Wild and cultivated.

Flora: Perennial, with purple flowers June–September.

Folklore: For centuries lavender has been used as a perfume, a sedative, a stimulant and for antiseptic purposes. The Romans used the plant in their bathwater and placed linen bags of it among their clothes as a natural deodorant. Its specific name is connected with the idea of washing. In the Middle Ages lavender oil was used to kill lice and bed bugs, while in warfare it was used as a natural antiseptic to cleanse sword cuts: modern scientists have discovered that lavender contains an essential oil which destroys bacteria on contact. In folk belief it is considered lucky to have a lavender bush growing in your garden, but the luck would vanish if flowers were cut and dried.

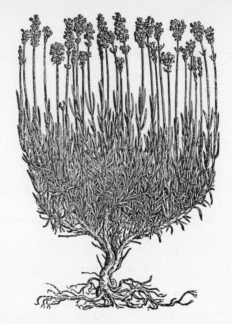

General medical properties: Antispasmodic, antibacterial, antiseptic, diuretic and sedative.

Specific properties: The principal use of the herb in folk remedies is for treating nervousness, insomnia, headaches and stress, and as a general antiseptic and pain reliever. It can also be used to treat rheumatism, depression, toothache, loss of voice, fainting and low blood pressure. Externally, it can be used to treat skin rashes and insect bites. It also acts as an insect repellent.

Application and use: Infuse 1 teaspoon of the dried herb in 1 cup of boiling water for 15 minutes. Take 3 times a day.

LILAC

Botanical name: *Syringa vulgaris.*

Popular name: Common or garden lilac.

Habitat: Cultivated.

Flora: Perennial, with white, pinkish-mauve or purple flowers in summer.

Folklore: Originally a native of Asia Minor, lilac was introduced into western Europe as a cultivated plant as late as the sixteenth century. Its original Persian name, *lilak*, was anglicized as lilac. Medically, the herbalists used it to treat fevers, as it was regarded as an alternative to quinine, which was very expensive. In folklore lilac is regarded as an unlucky flower to have inside the house because it is an omen of death.

General medical properties: Diuretic and anti-inflammatory.

Specific properties: Principally lilac is used for the treatment of fevers, especially in tropical diseases such as malaria. It has also been found of use in cases of rheumatism.

Application and use: Infuse 1 teaspoon of the leaves in 1 cup of boiling water for 15 minutes. Take 1 cup a day.

LILY OF THE VALLEY

Botanical name: *Convallaria majalis.*

Popular names: Wood lily, May lily, Our Lady's tears, May blossom.

Habitat: Dry woodlands, and cultivated.

Flora: Perennial, with white flowers May–June.

Folklore: As one of its popular names suggests, this plant was sacred to the Virgin Mary, who is the Christianized version of the old pagan Moon Goddess. Lily of the valley grew wild in the depths of St Leonard's Forest in Sussex, allegedly from the spots of blood shed during the saint's fight with a local dragon. The sweet smell of the flowers is said to be a powerful attraction to nightingales. Medieval herbalists used the plant as a substitute for foxglove, because it has a stimulating effect on the heart. In the First World War it was used to treat soldiers who had suffered the effects of mustard gas, as it has a strengthening effect on the nervous system.

General medical properties: Cardiac stimulant, diuretic, laxative and antispasmodic.

Specific properties: Recent research has revealed that lily of the valley contains a substance known as convallamarin, which is a potent cardiac stimulant similar to digitalis. This ingredient is now widely used by pharmaceutical companies in the manufacture of cardiac drugs. The flowers were believed to stimulate the mucous membranes of the nasal passages, and were recommended for treating sinusitis and vertigo. A spirit distilled from the flowers was applied externally for rheumatic pain. The traditional use of the plant is as a cardiotonic, but it also has a limited use in cases of water retention and nervous debility.

Application and use: *Only on the advice, and under the direction of, a medical herbalist.*

LIME TREE

Botanical name: *Tilia europea.*

Popular name: Linden.

Habitat: Cultivated.

Flora: Decidous tree, with yellow and white flowers at midsummer.

Folklore: The lime was a sacred tree to the ancient Teutonic peoples of northern Europe, possibly because, under ideal conditions, it can live for a thousand years. In popular folklore the tree was associated with death. At Cuckfield Hall in Sussex a famous lime tree stood for many years in the drive; everytime a branch fell from this old tree, a member of the family who lived in the house was said to die shortly afterwards. Medieval herbalists used a tea distilled from limeflowers to cure epilepsy; it was even said that an epileptic could be cured of their fits by just sitting under the tree. The bark of the tree was once used to make rope, and its wood was used in the manufacture of charcoal.

General medical properties: Antispasmodic, nervine, diuretic, expectorant and sedative.

Specific medical properties: Lime is recommended for the treatment of coughs, nervous disorders, hypertension, chills, fevers, migraine and catarrh, and externally as a soothing balm for skin rashes.

Application and use: Infuse 1 teaspoon of the fresh flowers in ½ cup of boiling water for 10 minutes. Take ½ cup a day.

LIQUORICE

Botanical name: *Glycyrrhiza glabra*.

Popular name: Liquorice.

Habitat: Cultivated.

Flora: Perennial, with lilac flowers June–July.

Folklore: The medical use of this plant dates back over three thousand years and is recorded in ancient Egyptian papyri. The ancient Greeks used liquorice as a thirst quencher, and children throughout the ages have eaten it as a confection. Liquorice grows wild in many parts of eastern Europe and Asia. It was first introduced into Europe in the fifteenth century, and brought to England by Dominican monks who grew it in their monastery garden at Pontefract in Yorkshire. Medieval herbalists used the plant as a natural sweetener to cover up the bitterness of other less palatable herbs in their compounds; it is some fifty times sweeter than sugar. Liquorice was also widely used as a cough medicine. In the 1940s a Dutchman, Dr F.E. Revers, discovered that his patients recovered more quickly from the effects of peptic ulcers if they took a herbal pill manufactured by a local pharmacist; when he analysed these pills he found that their main ingredient was liquorice.

General medical properties: Demulcent, anti-catarrhal, anti-spasmodic, laxative and anti-inflammatory.

Specific properties: Liquorice is used to treat bronchitis, coughs, gastric ulcers and indigestion, and externally as a wash for inflamed eyelids.

Application and use: Infuse 1 teaspoon of dried liquorice in 1 cup of boiling water for 15 minutes. Take 1 cup a day. *Overdosing can cause water retention.*

LOVAGE

Botanical name: *Levisticum officinale.*

Popular name: Sea parsley.

Habitat: Wet places, and cultivated.

Flora: Perennial, with whitish-yellow flowers July–September.

Folklore: Lovage derives its popular name from the fact that it was commonly eaten by sailors and fishermen as a cure for scurvy, caused by a lack of fresh vegetables; lovage contains an essential oil rich in vitamin C. The young leaves can be eaten raw in salads or cooked as a vegetable. The stems were once candied as a confection, and the root chewed as a tobacco substitute.

General medical properties: Diuretic and stimulant.

Specific properties: Lovage is recommended for use in cases of water retention and vitamin C deficiency.

Application and use: Infuse 1 teaspoon of the dried root or leaves in 1 cup of boiling water for 10 minutes. Take 1 cup a day.

LUNGWORT

Botanical name: *Pulmonaria officinalis.*

Popular names: Beggar's basket, Jerusalem cowslip, Jerusalem sage.

Habitat: Shady places and woodland.

Flora: Perennial, with pink and blue flowers March–May.

Folklore: The common name refers to the spotted leaves and the change in its flower colour from blue to pink, which resembled the symptoms of a diseased lung. For this reason lungwort was used in folk medicine to cure tuberculosis. Certainly its ingredients, such as tannin, silica and lime, can have a soothing effect on inflamed bronchial tubes.

General medical properties: Demulcent, expectorant, diuretic, astringent and anti-inflammatory.

Specific properties: The plant is recommended for the treatment of all lung diseases, bronchitis, coughs, catarrh and sore throats.

Application and use: Infuse 1 teaspoon of the dried herb in 1 cup of boiling water for 15 minutes. Take 1 cup a day.

MADDER

Botanical name: *Rubia peregrina.*

Popular name: Dyer's madder.

Habitat: Woodland and dry places, and cultivated.

Flora: Perennial, with greenish-yellow flowers June–September.

Folklore: As its common name suggests, madder was traditionally a source of a natural red dye called Turkey red or alizarin. Originally the plant was imported into Europe from Greece and Turkey as a commercial product for use by the linen industry. Until the end of the nineteenth century a compound of madder root, sheep's dung and alkali was used to dye wool and cotton; today it has been replaced by a synthetic substitute. In folk medicine madder root was used extensively to dissolve kidney stones.

General medical properties: Astringent, tonic, vulnerary, diuretic, laxative, antispasmodic and antiseptic.

Specific properties: Madder is used in the treatment of water retention, urinary infections and gall and kidney stones, and to cleanse open wounds.

Application and use: Infuse 1 teaspoon of the dried root in 1½ pints of boiling water in a closed container for 30 minutes. Cool and strain. Take 1–2 cups, cold, a day. Boil the root in honey and sugar to make a syrup. For removing skin blemishes, apply the bruised leaves externally.

MAIDENHAIR

Botanical name: *Adiantum capillus-veneris*.

Popular names: Venus hair, lady's hair.

Habitat: Wet places.

Flora: Perennial fern.

Folklore: Maidenhair derives its name from Greek *adiantos*, 'unwetted', because the foliage repels water and the plant generally is found in a damp environment. The popular folk names refer to the resemblance between the silky fronds of the fern and female pubic hair. Maidenhair was once a popular ingredient in a herbal cough medicine which was used until the end of the nineteenth century. Folk healers recommended its use in a herbal remedy to cure dandruff: the ashes of the burnt fern were added to vinegar and olive oil and then massaged into the scalp.

General medical properties: Expectorant, emmenagogue and diuretic.

Specific properties: Used in the treatment of asthma, bronchitis and water retention, and also to inhibit menstrual flow, dissolve kidney stones and purify the blood.

Application and use: Infuse 1 teaspoon of the fresh leaves in 1 cup of boiling water for 10 minutes. Take 1 cup daily.

MALLOW

Botanical name: *Malva sylvestris.*

Popular name: Common mallow.

Habitat: Ditches and riverbanks.

Flora: Perennial, with pinkish-violet flowers June–September.

Folklore: Mallow has been cultivated since earliest times for both medicinal and culinary uses. In the sixteenth century the herbalists called it *Omnimorbia*, which means 'cure all', because of its superior powers. Its generic name, *Malva*, means 'soft', which refers to the texture of its leaves. Pliny the Elder, with his usual degree of exaggeration, claimed that anyone who took a spoonful of mallow would be instantly cured of any malady. Its leaves were once cooked as a vegetable and used raw in salads.

General medical properties: Demulcent, emollient, anti-inflammatory and laxative.

Specific properties: Mallow is used in the treatment of inflamed tissues, bronchitis, gastro-enteritis, sore throats and constipation.

Application and use: Infuse 1 teaspoon of the dried leaves or flowers in ½ cup of cold water for 8 hours. Then heat, but do not boil. Cool, strain and take ½ cup a day.

MARIGOLD

Botanical name: *Calendula officinalis.*

Popular names: Mary's gold, summer pride, garden marigold.

Habitat: Cultivated.

Flora: Annual, with orange flowers June–September.

Folklore: Marigold is a popular garden plant with an ancient history. It was known to the Romans, Greeks, ancient Egyptians, Arabs and Hindus. The generic name derives from Latin *calends*, 'throughout the months', a reference to the lengthy flowering season of the marigold. It was popularly called summer's pride, because it followed the sun and bloomed all through the hot weather. The plant has never been found in the wild and has only ever been cultivated. In folklore it is said that the flowers give off bright sparks during a thunderstorm. It was widely used in wedding bouquets because in flower symbolism it represents constant love. William Turner in his herbal says of the marigold, 'Some use it to make their hair yellow, not content with with the natural colour God has given them.' Rubbed on wasp stings, the flowers were said to bring instant relief. According to an old West Country belief, if you pick a bunch of marigolds at dawn you risk turning into an alcoholic. Welsh country folk say that if the blooms of marigold are not open by 7 a.m. there will be a thunderstorm by the end of the day. Marigolds were generally used in folk remedies as a natural antiseptic and to induce perspiration in fevers.

General medical properties: Astringent, antiseptic and anti-inflammatory.

Specific properties: Scientific tests with marigold have indicated that the plant lowers blood pressure and has a slight sedative effect. In folk medicine it is recommended for use externally to soothe burns, inflammation, skin rashes, irritated eyes and conjunctivitis.

Application and use: Infuse 2 teaspoons of the flowers in 1 cup of boiling water for 15 minutes. Take 3 times a day.

MARJORAM

Botanical name: *Origanum vulgare*.

Popular names: Wild marjoram, oregano, wintersweet, mountain mint.

Habitat: Dry grassland, and cultivated.

Flora: Perennial, with purple or pinkish-white flowers July–October.

Folklore: Marjoram is widely cultivated in western Europe but originated in the Mediterranean area. Its popular name of oregano comes from Greek *oros* and *ganos*, meaning 'joy of the mountain', because of the plant's attractive appearance. The ancient Greeks are reputed to have planted clumps of the herb over their tombs to give peace to the departed spirits and to stop them haunting the living. In folk belief marjoram seems to have been associated with fertility, because newly married couples were crowned with ringlets of the flowers. Today it is extensively cultivated for commercial use: as a herb it is used in meat dishes, and the oil has various uses in the cosmetic industry.

General medical properties: Expectorant, antiseptic, antispasmodic, anti-inflammatory, stomachic, nervine, appetizer, sedative and tonic.

Specific properties: As the list above indicates, this herb has many medical uses. It cleanses the body of impurities, purifies the bloodstream, cures yellow jaundice, stimulates the appetite, relieves deafness, eases toothache, calms nerves, cures stomach upsets, treats bronchitis and stops seasickness. Stuffed in a herbal pillow, the bruised leaves make a natural remedy for insomniacs.

Application and use: Infuse 2 teaspoons of the dried flowers in 1 cup of boiling water. Take 1–2 cups daily.

MARSHMALLOW

Botanical name: *Althaea officinalis.*

Popular name: Sweetweed.

Habitat: Wet places, ditches, riverbanks and cultivated.

Flora: Perennial, with white flowers July–September.

Folklore: This is another herb which has been cultivated for centuries. The Romans used it as a vegetable, the Greeks extolled its medical properties, and the Emperor Charlemagne promoted its use in Europe in the ninth century. Its most popular use is as a confection. During the Middle Ages folk healers recommended its use to treat various types of venereal diseases.

General medical properties: Demulcent and emollient.

Specific properties: When exposed to water marshmallow root swells to form a soothing gel; it therefore has wide uses in treating burns, skin diseases, rashes and cuts. The plant also reduces inflammation and has a pain-relieving effect on sore or cut skin. A poultice made of the ground root is effective for treating insect bites, and a wash made from the root or leaves can be used for dandruff or itchy scalps.

Application and use: Infuse 2 teaspoons of the dried leaves in 1 cup of boiling water for 10 minutes. Take 1 cup a day. Boil the flowers in water and strain off the liquid to use as a gargle. Dried root boiled in milk was an old folk remedy for whooping cough. For colds take 5 oz of flowers, 5 oz of dried root and 2 oz of raisins. Boil up in 5 pints of water until only 3 pints are left. Strain, and take ½ a wineglass a day until the symptoms ease.

MEADOWSWEET

Botanical name: *Filipendula ulmaria.*

Popular names: Queen of the meadow, bridewort, meadwort.

Habitat: Fields and meadows.

Flora: Perennial, with white flowers June–September.

Folklore: The original use of meadowsweet was as a flavouring agent in mead. In 1839 the flowers of the plant were found to contain salicylic acid, from which aspirin was synthesized. In folklore meadowsweet was associated with death, possibly because of its sweet-smelling flowers: its heavy scent was said to be able to induce a deep sleep from which the sleeper would never wake. For this reason it was never placed in bedrooms or sick rooms.

General medical properties: Antispasmodic, astringent, stomachic, anti-inflammatory and antirheumatic.

Specific properties: Meadowsweet can be used to prevent stomach disorders and for the treatment of heartburn, colic and peptic ulcers. It can also be used as an effective pain reliever for rheumatism, arthritis, fevers and chills.

Application and use: Infuse 1 teaspoon of the dried flowers or root stock in 1 cup of boiling water for 15 minutes. Take 1 cup a day.

MILKWORT

Botanical name: *Polygala vulgaris.*

Popular name: Rogation flower, gong flower, common milkwort.

Habitat: Meadows and hillsides.

Flora: Perennial, with blue flowers May–September.

Folklore: The generic name derives from Greek words meaning 'much milk', a reference to the milkwort's ability to increase the flow of breast milk in nursing mothers. Its other two popular names originated in its use in garlands carried by people following the old folk custom of Beating the Bounds.

General medical properties: Expectorant, diuretic, laxative, stomachic, appetizer and galactagogue.

Specific properties: As well as its common usage by mothers with new-born babies, milkwort was also recommended in folk remedies for treating coughs and stomach pains and for improving the appetite.

Application and use: Infuse 1 teaspoon of the dried root or plant in 1 cup of boiling water for 15 minutes. Take 1 cup a day.

MONEYWORT

Botanical name: *Lysimachia nummularia*.

Popular names: Herb twopence, creeping Jenny.

Habitat: Hedgerows and fields.

Flora: Perennial, with yellow flowers June–July.

Folklore: In his *Herbal* Culpeper places this plant astrologically under the rulership of the planet Venus and the goddess of love, for which reasons he recommends it for preventing the excessive flow of menstrual fluids. In folk medicine it was also used to curb internal bleeding.

General medical properties: Anticoagulant and stomachic.

Specific properties: As in the days of Culpeper, the primary use of this herb nowadays is for controlling menstruation and preventing internal haemorrhaging.

Application and use: Infuse 1 teaspoon of the dried herb in 1 cup of boiling water. Take 1 cup a day as required.

MOTHERWORT

Botanical name: *Leonurus cardiaca*.

Popular names: Lion's tail, throw wort.

Habitat: Rare, on wasteland and roadsides.

Flora: Perennial, with pink-purple flowers July–September.

Folklore: This plant was originally a native of central Asia. Its common name derives from its use by the ancient Greeks as a nerve tonic for pregnant woman, and it has been used in folk healing to cure infections of the vagina. The botanical name comes from Latin *leo*, 'lion', and Greek *oura*, 'tail', description of the leafy stem of the plant, with Greek *kardiaca*, 'heart', referring to its use in heart conditions. According to an old country saying, if you ate motherwort regularly you would 'live to be a source of continuous astonishment and grief to your waiting heirs'. So common was the belief that this herb had regenerative powers that it was sometimes called 'the herb of life'. Folk healers used it extensively for treating women suffering from menstruation problems and difficulties in childbirth. In the seventeenth century a distillation of mother-wort was used to calm those suffering from epileptic fits. The plant was generally cultivated for its medicinal powers and was seldom found in the wild.

General medical properties: Sedative, nervine, anti-spasmodic, cardiac and tonic.

Specific properties: Medical tests indicate that extracts of this herb do have a tonic effect in some heart conditions. It has also been proved to have sedative and anti-epileptic properties. Motherwort is therefore recommended for treating female disorders, heart disease, hysteria, low blood pressure, extreme nervousness and palpitations.

Application and use: Infuse 1 teaspoon of the dried or fresh flowers in ½ cup of boiling water for 15 minutes. Take 1 cup a day.

MOUSE-EAR HAWKWEED

Botanical name: *Hieracium pilosella.*

Popular name: Mousewort.

Habitat: Wasteland, meadows and ditches.

Flora: Perennial, with yellow flowers in October.

Folklore: The name originates in the shape of the leaf which country folk thought resembled the shape of a mouse's ear, while 'Hawkweed' is a reference to the folk belief that hawks consumed the juice of this plant to increase their already considerable eyesight. For this reason medieval herbalists used extracts of the herb for treating eye diseases. In his *Herbal* Gerard claimed that it had the additional power of hardening metal! No scientific proof has been found to support his claim.

General medical properties: Expectorant, antispasmodic, anti-catarrhal, astringent, diuretic and anti-bacterial.

Specific properties: Mouse-ear hawkweed can be recommended for treating liver disorders, bronchitis, whooping cough and asthma, and as a natural antiseptic for open wounds.

MUGWORT

Botanical name: *Artemisia vulgaris.*

Popular names: Felon's herb, sailor's tobacco.

Habitat: Wasteland, hedgerows and banks.

Flora: Perennial, with yellow-red flowers July–October.

Folklore: Mugwort is a very ancient herb. Its common name dates from Anglo-Saxon times and is from Old English *muggia wort*, 'midge plant': it was evidently used to repel insects. Its generic name comes from the Greek goddess Artemis. Opinions differ among the experts as to why this plant became associated with this pagan Moon Goddess: most herbalists suggest it is because mugwort has proved successful in dealing with problems arising from the menstrual cycle, which is linked with the lunar phases; the Greeks also used the plant to ease difficult childbirth and to assist in the expelling of the placenta. Pliny the Elder suggested that all travellers should carry a sprig of Mugwort to prevent tiredness on a long journey. In 1656 William Coles, in his book *The Art of Simpling*, said that if a footman placed a mugwort leaf in his shoe he would be able to walk forty miles before noon without stopping or becoming tired. Mugwort leaves were placed under the pillows of sick people in the hope that they would be cured of their malady when they awoke. It was also an old country belief that a bunch of mugwort hung up in the kitchen would protect the house from lightning during a thunderstorm.

In the old days mugwort leaves were used to create a substance known as moxa. The dried leaves of the plant were bruised and rubbed between the hands until they became shredded; this substance was formed into a cone and placed upon the skin. It was then set alight and allowed to burn down until a blister was created on the skin. Incredibly this painful quasi-medical practice was still in use in France during the 1830s as a cure for a variety of diseases including asthma, rheumatism and paralysis of the limbs.

General medical properties: Nerve tonic, appetizer, laxative, sedative and emmenagogue.

Specific properties: Medical testing of this herb has indicated that it does stimulate uterine muscle, which would make it an effective treatment for inhibited menstruation. It has also been proved to have a limited sedative effect. Mugwort can be used as a tonic for nervousness, to ease tension and cure depression. It also helps to aid the normal flow of the menses, and its sedative properties have some use in treating epilepsy. Externally, it can be used to treat bruises and chilblains.

Application and use: Infuse 1 teaspoon of the dried leaves or flowers in 1½ cups of boiling water. Take 1 cup a day.

MULLEIN

Botanical name: *Verbascum thapsus.*

Popular names: Beggar's blanket, Adam's fennel, hare's beard, cow's lungwort, Aaron's rod, donkey's ears, candlewick, rabbit's ear, bull's ear, velvet dock, flannel dock, great mullein.

Habitat: Wasteland, woodland and hedgerows.

Flora: Perennial, with yellow flowers June–October.

Folklore: The common name of mullein comes from Latin *mollis*, 'soft'. This, like many of its popular names, is a reference to its large leaves, which have a velvety texture. Its folk name of candlewick dates back to the days when the stem was dried, dipped in tallow and used as a torch. Mullein leaves, greatly prized for decorative purposes, were included in herbal smoking mixtures and in the preparation of herbal cosmetics. In magical lore mullein was regarded as a herb of protection; it is even said that medieval monks grew it in their monastery gardens to ward off the Devil. In the Middle Ages the juice from the plant was used in folk remedies to cure gout and piles; the leaves and flowers were compounded, and then left to decay in a sealed wooden tub. After three months the juice was pressed out of the rotted plant material and corked in glass bottles ready for use.

General medical properties: Demulcent, expectorant, diuretic and sedative.

Specific properties: Mullein is recommended for treating bronchitis and asthma, as it has a beneficial effect on the respiratory system. Mullein leaves in hot vinegar and water can be applied to piles, and boiled with lard or vegetable fat they can be made into an ointment for dressing wounds. A poultice of the leaves or flowers can be applied to burns. Because of its unpleasant taste, mullein is sometimes best mixed with another herb.

Application and use: Infuse 1 teaspoon of the leaves or flowers in 1 cup of boiling water. Take ½ cup a day. Alternatively, boil 2 oz of leaves in 2 pints of water for 20 minutes. Drink the resulting liquid every 3 hours for severe bronchial congestion. Apply externally for swellings and itching, or use as a gargle.

NETTLE

Botanical name: *Urtica dioica.*

Popular name: Stinging nettle.

Habitat: Wasteland and roadsides.

Flora: Perennial.

Folklore: The common name of this well-known plant comes from an old word meaning 'to twist', and dates from the time when it was used to make fibre. In the past nettle was even cultivated for cloth manufacture. In ancient Greece it was used as an antidote for hemlock poisoning and as a cure for scorpion stings and snakebites. The medieval magician Albertus Magnus said that if you made an infusion of houseleek juice and nettles and rubbed it into your hands it would attract fish. In folklore, if you threw a bunch of nettle tops on the fire during a thunderstorm the house would be protected from lightning. A bunch of dried nettles hung in the larder warded off flies, and if hung near a hive drove away frogs. The popular phrase 'to grasp the nettle', meaning to take on an unpleasant task or face a difficult problem, originated in the folk belief that a person could be cured of a fever by pulling up a nettle with his or her bare hands.

The nettle is infamous because of the formic acid secreted by the hairs on the plant, which cause intense itching and skin blisters. Young nettles, before their stinging ability develops, have always been popular as a salad or an alternative to spinach. The plant is rich in vitamin A and C and various minerals, so is recommended for improving the complexion. Nettle seeds were once regarded as an aphrodisiac, and nettles were cultivated commercially as a source of chlorophyll.

General medical properties: Astringent, diuretic, appetizer, galactagogue and anti-coagulant.

Specific properties: Scientific tests have proved that nettle has the effect of lowering the blood sugar level, so it could have a use in treating diabetes. It can also be recommended as a stimulant to the appetite, a blood purifier and an aid to the digestion system; it lowers the blood pressure, increases the secretion of breast milk, can treat anaemia and stimulates the scalp in cases of premature baldness. Used as a snuff, the powdered leaf prevents nosebleeds and cures water retention.

Application and use: Only use fresh leaves, or cook them first. Infuse 2–3 tablespoons in 1 cup of boiling water and leave for 10 minutes. Take 1 tablespoon of the resulting liquid 4 times daily.

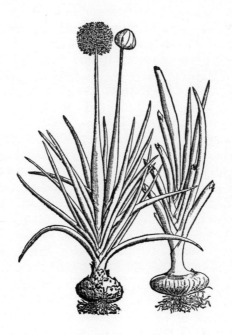

ONION

Botanical name: *Allium cepa*.

Popular name: Common onion.

Habitat: Cultivated.

Flora: Biennial or perennial, with whitish-green flowers June–August.

Folklore: The common onion has been cultivated as a food for thousands of years and is mentioned by the Assyrians, ancient Egyptians, Greeks and Romans. It is the most widely grown vegetable worldwide. In folklore it was claimed that onion seeds had to be sown on St Gregory's Day (12 March) to ensure a good crop. It was also believed that a raw onion would draw out the poison from a snakebite. Bunches of onions were hung outside houses in the Middle Ages to prevent the outbreak of bubonic plague. As late as 1968 a Cheshire farmer's wife claimed that an outbreak of foot and mouth disease had been prevented because she had placed a ring of onions around the cowshed.

General medical properties: Antiseptic, antibacterial, diuretic, expectorant, stomachic and antispasmodic.

Specific properties: Onions lower the blood pressure, restore sexual potency, promote urinary flow, and act as a natural antiseptic due to their sulphur content. Onion juice is known to be beneficial in the treatment of skin blemishes. Externally, onion juice can be used to treat chilblains and insect bites. Onions can also be used in syrups for persistent coughs.

Application and use: Take 1 teaspoon of onion juice 3 times daily. *Use with care, because in large doses the juice can be an irritant.*

PANSY

Botanical name: *Viola tricolor.*

Popular names: Stepmother, garden violet, heartsease, garden gate, love-in-idleness, Johnny-jump-in.

Habitat: Grassy places, and cultivated.

Flora: Annual, with purple, white and yellow flowers May–September.

Folklore: The common name pansy comes from the French *pensée*, meaning 'thought' or 'remembrance'. The white pansy flowers represented long thoughts, the yellow were souvenirs and the purple were memories, so a gift of pansies was used to ease the heartbreak between separated lovers. Folklore claims that to pick a pansy with dew on it will cause the death of a loved one; to pick pansies on a fine day will make it rain. Until about sixty years ago the pansy was cultivated in several European countries as a herbal treatment for heart disease.

General medical properties: Cathartic, demulcent, diuretic and anti-inflammatory.

Specific properties: Pansy is used in folk remedies as a safe and gentle laxative, for water retention, heart disease, hysteria and for easing childbirth. Externally, it can be used as a soothing balm for skin diseases.

Application and use: Infuse ½ oz of the flowers in 1 pint of water and steep for 15 minutes. Take 1–2 cups a day.

PARSLEY

Botanical name: *Petroselinum crispum*.

Popular name: Common parsley, garden parsley.

Habitat: Dry places, and cultivated.

Flora: Biennial and perennial, with whitish-green flowers June–August.

Folklore: Despite its common use as a culinary herb, parsley has always been regarded as an unlucky plant associated with death and funerals. The Romans believed that parsley had the power to make a pregnant woman miscarry, this may be the origin of the later folk belief that unwanted babies could be aborted if a woman ate a large quantity of parsley. It should be added that there is medical evidence to support this assertion. It was widely believed by country folk that parsley should never be transplanted or given away; it was even believed that if you mentioned a person's name while you were picking parsley he or she would sicken and die within seven days. Parsley was also said to have the magical power to weaken the structure of glass. A glass washed in parsley water would break, it was said, if only touched lightly. A green dye can be obtained from the stems, and the plant itself is a popular ingredient in sauces and garnish for fish dishes.

General medical properties: Antispasmodic, diuretic, expectorant, antiseptic and appetizer.

Specific properties: Parsley has a wide range of medical uses including the treatment of bronchitis, water retention, asthma and high blood pressure. It also helps the circulation; cleanses the kidneys and improves the appetite.

Application and use: Infuse 1 tablespoon of the dried herb in 1 cup of boiling water for 20 minutes. Take 1 cup a day. *Use with caution. Do not overdose. Not to be taken by pregnant women.*

PARSLEY PIERT

Botanical name: *Aphanes arvensis.*

Popular name: Breakstone parsley.

Habitat: Wasteland.

Flora: Annual, with green flowers May–October.

Folklore: The common name of this herb is derived from the French *perce pierre*, meaning a plant able to grow on common ground and which resembles parsley. Its popular name of breakstone parsley refers to its use by medieval herbalists to dissolve kidney and gall stones.

General medical properties: Diuretic and demulcent.

Specific properties: Used specifically to dissolve kidney and gall bladder stones and for the treatment of cystitis.

Application and use: Infuse 1 teaspoon of the dried herb in 1 cup of boiling water for 15 minutes. Take 1 cup a day.

PENNYROYAL

Botanical name: *Mentha pulegium.*

Popular names: Pudding grass, tickweed.

Habitat: Woodland and fields.

Flora: Perennial, with mauve flowers July–October.

Folklore: Pennyroyal belongs to the same family of plants as peppermint and spearmint. The name is a corruption of the French *puliol royale*, or royal thyme. Its specific name, *pulegium*, was given to the plant by Pliny the Elder and means 'flea': in Roman times pennyroyal was burnt to kill that insect.

General medical properties: Antispasmodic, stimulant, carminative and stomachic.

Specific properties: In medical tests pennyroyal has been proved to act as a stimulant to the uterus, and can therefore be used in any cases of suppressed menstruation. However, because of its toxic nature in large doses it has largely been superseded by peppermint for treating headaches, nervous tension and indigestion.

Application and use: *Only on the advice of a medical herbalist.*

PEPPERMINT

Botanical name: *Mentha × piperita*

Popular name: Mint.

Habitat: Cultivated.

Flora: Perennial, with mauve flowers July–October.

Folklore: Peppermint, one of the oldest cultivated herbs, was grown in ancient Egypt, used by the Greeks as a perfume, and employed by the Romans to flavour sauces and wine. Wealthy Roman noblewomen chewed peppermint leaves to stop bad breath. The leaves were also strewn in granaries in the ancient world to keep away rats and mice. Despite this long history, the use of peppermint in England is not recorded until the end of the seventeenth century, when a botanist saw it growing in a field in Hertfordshire and gave it the name by which it is now internationally well known. Today it is used in the manufacture of confectionery.

General medical properties: Antispasmodic, analgesic, nervine, carminative and appetizer.

Specific properties: Scientific tests have proved the use of peppermint as a muscle relaxant; for this reason it can be used to treat spasms and to relieve stomach cramps. It is also recommended for the relief of indigestion and flatulence and for promoting a healthy appetite. As in Roman times, it is recommended for the antisocial condition known as halitosis. Externally, it can be used to treat skin complaints.

Application and use: Infuse 2–3 teaspoons of the dried leaves in 1 cup of boiling water. Take 2 cups a day. *Do not prolong dosage any longer than 7 days.*

PERIWINKLE

Botanical names: *Vinca major, Vinca minor.*

Popular names: Greater and lesser periwinkle, sorcerer's violet, cut finger, blue buttons.

Habitat: Woodland, and cultivated.

Flora: Perennial, with pale blue flowers March–April.

Folklore: Periwinkle derived one of its popular names, cut finger, from its ability to stem bleeding. Sorcerer's violet comes from its use in medieval magic. Albertus Magnus says, in a grimoire or textbook written for aspiring magicians, 'Perrywinkle when it is beate into powdre with worms of ye earth wrapped around it names: *Vinca major, Vinca minor.*

Popular names: Greater and lesser periwinkle, sorcerer's violet, cut finger, blue buttons.

Habitat: Woodland, and cultivated.

Flora: Perennial, with uch in vogue in Victorian times, periwinkle represented virginity; it was also said to symbolize eternity, and for this reason was included in wreaths at the funerals of young children.

General medical properties: Astringent, sedative and anti-coagulant.

Specific properties: In the 1960s doctors extracted from the leaves of the tropical version of this plant a chemical which is used today in the treatment of leukaemia and Hodgkin's disease. The principal use of the English native species is to treat excessive bleeding, including menstruation. It can also be used in cases of dysentery, mouth ulcers, hysteria, epilepsy and bleeding gums caused by bad teeth.

Application and use: Infuse 1 teaspoon of the dried flowers in 1 cup of boiling water. Take 1 cup a day.

PINK

Botanical name: *Dianthus caryophyllus.*

Popular names: Gillyflower, old carnation, clove pink.

Habitat: Rocky places, and cultivated.

Flora: Perennial, with rose, purple or white flowers July–October.

Folklore: Gilly was the Old English name for July, referring to the month when the flower first appears. This traditional flower has been largely replaced by horticulturists with the more common carnation, which does not have the same potent scent. It is used commercially to flavour liqueurs and cordials.

General medical properties: Tonic, diuretic and anti-inflammatory.

Specific properties: Although it is seldom used by modern herbalists, pink can be recommended for soothing the symptoms of fever as it promotes perspiration and urine.

Application and use: Infuse 1 teaspoon of the dried flowers in 1 cup of boiling water for 15 minutes. Take 1 cup a day, as required.

PIMPERNEL

Botanical name: *Anagallis arvensis*.

Popular names: Poor man's weather glass, shepherd's barometer, laughter bringer, scarlet pimpernel.

Habitat: Fields and pastures.

Flora: Annual, with scarlet flowers May–September.

Folklore: The Greek name of this flower is a word meaning 'to delight'. Its popular name of laughter bringer also refers to the belief that this herb could cure depression. Traditionally, country people told the time by observing the flowers, which open in the morning and close in early afternoon – hence its other popular names. The flowers also close shortly before rain.

General medical properties: Diuretic.

Specific properties: Used for treating water retention and depression.

Application and use: *Only on the advice of a medical herbalist.*

PLANTAIN

Botanical name: *Plantago major.*

Popular names: Greater plantain, ripplegrass, fireweed, rat tail, waybread, broadleaf, ribwort, lamb grass, lanceleaf, soldier's herb, ribgrass.

Habitat: Meadows and hedgerows.

Flora: Perennial, with white flowers April–November.

Folklore: Plantain has a long history in folk medicine for treating sores and ulcers. Country folk placed bruised leaves on open wounds as an emergency dressing: they believed it had the ability to close an open wound and heal it. Recently, medical tests have established that the plant contains a powerful antibacterial agent.

General medical properties: Demulcent, expectorant, vulnerary, diuretic, astringent and antibacterial.

Specific properties: This herb is recommended for treating bronchitis, coughs and sore throats, and for promoting urinary flow. Externally, the leaves can be applied in poultice form to treat wounds, sores and insect bites.

Application and use: Infuse 1 tablespoon of the dried leaves in ½ cup of water for 5 minutes. Take 1 cup a day.

POPPY

Botanical name: *Papaver rhoeas*.

Popular names: Corn poppy, Flanders poppy, opium poppy.

Habitat: Fields and hedgerows.

Flora: Annual with red flowers (*P. rhoeas*) or mauve flowers (*P. somniferum*) June–August.

Folklore: Poppies have been used as a colouring agent since at least the fifteenth century. A cough syrup made from the plant was employed by Arab physicians in the eleventh century. Country folk used to add poppy juice to their babies' bottles to get a good night's rest at teething time. Although the poppy is a source of the narcotic opium, it has also provided medical science with the greatest painkiller, morphine. The popular name of Flanders poppy refers to their widespread occurrence on the battlefields of the First World War.

General medical properties: Sedative, antihydrotic and anti-spasmodic.

Specific properties: Poppy promotes perspiration, soothes coughs and calms nervous restlessness. It is also good for treating anxiety attacks, hysteria, insomnia and fits.

Application and use: *Only on the direction of a medical herbalist.*

PRIMROSE

Botanical name: *Primula vulgaris.*

Popular name: Butter rose.

Habitat: Woods, hedgerows, roadsides and pastures.

Flora: Perennial, with yellow flowers April–June.

Folklore: Primrose comes from Latin *prima rosa*, 'first rose' (of the year), because it appears very early in the spring. According to folk belief it is very unlucky to bring a posy of these flowers into the house if they number fewer than thirteen plants. A smaller number indicates the number of eggs which the hens of the household will hatch that year. In magical lore primroses were used to protect barns and cowsheds from the evil spells of black witches. Children who eat primrose flowers are said to be able to see the fairies. In the New Forest wood cutters treated cuts with an ointment made of primrose oil boiled with lard. The flowers were also candied as a confection and used in salads.

General medical properties: Antispasmodic, expectorant and diuretic.

Specific properties: The principal use of primrose is to relieve lung congestion and treat bronchitis. It can also be used to ease childbirth and to treat pre-menstrual tension and nervous headaches. Externally, it reduces the swelling of bruises.

Application and use: Infuse 2 teaspoons of the dried flowers in ½ cup of boiling water. Take 1 cup a day.

PURPLE FLAG

Botanical name: *Iris versicolor.*

Popular names: Liver lily, flag lily, water flag, wild iris, fleur de lys.

Habitat: Wet places and cultivated.

Flora: Perennial, with blue or violet flowers June–August.

Folklore: One of this plant's popular names, liver lily, refers to its use in folk medicine to treat complaints of the liver. Folk healers also recommended its use for treating gastric disorders, as a blood purifier and for treating skin eruptions.

General medical properties: Diuretic, cathartic and alterative.

Specific properties: The root of the purple flag can be used to cure vomiting, heartburn, liver disorders, gall bladder infections and sinus problems. It is also widely used by folk healers and herbalists in the treatment of skin diseases, including eczema and psoriasis. It has a stimulating effect on the flow of saliva and the gastric juices. Externally, the bruised leaves relieve the swelling caused by bruises. *Use with caution, as large dosages can cause nausea.*

Application and use: Infuse 1 teaspoon of powdered root in 1 pint of boiling water. Cool, and take 2 tablespoons twice a day.

PURPLE LOOSESTRIFE

Botanical name: *Lythrum salicaria.*

Popular names: Grass Polly, willowherb.

Habitat: Riverbanks, ditches and wetlands.

Flora: Perennial, with purple flowers June–July.

Folklore: The botanical name is derived from Greek *lythrum*, 'blood', and *salaicaria*, 'willow', which refers to the shape of the leaves. In folklore loosestrife was said to have the power to calm wild animals, including horses. It was also popularly used as an insect repellent: in his *Herbal* Gerard says, 'The smoke of this burned herb driveth away serpents and kills gnats and flies in the house.' In magical lore loosestrife had the ability to encourage the development of psychic powers and restore the memory of past lives. The plant was once used commercially in tanning leather.

General medical properties: Astringent, antibacterial, tonic and antiseptic.

Specific properties: Widely used in folk medicine as an antiseptic for throat gargles and cleansing wounds.

Application and use: Infuse 1 teaspoon of the dried flowers in 1 cup of boiling water for 15 minutes. Take 1 cup a day.

RASPBERRY

Botanical name: *Rubus idaeus*.

Popular name: Wild raspberry.

Habitat: Shady places, and cultivated.

Flora: Perennial, with white flowers in spring and summer.

Folklore: Wild raspberries have been gathered since pre-historic times, but the cultivated variety was not introduced into Europe until the Middle Ages. In prehistoric times hunters used them as bait because bears loved them. Medieval folk healers used raspberry tea to cool fevers and as a proven cure for severe cases of insomnia.

General medical properties: Cardiac, laxative, galactagogue and astringent.

Specific properties: The astringent qualities of raspberry may be due to the high concentration of tannin in the leaves. The plant is believed to prevent vomiting, and is therefore recommended for treating morning sickness in pregnant women. It can also increase the secretion of breast milk, deaden labour pains, treat mouth ulcers, stop diarrhoea, act as a mouthwash for sore gums and mouth ulcers, and externally treat sores and cuts.

Application and use: Infuse 2 teaspoons of the fruit in 1 cup of boiling water for 15 minutes. Drink 1 cup as required.

RESTHARROW

Botanical name: *Ononis repens.*

Popular names: Cammock, stayplough.

Habitat: Meadows and pastures.

Flora: Perennial, with reddish-pink flowers.

Folklore: Restharrow is a pleasant-looking plant but should be treated with some respect as it possesses sharp spines. It also has a long root which makes it difficult to prise from the earth. Farmers called it stayplough, because the plant often became entangled around the plough and held it up. Not surprisingly, Culpeper placed this prickly plant under the dominion of the planet of war, Mars. In the Middle Ages folk healers used it to dissolve kidney and gall stones. They also mixed the powdered root with silver birch, meadowsweet and horsetail to make a herbal compound which promoted the flow of urine in cases of dropsy or water retention.

General medical properties: Laxative and diuretic.

Specific properties: Its principal uses are as a laxative, to treat water retention and to dissolve kidney and gall stones. It has some limited use for treating rheumatic pain, and externally for skin blemishes.

Application and use: Infuse 3–4 tablespoons of the root stock in 1 cup of boiling water for 15 minutes. Take 1 cup a day, lukewarm.

ROSEMARY

Botanical name: *Rosmarinus officinalis.*

Popular names: Rosa maria, dew-of-the-sea.

Habitat: Cultivated

Flora: Perennial, with pale blue flowers May–August.

Folklore: The plant's generic name translates from Latin as 'dew of the sea', this may be because the herb thrives near the sea. It was a sacred plant to the Romans, who burnt it as incense during religious ceremonies and planted it in wreath shapes for decorating the tombs of important people. The early Christian Church adopted rosemary as the sacred flower of the Virgin Mary. According to one legend, Mary sheltered under a rosemary bush with the baby Jesus during her flight to Egypt. Folk tradition states that, like the famous Glastonbury thorn, rosemary blooms at Christmas. Country people used branches of the plant to protect their homes from witches, evil spirits, fairies and lightning. A spring of rosemary placed under the pillow stopped nightmares, and it was even said that a comb made of the wood would cure baldness.

In an echo of the pagan Roman custom, bunches of rosemary were sometimes placed in the coffin at rural funerals. In the Middle Ages, folk belief credited rosemary with the ability of being an antidote to bubonic plague. A flourishing black market in the herb grew up, with one contemporary writer remarking that rosemary, which had been selling for 'twelve pence an armful', was being offered at 'six shillings a handful' when the plague broke out. Rosemary was also believed to be a protective plant which kept bad luck away, and a sprig placed in the buttonhole assisted business success and improved the memory. It was also used in love magic, for a sprig burnt slowly in a candle flame was said to be able to warm the heart of a cool lover. Oil of rosemary was first distilled in the fourteenth century and was extensively used in the manufacture of perfumes.

General medical properties: Tonic, diuretic, antispasmodic, stimulant, antiseptic, anti-depressive and appetizer.

Specific properties: Rosemary promotes regular liver function and can be used to treat neuralgia, high and low blood pressure, headaches, halitosis, depression, flatulence, premature baldness and loss of appetite; it also acts as a general tonic. Externally, it can be used to treat bruises and skin diseases, and it is an insect repellent.

Application and use: Infuse 1 teaspoon of the dried flowers in ½ cup of boiling water. Take one cup daily. *Use with caution.*

ROWAN

Botanical name: *Sorbus aucuparia.*

Popular names: Mountain ash, quicken tree.

Habitat: Woodland and gardens.

Flora: Perennial shrub or tree, with white flowers in May–June and red berries in autumn.

Folklore: Rowan was traditionally a tree which offered protection from the powers of darkness. Following Britain's conversion to Christianity this description usually referred to the old gods and goddesses who were worshipped in pagan times. Rowan twigs bound with red ribbons were hung over barn doors on May Eve (30 April) and Hallowe'en (31 October) to keep evil influences away from the livestock. Farmers' wives wore a necklace of dried rowan berries, to protect them from spells in case they met the local witch out walking. It was said that a plentiful crop of rowan berries signified a poor harvest the following season.

General medical properties: Aperient, astringent, diuretic and laxative.

Specific properties: Rowanberries can be used for water retention, as a purgative and as a gargle for sore throats.

Application and use: Take 1 teaspoon of rowanberry juice as required.

RUE

Botanical name: *Ruta graveolens*.

Popular name: Herb of grace.

Habitat: Cultivated and wild.

Flora: Perennial, with white and pink flowers July–September.

Folklore: Rue has always been regarded as an important plant, renowned for its medicinal and magical uses. The Romans claimed that eating it granted the gift of second sight or psychic vision. Musket balls soaked in rue water were said always to hit their target. The herb was also used for cursing rituals, but oddly was also said to be a protection against the evil spells of witches. The popular expression, 'You will rue the day . . .' originated in the folk belief that rue was a plant of misfortune. Traditionally rue was said, like rosemary, to be a powerful antidote to bubonic plague. In 1760 a rumour spread through London that the plague had broken out in St Thomas's Hospital: before the doctors at the hospital could issue a denial the price of rue in Covent Garden had doubled in price.

General medical properties: Antispasmodic, emmenagogue, nervine and stomachic.

Specific properties: The general use of rue is for treating stomach upsets and difficult menstruation, lowering blood pressure, easing nervous tension and relieving muscular cramps.

Application and use: *Use with caution. Over-dosing can cause abortions or skin allergies.* Infuse 1 teaspoon of dried herb in 1 cup of boiling water for 15 minutes. Take 1 cup a day, as required.

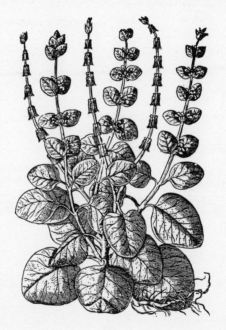

SAGE

Botanical name: *Salvia officinalis*.

Popular name: Garden sage:

Habitat: Cultivated.

Flora: Perennial, with purple, red, blue or white flowers June–July.

Folklore: Sage is a very ancient herb, whose generic name, *Salva*, means 'good health'. The Romans treated it as a sacred plant which had to be picked according to special religious rites: the gatherer had to wear a white robe, have bare feet and first indulge in a ritual bath; the plant also had to be gathered without using iron tools. Today we know that iron salts are incompatible with sage. According to the Roman belief a woman who cannot conceive should take sage juice, abstain from sexual intercourse for four days, and then go to bed with her husband. During the Middle Ages the herb was generally regarded as a cure-all. Culpeper said that it 'provoked the urine, expels the dead child, brings down women's courses and causes the hair to become black'. In folklore, it symbolized domestic virtue and was said to grow properly only in gardens where the wife ruled the household. Sage represented immortality, and eating it was said to rejuvenate the aged. In the old days a sprig of sage was hung in the kitchen when a member of the family was away; if it stayed fresh, the absent person was said to be happy. Eaten in May, the herb was said to be able to grant the eater a long and healthy life.

General medical properties: Antiseptic, anti-inflammatory, astringent and stomachic.

Specific properties: Sage reduces the flow of perspiration, treats dysentery, gastro-enteritis, sore throats and nervous disorders, and applied externally eases insect bites.

Application and use: Infuse 1 teaspoon of the leaves in ½ cup of boiling water for 30 minutes. Take 1 cup a day, a tablespoon at a time.

SAVORY

Botanical name: *Satureja hortensis*.

Popular names: Summer savory, garden savory.

Habitat: Cultivated.

Flora: Annual, with rose and lilac flowers August–October.

Folklore: Savory has been cultivated since the ninth century as a culinary herb, although its use as a medicinal plant dates back nearly two thousand years. It was renowned as an aphrodisiac, as indicated by its generic name, *Satureja*, which originated in the Greek word for a satyr, a lusty wood spirit. The Roman poet Virgil recommended that the herb should be planted around hives to attract bees. As a culinary herb savory is added to salads, sauces and vegetables. It is especially used on the Continent with haricot beans, hence its German name of *Bohnenkraut* or 'bean herb'.

General medical properties: Antiseptic, expectorant, carminative, stomachic, stimulant, diuretic and appetizer.

Specific properties: The principal use of savory is to stimulate the appetite and treat gastric complaints. It can also be used as an antiseptic gargle for sore throats and mouth ulcers.

Application and use: Infuse 2–4 teaspoons of the dried leaves in 1 cup of boiling water Take 1 cup a day.

SELF HEAL

Botanical name: *Prunella vulgaris*.

Popular names: Healwort, woundwort, heal all, sicklewort.

Habitat: Woodlands and pastures.

Flora: Perennial, with violet or purple flowers June–September.

Folklore: As its name suggests, self heal has a long history as a medicinal plant. Medieval herbalists who ascribed to the Doctrine of Signatures saw a resemblance between this plant and the throat, for which reason it was often included in folk remedies which treated this part of the body. The generic name is derived from a German word for quinsy, *Bräune*.

General medical properties: Astringent, tonic, antiseptic and carminative.

Specific properties: It is used to treat diphtheria, mouth ulcers, sore throats and burns.

Application and use: Infuse 2 teaspoons of the dried leaves for 15 minutes in 1 cup of boiling water. Take 1 cup a day, or use as a gargle as required.

SHEPHERD'S PURSE

Botanical name: *Capsella bursa-pastoris.*

Popular names: Shovelweed, St James' weed, toywort.

Habitat: Woodland and old ruins.

Flora: Annual or biennial with white flowers throughout the summer.

Folklore: The botanical name means 'the little case of the shepherd', a reference to its small triangular seedcases which resemble the purses once commonly worn by shepherds on their belts. Shepherd's purse grows as far north as Greenland, where it was introduced by the Vikings over a thousand years ago.

General medical properties: Anti-haemorrhagic, diuretic, emmenagogue, anti-inflammatory and astringent.

Specific properties: This herb is recommended for treating kidney disorders, low blood pressure, diarrhoea, wounds and nosebleeds, and for stimulating menstrual flow. Externally, it reduces the inflammation of chilblains.

Application and use: Infuse 2 teaspoons of the dried flowers in ½ cup of boiling water. Take 1 cup a day.

SKULLCAP

Botanical name: *Scutellaria galericulata*.

Popular names: Mad dog, mad weed, hooded willow herb.

Habitat: Wet places, ditches and riverbanks.

Flora: Perennial, with pale blue or purple flowers July–September.

Folklore: In the eighteenth century herbalists recommended this plant to treat rabies, hence its popular name of mad dog. It was also used to treat nervous tremors, lockjaw and convulsions. Its common name of skullcap refers to its use for mental patients.

General medical properties: Tonic, nervine, sedative and antispasmodic.

Specific properties: Skullcap is used principally to treat nervous disorders, insomnia, pre-menstrual tension, hysteria, muscular spasms and high blood pressure.

Application and use: Use with caution as can cause drowsiness. Infuse 1 teaspoon of the dried herbs in 1 cup of boiling water for 20–30 minutes. Take 2–3 times a day.

SLIPPERY ELM

Botanical name: *Ulmus fulva*.

Popular names: Red elm, sweet elm.

Habitat: Woodland.

Flora: Deciduous tree.

Folklore: This tree takes its name from the moist inner bark, which in powdered form is a very effective laxative and aid to childbirth. It is widely available as a commercial product in health food stores.

General medical properties: Demulcent, emollient and purgative.

Specific properties: Slippery elm can be used internally as a safe laxative for constipation, and externally for treating boils.

Application and use: Decoct 1 part of powdered bark to 8 parts of water. Boil, and simmer slowly for 15 minutes. Take ½ cup a day.

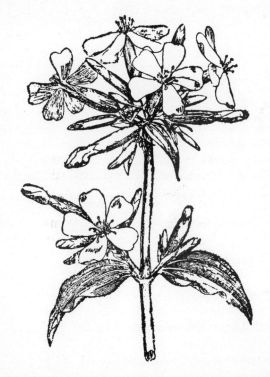

SOAPWORT

Botanical name: *Saponaria officinalis.*

Popular names: Bouncing Bet, fuller's herb, bruisewort, sheepweed.

Habitat: Wasteland and roadsides.

Flora: Perennial, with pink or white flowers June–September.

Folklore: The common name derives from the fact that in water the root exudes a substance known as saponin which creates a lather similar to soap. The detergent effects led to the plant's use as a natural alternative for soap, especially in the cleansing of wool before dyeing. The popular name of fuller's herb is a reference to the fullers who worked in the weaving industry. In 1548, in his book *The Names of Herbs*, William Turner first gave this plant its name of soapwort. However, it was known earlier to the Arab physicians, who used it to treat leprosy and other serious skin diseases. Medieval herbalists recommended soapwort for treating skin blemishes.

General medical properties: Antirheumatic, diuretic, depurative and expectorant.

Specific properties: Soapwort can be used to treat exzema, psoriasis, acne, scabies and other skin diseases. It also acts as a blood purifier, cures water retention and calms bad coughs.

Application and use: *Use only as directed by a medical herbalist.*

SORREL
See Wood Sorrel.

SOUTHERNWOOD

Botanical: *Artemisia abrotanum.*

Popular names: Lad's love, old man.

Habitat: Wild, and cultivated

Flora: Perennial, with yellowish-white flowers July–September.

Folklore: The common name originated in the Old English word *suthernwuld*, meaning 'a wooded plant from the south', a reference to its botanical origins in southern Europe. Because it is a strong-smelling herb it was formerly used to repel insects and as a nosegay to be carried by wealthy people to disguise the nastier smells of the streets. Medieval herbalists thought the herb had aphroidisiac powers, hence its name lad's love.

General medical properties: Stimulant, insecticide, antiseptic and emmenagogue.

Specific properties: It is principally used to promote menstruation in difficult cases, and as a general herbal antiseptic.

Application and use: Infuse 1 teaspoon of the dried herb in boiling water for 15 minutes. Take 1 cup a day.

SPEARMINT

Botanical name: *Mentha spicata*.

Popular name: Mint.

Habitat: Cultivated.

Flora: Perennial, with purple flowers July–September.

Folklore: Spearmint was introduced into Europe by the Romans, although its name dates only from the sixteenth century. Today, like peppermint, it is widely used as an essential oil for making confectionery. Spearmint has a sweeter, smoother taste than peppermint, which can be harsh. Folk healers used spearmint to cover the taste of unpleasant herbs in their remedies, or on its own as an aid to digestion.

General medical properties: Antispasmodic, digestive, stimulant and diuretic.

Specific properties: Spearmint is generally used in folk remedies to cure indigestion, flatulence, cramp, headaches, and colds.

Application and use: Infuse 1 teaspoon of the leaves in 1 cup of boiling water for 15 minutes. Take 1 cup a day.

SPEEDWELL

Botanical name: *Veronica officinalis.*

Popular names: St Llewellyn herb, gypsyweed, bird's eye, cat's eye.

Habitat: Hedgerows, woodland and heaths.

Flora: Perennial, with pale blue flowers May–August.

Folklore: This herb, as its common name suggests, was widely praised by folk healers for its fast-working curative powers. It was generally used in folk remedies for curing skin diseases and for both stomach and respiratory problems. In several European countries, including France and Germany, it was used as a substitute for tea.

General medical properties: Expectorant, stomachic, diuretic and appetizer.

Specific properties: Today the medicinal qualities of speedwell are treated with some scepticism by most herbalists. It is generally used in herbal tea mixtures, but can also be used to treat bronchitis, water retention and stomach upsets.

Application and use: Infuse 2 teaspoons of the dried flowers in ½ cup of boiling water. Take 1 cup a day.

ST JOHN'S WORT

Botanical name: *Hypericum perforatum.*

Popular name: Fairy herb.

Habitat: Woodland and meadows.

Flora: Perennial, with yellow flowers June–October.

Folklore: St John's wort derives its generic name of *Hypericum* from the Greek, which indicated that it smelt strong enough to drive away evil influences. It has always been recognized in folk belief as a plant which had the power to drive away witches, ghosts and demons. It could also protect a house from lightning. One Latin name for the herb used by medieval herbalists was *Euga daemonum*, or 'flight of demons'. Its common name derives from the fact that it is in full bloom at midsummer, which coincides with the Christian feast day of St John (24 June). Culpeper recommended a tincture of the flowers in spirits of wine to ward of melancholy and insanity. In the Doctrine of Signatures the red juice of the plant, which resembles blood, led to its use to treat open wounds. The popular name of fairy herb may refer to the belief on the Isle of Man that anyone who stepped on this plant would be carried off by the little people.

General medical properties: Diuretic, sedative, anti-inflammatory, astringent and anti-depressant.

Specific properties: *St John's wort has been found to contain a phototoxic agent which can react on fair-skinned people who are sensitive to sunlight. It should therefore only be used externally to treat skin irritations and insect bites.*

Application and use: *Only on the advice of a medical herbalist.*

STRAWBERRY

Botanical name: *Fragaria vesca.*

Popular names: Wild strawberry, wood strawberry.

Habitat: Grass and woodland, and cultivated.

Flora: Perennial, with white flowers May–June followed by red fruits.

Folklore: Although the strawberry has been cultivated since the sixteenth century in England as a dessert fruit, it was used for centuries before as a medicinal plant. Because of its high iron content strawberry has been recommended for people suffering from anaemia. It has also shown beneficial effects on the kidneys as well as lowering high blood pressure and treating gastro-enteritis. Externally, crushed strawberries have been used by women as a face pack to cleanse the complexion. Strawberries rubbed on chilblains are said to ease the severe itching sensation. It also has a use as a general tonic for children and sick adults, and many orthodox pharmaceutical products use strawberry syrup as a base.

General medical properties: Astringent, tonic, laxative and diuretic.

Specific properties: Strawberries are recommended as a gentle laxative, for water retention and as a tonic.

Application and use: Infuse the fruit in boiling water and take as required. *Caution: strawberries can cause allergic reactions in some people.*

SWEET FLAG

Botanical name: *Acorus calamus.*

Popular names: Sweet sedge, myrtle, sweet root.

Habitat: Wet places, riverbanks and ditches.

Flora: Perennial, with greenish-yellow flowers May–June.

Folklore: This ancient herb is mentioned in the biblical book of Exodus. It was introduced into Russia by the Mongols in the eleventh century, and from there to Poland in the thirteenth century; by the end of the sixteenth century it was widely distributed all over Europe. The medical properties of the root were well known to the ancient Greek and Arab physicians who used it as an aid to digestion, for expelling worms and for the treatment of colic.

General medical properties: Carminative, sedative and appetizer.

Specific properties: The general use of the root is in the treatment of severe cases of colic and flatulence. It has also been given as a sedative for the nervous system and as an appetite improver.

Application and use: Infuse 1 teaspoon of the dried root in 1½ pints of water. Drink 1–2 cups a day, lukewarm, as required.

SWEET VIOLET

Botanical name: *Viola odorata*.

Popular name: Sweet violet.

Habitat: Woodlands and hedges, and cultivated.

Flora: Perennial, with violet flowers April–May.

Folklore: This plant has been used in perfumery for nearly two thousand years. In the nineteenth century violet water was the most popular perfume used by ladies of distinction. It has also been used as a colouring agent for soft drinks and confectionery. Sweet violet also has important medical properties.

General medical properties: Purgative, expectorant and diuretic.

Specific properties: Sweet violet is recommended for treating bronchitis, catarrh and asthma. It can also be used as a laxative and to treat water retention.

Application and use: Infuse 1 teaspoon of the dried herb in 1 cup of boiling water for 10 minutes. Take 1 cup a day, as required.

TANSY

Botanical name: *Tanacetum vulgare.*

Popular names: Bitter button, wormwort, parsley fern.

Habitat: Woodland and wasteland.

Flora: Perennial, with yellow flowers July–September.

Folklore: Tansy was once used extensively to treat parasitic worms. In ancient times tansy oil was smeared on corpses, or bunches of it were placed in the shrouds of the dead, to keep away maggots. In the Middle Ages the herb was strewn on cottage floors to repel insects; it was also rubbed over meat to keep flies away. In the eighteenth century its bitter juice was used to flavour special cakes eaten at Lent; the idea was that the bitterness would remind the eater of the agonies suffered by Jesus on the cross. According to the old rhyme,

> On Easter Sunday is the pudding seen
> To which the Tansy lends her sober green.

General medical properties: Vermifuge, carminative, insectide and digestive.

Specific properties: The principal use of this herb is for expelling worms, but it should be taken with caution. Externally, it can be used to treat skin diseases and bruises.

Application and use: *Use only on the advice of a medical herbalist.*

TARRAGON

Botanical name: *Artemisia dracunculus.*

Popular name: French tarragon.

Habitat: Cultivated.

Flora: Perennial, with lilac or white flowers June–September.

Folklore: This herb is generally used to flavour chicken, seafood and meat. As its popular name suggests, it was widely used in French cuisine. Originally a native of Siberia, this herb has a number of medical uses.

General medical properties: Stomachic, digestive, diuretic and appetizer.

Specific properties: Tarragon is used for treating colic, flatulence, indigestion and nausea. It also has the ability to improve the appetite.

Application and use: Infuse ½ teaspoon of the dried herb in ½ cup of boiling water. Take ½ cup 3 times daily.

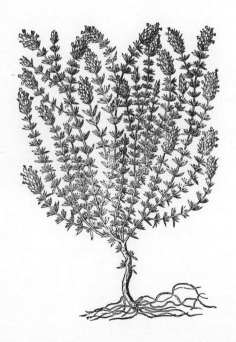

THYME

Botanical name: *Thymus vulgaris.*

Popular names: Common thyme, garden thyme.

Habitat: Cultivated.

Flora: Perennial, with lilac or white flowers June–September.

Folklore: According to legend, this plant grew from the tears shed by the beautiful Helen of Troy. The ancient Egyptians used it in the compound they mixed to embalm their dead. Opinions differ as to when it was first introduced into the British Isles: some botanists claim that the Romans introduced it, while others say that it did not arrive until the ninth century. Thyme's essential oil was not isolated until the eighteenth century, when it was found to be a powerful antiseptic. In modern scientific tests it was discovered that bacteria are destroyed by thyme oil essence within thirty minutes. In folklore this herb is associated with death, and in Wales it was often seen planted on graves. Thyme was also linked in folk belief with the fairies: a seventeenth-century recipe preserved in the Ashmolean Museum in Oxford mentions thyme as one of the ingredients of a magical elixir that can be used to see the little people.

General medical properties: Antiseptic, antispasmodic, expectorant, astringent, digestive and appetizer.

Specific properties: Thyme can be used medically for soothing sore throats, treating bronchitis and asthma and easing indigestion. Externally, it can be used to treat insect bites.

Application and use: *Use with caution, as an overdose can be poisonous.* Infuse ½ teaspoon of the fresh herb in ½ cup of boiling water for 5 minutes. Take 1 cup a day.

VALERIAN

Botanical name: *Valeriana officinalis.*

Popular names: Common valerian, all heal.

Habitat: Meadows, riversides and ditches.

Flora: Perennial, with white and pinkish flowers June–September.

Folklore: Valerian, named in the tenth century, was much sought after by Arab physicians. It has been described as the perfect herbal tranquilliser, and was used for this purpose in the First World War to treat soldiers suffering from shell shock. In the Middle Ages it was widely used by folk healers to treat the symptoms of epilepsy. The herb attracts rats, and it has been suggested that the secret weapon used by the Pied Piper of Hamelin may have been sprigs of valerian. In English folklore this herb was reputed to have aphrodisiac qualities: a young woman who carried a sprig of this herb was said never to lack ardent lovers. It was also said to possess the ability to increase psychic perception.

General medical properties: Sedative, antispasmodic, nervine and stomachic.

Specific properties: Medical tests have revealed that the roots of this plant contain substances known as valepotriates, which have a sedative effect. It is principally used in folk medicine to treat nervous tension, hyperactivity and insomnia, and as a general nerve tonic and sedative. As a pain reliever it can be recommended for severe headaches and rheumatic pains.

Application and use: Infuse 1 teaspoon of the dried root in 1 cup of boiling water for 15 minutes. Take 1 cup a day.

VERVAIN

Botanical name: *Verbena officinalis*.

Popular names: Simpler's joy, holy herb.

Habitat: Hedgerows and wasteland.

Flora: Perennial, with lilac flowers July–October.

Folklore: Vervain has an ancient history as a magical plant dating back to Greek times. The Romans called it *Herba Veneris* because they regarded it as sacred to the goddess of love, Venus. The Celtic druids were said to have washed their stone altars with water made from this herb before offering sacrifices to their gods. Country folk gathered the herb at specific phases of the moon and wore it as a protection against black magic. It allegedly possessed the mystical power of opening locked doors, and so was much valued by burglars. Hung around the neck, it was said to drive away bad dreams. In the Middle Ages the plant was used in love potions by white witches. Medically, vervain was used in folk remedies to cleanse the body of impurities, and was regarded as an antidote to poison and a cure for the bites of mad dogs and snakes.

General medical propertes: Tonic, astringent, diuretic and antispasmodic.

Specific properties: Vervain is recommended for treating disorders of the nervous system, depression, stress, hysteria, anaemia, pre-menstrual tension and muscular spasms. It can also be used to treat inflammation of the gall bladder and sore gums. Externally, an ointment made from the herb cures piles.

Application and use: Infuse 2 teaspoons of the dried herb in 1 cup of boiling water for 15 minutes. Take 1 cup a day.

VIOLET

See Sweet Violet.

WATERCRESS

Botanical name: *Nasturtium officinale.*

Popular name: Common watercress.

Habitat: Wet places, and cultivated.

Flora: Perennial aquatic, with white flowers June–September.

Folklore: Watercress is such a popular summer salad ingredient that its medical properties have largely been ignored. Its generic name means 'distortion of the nose', and refers to its pungent smell, caused by the high iron content. Medieval herbalists recommended people to wash their hair in watercress water to stimulate its growth.

General medical properties: Diuretic, stimulant, stomachic and expectorant.

Specific properties: It is recommended for treating anaemia (because of its high iron content), nervousness, bronchitis, asthma, urinary infection, water retention, diabetes, vitamin C deficiency and lack of appetite. Externally, it treats chilblains.

Application and use: *Use with caution, as prolonged dosage at high levels can cause kidney problems.* Infuse 1 teaspoon of young shoots in ½ cup of cold water. Do not boil. Take 1 cup 3 times a day.

WHITE BRYONY

Botanical name: *Bryonia dioica.*

Popular names: Ladies' seal, mandragora, English mandrake, devil's turnip, wild vine.

Habitat: Woodland and hedgerows.

Flora: Perennial, with greenish-white or pale green star-shaped flowers with five petals. The root resembles a large turnip in shape and is yellowish-grey on the outside and white inside. The berries are red.

Folklore: The name Bryony is derived from the Greek word *bruein*, meaning 'to grow luxuriantly'. In the Middle Ages white bryony was the English equivalent of mandrake, used for magical purposes on the Continent, and was therefore much sought after by witches, magicians, alchemists and other practitioners of the occult arts. Bryony roots carved into the shape of human forms were used as shop signs by eighteenth-century herbalists. The plant was popularly regarded as having aphrodisiac properties, but this has never been proved. The ancient Romans regarded it as a protection against lightning: the Emperor Augustus Caesar always wore a wreath of bryony leaves on his head during thunderstorms. White bryony is not related to black bryony, *Tamus communis*.

General medical properties: Hydrogogue and cathartic.

Specific properties: The dried root is the part used in folk remedies. *However it is toxic and can cause vomiting and gastric pains; both berries and root are poisonous.*

Application and use: *Only under the direction of a medical herbalist.*

WINTERGREEN

Botanical name: *Pyrola minor.*

Popular names: Spice berry, mountain tea, deerberry.

Habitat: Woodland, and damp and hilly places.

Flora: Evergreen, with white flowers June–September.

Folklore: The principal ingredient of this important medical plant is methyl salicylate, which is the basis of opium! For this reason wintergreen has been used in folk remedies to alleviate pain.

General medical properties: Astringent, demulcent, diuretic and tonic.

Specific properties: Oil of wintergreen is recommended for soothing all forms of pain, including rheumatic, arthritis and migraine. It can also be used as a gargle, and externally to treat bruises.

Application and use: Infuse 1 teaspoon of the leaves in 1 cup of boiling water for 15 minutes. Take 1 cup a day.

WITCH HAZEL

Botanical name: *Hamamelis virginiana.*

Popular names: Spotted hazel, winterbloom.

Habitat: Woodland and gardens.

Flora: Tree or shrub, with yellow flowers September–October.

Folklore: Witch hazel is commercially produced for a liniment to treat bruises and cuts. The North American Indians used its branches as divining rods to find water.

General medical properties: Astringent and anti-inflammatory.

Specific properties: Witch hazel can be used to stop bleeding and to treat boils, insect bites, swellings, bruises, burns and cuts.

Application and use: Infuse 1 teaspoon of the dried leaves in 1 cup of boiling water for 15 minutes. Take 1 cup a day as required.

WOODRUFF

Botanical name: *Galium odoratum.*

Popular names: Sweet woodruff, Waldmeister's tea.

Habitat: Woodland and hedgerows.

Flora: Perennial, with white flowers May–June.

Folklore: Woodruff was renowned for its fragrance, and in the Middle Ages its flowers were strewn on the floors of houses and churches. Bundles of the herb were hung in houses during the summer to cool and freshen the air; it was also placed in wardrobes to scent linen and ward off moths. In some European countries the plant is distilled into a fragrant wine which is sold as a herb tonic.

General medical properties: Carminative, diuretic, tonic, stomachic and cardiac.

Specific properties: Woodruff is used for the relief of stomach pains, as a heart tonic and a cure for insomnia, and for liver and kidney disorders.

Application and use: *Only under the direction of a medical herbalist.*

WOOD SORREL

Botanical name: *Oxalis acetosella.*

Popular name: Irish shamrock.

Habitat: Woodland.

Flora: Perennial, with white flowers May–June.

Folklore: The generic name comes from Greek *oxalis*, 'sour'. The principal ingredient of wood sorrel is oxalic acid, which if taken in excess can cause the formation of kidney stones. The plant has been cultivated as a culinary herb for sauces since the fourteenth century, but has now largely been replaced by common sorrel, which is of French origin.

General medical properties: Diuretic and antiseptic.

Specific properties: It is used as a gargle, and externally for treating skin diseases.

Application and use: *Only on the advice of a medical herbalist.*

WORMWOOD

Botanical name: *Artemisia absinthium.*

Popular name: Absinthe.

Habitat: Waste places, and cultivated.

Flora: Perennial, with yellow-green flowers July–October.

Folklore: As its common name suggests this herb was extensively used in folk remedies to expel worms. Because of its

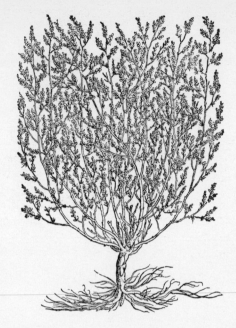

bitterness it has also been used commercially in the production of various aperitifs; absinthe itself had very dangerous side-effects, including hallucinations and brain damage. Medieval herbalists recommended this herb for treating water retention and as an antidote to poison.

General medical properties: Antiseptic, astringent and diuretic.

Specific properties: It is used for treating worms and as an appetizer.

Application and use: *Only on the advice of a medical herbalist. An overdose causes severe vomiting.*

YARROW

Botanical name: *Achillea millefolium.*

Popular names: Milfoil, woundwort, carpenter's weed, devil's plaything, nosebleed.

Habitat: Pastureland.

Flora: Perennial, with white and pink flowers May–September.

Folklore: The generic name comes from the classical legend that the Greek hero Achilles used to make poultices from its leaves to treat his warriors after a battle. It has been traditionally used to heal open wounds and stop the flow of blood, hence its popular name of woundwort. In Scandinavian countries it was sometimes used as a substitute for hops. In folklore, yarrow stems featured in divination: young women sewed an ounce of it into a sachet and, placing it under their pillows at night, said,

> Thou pretty herb of the Venus tree,
> Thy true name is Yarrow.
> Who is my true bosom friend to be?
> Pray tell me tomorrow.

They then allegedly went to sleep and dreamed of their future lover. The yarrow used in this love charm had to be picked from a graveyard on the night of the full moon. Yarrow leaves were often hung above the cradles of new-born babies in country districts to protect them from the spells of witches.

General medical properties: Diuretic, antiseptic, digestive, antibacterial and anti-inflammatory.

Specific properties: Medical tests have shown that yarrow stimulates the gastric juices and is therefore an aid to digestion. It also has proven antiseptic and antibacterial qualities and is capable of reducing inflammation.

Application and use: Infuse 1 teaspoon in 1 cup of boiling water for 15 minutes. Take 1 cup a day.

Bibliography

Addey, S. Oddall, *Household Tales*, David Nutt, 1895.

Agrippa, Henry Cornelius, *The Philisophy of Natural Magic*, Antwerp, 1533.

Baker, Margaret, *Discovering the Folklore of Plants*, Shire, 1969.

Ballow, M., *County Folklore: Northumberland*, David Nutt, 1904.

Black, William George, *Folk Medicine*, Elliot Stock, 1893.

Briggs, Katherine M., *The Folklore of the Cotswolds*, Batsford, 1974.

Briggs, Katherine M., *Botonologia: The British Physician or the Nature and Virtue of English Plants*, 1687.

Brown, Theo, 'Charming in Devon', *Folklore*, Vol. 1 81, spring 1970.

Burnby, J.G.L., *A Study of the English Apothecary 1660–1760*, Wellcome Institute, 1983.

Burne, Charlotte Sophia, *Shropshire Folkore*, Trübner & Co., 1893.

Bryan, Cyril P., *The Ebers Papyrus*, Geoffrey Bles, 1936.

Camp, John, *Magic, Myth and Medicine*, Priory Press, 1973.

Chamberlain, Mary, *Old Wives' Tales*, Virago Press, 1981.

Clark A. *The Working Life of Women in the Seventeenth Century*, Routledge, 1919.

Cockayne, Rev. O., *Leechdoms, Wort Cunning and Star Craft of Early England*, Vols. I and II, Longmans, 1864.

Coles, William, *The Art of Simpling*, 1656.

Creighton, A., *A History of Epidemics*, Cambridge University Press, 1891.

Crow, Dr. W.B., *The Occult Properties of Herbs*, Aquarian Press, 1969.

Cullum, Elizabeth, A Cottage Herbal, David and Charles, 1975.

Culpeper, Nicholas, *Herbal*.

Dawson, W.R., *A Leech Book of Medical Recipes of the Fifteenth Century*, Macmillan, 1934.

Deare, Tony and Shaw, Tony, *The Folklore of Cornwall*, Batsford, 1975.

Drewitt, F. Dawtrey, *The Romance of the Apothecaries Garden at Chelsea*, Chapman and Dodd, 1924.

Ehrenreich, Barbara and English, Deidre, *Witches, Midwives and Nurses*, The Feminist Press, USA, 1973.

Falkland, Richard, *Plant Lore, Legends and Lyrics* Sampson, Masterton & Co., 1892.

'Some Notes on the Pharmacology and Therapeutic Value of Folk Medicines', *Folklore*, Vol. LIX, September and December 1948.

Forbes, T.R., *The Midwife and the Witch*, Yale University Press, USA, 1966.

Friend, Rev. H., *Flowers and Flower Lore*, Vol. II George Allen n.d.

Fulder, Stephen, *The Handbook of Complementary Medicine*, Cornet Books, 1984.

Garland, Sarah, *The Herb and Spice Book*, Frances Lincoln, 1979.

Garrison, Lt. Col., *An Introduction to the History of Medicine*, W.B. Sanders & Co., 1929.

Glyde, John, *The Norfolk Garland*, Jarrold, 1872.

Golsing, Narda, *Successful Herbal Remedies*, Thorson's, 1985.

Gurdon, Lady, *County Folklore: Suffolk*, David Nutt, 1893.

Harner, Michael J., *Hallucinogens and Shamanism*, OUP Inc., USA, 1973.

Hartmann, Dr Franz, *Occult Science in Medicine*, Theosophical Publishing House, 1893.

Henderson, William, *Notes on the Folklore of the Northern Counties of England and the Borders*, W. Satchell, Peyton & Co., 1879.

Hoffman, Dr David, *The Holistic Herbal*, Findhorn/Thorson's, 1984.

Hoffman, Dr. David, *Welsh Herbal Medicine*, Abercastle, 1978.

Hopper, M.M., *Notes on Herbs*, Stoke Lacey Herb Farm, n.d.

Hunt, R. *Popular Romances of the West of England*, 1897.

Huson, Paul, *Mastering Herbalism*, Abacus, 1977.

Inglis, Brian, *A History of Medicine*, Weidenfeld and Nicolson, n.d.

Jones Baker, Doris, *The Folklore of Herefordshire*, Batsford, 1977.

Kloss, Jethro, *Back to Eden*, Back to Eden Books, USA, 1946.

Kremens, E. and Urdang, G., *History of Pharmacy*, J.P. Lippincott, USA, 1944.

Laing, J.M., *Notes on Superstition and Folklore*, John Menzies, 1885.

Law, Desmond, *The Concise Herbal Encyclopedia*, J. Bartholomew, 1973.

Leather, E.M., *The Folklore of Herefordshire*, Sidgwick and Jackson, 1912.

Lehane, Brendan, *The Power of Plants*, John Murray, 1977.

Le Strange, Richard, *A History of Herbal Plants*, Angus and Robertson, 1977.

Lloyd, Gwynedd, *Lotions and Potions*, National Federation of Women's Institutes, n.d.

Lucas, Dr R., *Nature's Medicines*, Award Books, USA, 1968.

Lust, John, *The Herb Book*, Bantam, USA, 1974.

Maple, Eric, *Magic, Medicine and Quackery*, Robert Hale, 1968.

Maple, Eric, 'Witchcraft and Magic in the Rochford Hundred', *Folklore*, Vol. 76, autumn 1965.

Marshall, Simpkin, *The Folklore of East Yorkshire*, Hamilton Kent, 1890.

Miller, P.S.A., *The Magical and Ritual Use of Herbs*, Destiny Books, USA, 1983.

Milton F.V., *Milton's Practical Modern Herbal*, Foulsham & Co., 1976.

Murray, Dr M.A. *The Witch Cult in Western Europe*, Oxford University Press, 1921.

Palaiseul, Jean, *Grandmother's Secrets*, Barrie and Jenkins, 1972.

Peacock, Mabel and Gutch, Mrs, 'Examples of Printed Folklore Concerning Lincolnshire', *County Folklore*, Vol. V, David Nutt, 1908.

Porter, Enid, *The Folklore of East Anglia*, Batsford, 1974.

Porter, Enid, *Cambridgeshire Customs and Folklore*, Routledge, 1969.

Raven, Jan, *The Folklore of Staffordshire*, Batsford, 1978.

Ristater, Carol Ann, *A Dictionary of Medical Folklore*, Thomas Y. Crowell, USA, 1979.

Rivers, Dr W.H.R., *Medicine, Magic and Religion*, Kegan Paul, Trench & Trübner Co. Ltd., 1924.

Robbins, Prof. H., *The Encyclopedia of Witchcraft and Demonology*, Hamlyn, 1970.

Rohde, Sinclair, *The Old English Herbals*, Longman, Green & Co., 1929.

Simpson, Jacqueline, *The Folklore of Sussex*, Batsford, 1973.

Simpson, N.D., A Bibliographical Index of British Flora, privately printed, 1960.

Stabbart, Tom, *Herbs, Spices and Flavourings*, David and Charles, 1970.

Step, Edward, *Herbs and Healing*, Hutchinson, 1926.

Stuart, Malcolm, *The Encyclopedia of Herbs and Herbalism*, Orbis, 1979.

Swinger, Dr Charles, *Early English Medicine and Magic*, Oxford University Press, 1920.

Thiselton Dyer, T.F., *The Folklore of Plants*, Chatto and Windus, 1889.

Thomas, Keith, *Religion and the Decline of Magic*, Weidenfeld and Nicolson, 1971.

Thompson, J.S., *The Mystery and Art of the Apothecary*, Bodley Head, 1929.

Prof. Lynn Thorndike, *A History of Magic and Experimental Science*, Columbia University Press, USA, 1923–58.

Thorne-Quelch, Mary, *Herbs and How To Know Them*, Faber, 1936.

Turner, William, *The New Herball*, 1551.

Tynan, Katherine and Maitland, Frances, *The Book of Flowers*, Smith, Eder & Co. 1909.

Ulydent, Mollie, *The Psychic Garden*, Thorson's, 1980.

Waring, Phillip, *A Dictionery of Omens and Superstitions*, Souvenir Press, 1978.

Weiner, Dr Michael, *Weiner's Herbal*, Stein and Day, USA, 1980.

Whitlock, Ralph, *The Folklore of Wiltshire*, Batsford, 1976.

Woodville, William and Jackson, Dr William, *Medical Botany*, John Bohn, 1932.

Zilboorg, Dr Gregory, *The Medical Man and the Witch in the Renaissance*, Johns Hopkins University Press, USA, 1935.

The Dioxin War

The Dioxin War

Truth and Lies About a Perfect Poison

Robert Allen

Pluto  Press

LONDON • ANN ARBOR, MI

First published 2004 by Pluto Press
345 Archway Road, London N6 5AA
and 839 Greene Street, Ann Arbor, MI 48106

www.plutobooks.com

British Library Cataloguing in Publication Data
A catalogue record for this book is available from the British Library

ISBN   0 7453 2213 1 hardback
ISBN   0 7453 2212 3 paperback

Library of Congress Cataloging in Publication Data applied for

10   9   8   7   6   5   4   3   2   1

Designed and produced for Pluto Press by
Chase Publishing Services, Fortescue, Sidmouth, EX10 9QG, England
Typeset from disk by Stanford DTP Services, Northampton, England
Printed and bound in the European Union by
Antony Rowe Ltd, Chippenham and Eastbourne, England

Contents

Preface

This story starts in South Tipperary amidst a leafy townland called Ballydine in the picturesque Suir Valley in the Irish mid-south. A long time ago Ballydine became the location of a David and Goliath encounter between a farming family called the Hanrahans and one of the biggest chemical corporates in the world, Merck, Sharp and Dohme of the USA. The Hanrahans, like many of their neighbours, believed that there was no mystery about the cause of the illnesses that were killing their animals – to the farmers the cause was emissions from Merck's faulty incinerator. When the Hanrahans learned that these emissions included a chemical substance known as dioxin, experts baffled them with science and told them that dioxin was not a problem. Whatever was killing their animals, the experts said, was a mystery.

It might have been a mystery to Irish regulators but across the Atlantic, in the USA, a different story about dioxin was emerging – one that was linked with a biological weapon used by the US military in Vietnam. Returning soldiers gradually began to exhibit symptoms their doctors could not diagnose or even understand. Gradually other stories began to emerge, in England, in Sweden, in Germany, in Italy, and back in the USA, in Missouri, about dioxin and its effects on human health. Throughout the 1970s and into the 1980s these stories persisted. There wasn't a mystery, dioxin was a deadly poison, and it was ubiquitous in the environment, in the blood and in the bodies of workers, soldiers and individuals.

This book, however, is not about dioxin the poison, it is the story of the lies and the secrecy that have accompanied this accidental by-product of the chemical industry throughout the twentieth century, and the price that must be paid to those who have suffered exposure to it. That price is high, not least among the Vietnam veterans who were exposed to Agent Orange, the biological weapon that contained large amounts of dioxin, and among the population of Vietnam, which is trying to live with a poison that is in their blood. The Vietnamese claim that the US government is in denial about Agent Orange and its impact on the children and youth of Vietnam who are growing up with conditions associated with dioxin. They can't prove this of course because they don't have the funds or the resources to do the tests that would establish a connection between their illnesses and Agent Orange. Yet back in the USA the connection is clear and the manufacturers of Agent Orange have begun to face the consequences that for many years they did everything in their power to avoid.

The story of dioxin is characterised by David and Goliath stories, human stories that reveal a human tragedy that affects us all, so the purpose of this book is to show why it happened, why it was covered up and what we can do to make sure it never happens again. *The Dioxin War* is a book, written from a social perspective, for those interested in the history of dioxin and its environmental, ethical, legal, moral and political impact on our societies.

Acknowledgements

This book is dedicated to everyone who has willingly or unwillingly worked on dioxin politics. For my inspiration I'm deeply indebted to Anne Addicott, C.D. Stelzer, Christiane Jacobi, Rick Reese, Charlie Cray of Chicago Greenpeace, Aynia Brennan, Tim and Ali Barton, Derry Chambers, Lennart Hardell, Olav Axelson, Mikael Eriksson, Arnold Schecter, Éanna Dowling and Ade Peace. My thanks and gratitude also go to Daithi O'hF.'alaithe, Diarmuid McConville, Catherine Dillon, Brian Campbell, Robbie Smyth, Mark Dawson, Micheal McDonnacha, Sean Marlow, Bernie Marlow, Rex Carr and his extremely helpful staff, Dennis Goss, Jenny Martin, Joe Holland, Steve Taylor, Fred Striley, Don Fitz, Russell Bliss, John, Mary and Seline Hanrahan, David Wingrove, Peter Styles, John Waters, Phillip Mullally, Alan Care, Charlie Hopkins, Martyn Day, Pat Costner, Alan Watson, Jon Campbell, Michelle Allsop, Roger van Zwanenberg and all the good Pluto people. I was aided by many other people, particularly dioxin specialists and community activists, and I hope they will forgive me for leaving their credits in the notes. As always my daughters Jenny and Ciara and my grandchildren Conor and Matthew were my foundations.

Chronology

1872: German chemists synthesise octachlorinated dibenzo-p-dioxin.

1897: Chloracne – a skin disease associated with dioxin exposure – identified.

1900: Herbert Dow, founder of Dow Chemical, credited with modern chlorine chemistry.

1918: Outbreak of chloracne following exposure to chlorinated naphthalenes.

1920–40: Dramatic increase of polychlorinated dibenzo dioxins (PCDD) and polychlorinated dibenzofurans (PCDF) levels in north American lake sediments (reported 1984).

1929: Production of polychlorinated biphenyls (PCBs) begins, in USA.

1936: Production of Pentachlorophenol begins.

1940–47: Synthesis of 2,4,5-T and 2,4-D for US military use.

1949: Explosion at Monsanto trichlorophenol factory in Nitro, Virginia, USA.

1950: Dow begin 2,4,5-T production and discover toxic impurity in the process.

1952: US military contact Monsanto for information on the toxicity of 2,4,5-T.

1953: Explosion at Boehringer trichlorophenol factory in Hamburg, Germany.

1953: Explosion at BASF trichlorophenol factory in Ludwigshafen, Germany.

1956: Explosion at Rhone Poulenc trichlorophenol factory in Pont de Claix, France.

1956: 'Accident' at Hooker Chemicals trichlorophenol factory in Niagara Falls, USA.

1957: Tetra chloro dibenzo dioxin (TCDD) – the most toxic dioxin – identified as unwanted contaminant in production of chlorophenols.

1959: 'Accident' at Thompson Hayward trichlorophenol factory, New Jersey, USA.

1961: Further research relates TCDD to chloracne and liver damage.

1961:   US military and trichlorophenol producers collaborate on production of 50:50 blend of 2,4,5-T and 2,4-D – Agent Orange

1963–70:   Agent Orange used in Southeast Asia.

1963:   Explosion at Philips Duphar trichlorophenol factory in Amsterdam, The Netherlands.

1963:   Rachel Carson's book *Silent Spring* published.

1964:   Dow identify TCDD in 2,4,5-T.

1965–66:   Sixty volunteers at Holmsburg prison in US treated with dioxin experience no immediate ill effects until dosage is increased 1,000-fold.

1965–66:   Reproductive and developmental effects noted in North American Great Lakes fish-eating birds.

1966:   US military demand for Agent Orange reaches limit of industry capacity.

1967:   Monsanto analyse their 2,4,5-T for TCDD contamination.

1968:   PCB/PCDF contamination of rice oil in Yusho, Japan.

1968:   Explosion at Coalite trichlorophenol factory in Bolsover, England.

1969:   Bionetics report reveals 2,4,5-T as teratogenic (birth deforming) in mice.

1970:   English scientists contract chloracne and high cholesterol levels after synthesising dioxin in their laboratory.

1970–71:   Thomas Whiteside articles on phenoxy herbicides in the *New Yorker*.

1971:   TCDD found to cause birth defects in mice.

1971:   Poisoning of Missouri, USA.

1972–76:   AH receptor hypothesis (how dioxin reacts in the body) developed.

1973:   Poly brominated biphenyls (PBBs) accidentally added to cattle feed in Michigan, USA.

1974:   TCDD found in breast milk from south Vietnam.

1976:   Explosion at Hoffman La Roche trichlorophenol factory in Meda (Seveso), Italy.

1977–79:   Lennart Hardell and Olav Axelson health studies of phenoxy herbicide exposed workers in Sweden.

1977:   TCDD found to cause cancer in rats.

1978:   TCDD found in emissions from domestic waste incinerators.

1979:   Class action filed against seven US manufacturers of Agent Orange, including Dow and Monsanto.

1979:   USEPA suspends use of herbicide 2,4,5-T.

1979:   PCB/PCDF contamination of rice oil in YuCheng, Taiwan.

1979:   Association of rare cancers – soft tissue sarcomas – with TCDD and phenoxyacetic acids.

1979:   TCDD found to modulate hormones and their receptors.

1980:   Toxic contamination of Love Canal community revealed.

1981:   Capacitor fire in Binghampton, New York, contaminates state office building with PCBs and PCDFs.

1982–87:   US Centers for Disease Control study on Agent Orange and Vietnam vets health effects.

1983:   USEPA halts production of 2,4,5-T.

1983:   First Agent Orange class action begins.

1983–85:   General industrialised populations found to be contaminated with PCDFs and PCDDs.

1983:   Evacuation of Times Beach, Missouri, USA.

1984:   Judge forces $180m settlement in Agent Orange action.

1985:   USEPA assessment of TCDD.

1985–88:   Kemner–Monsanto trial.

1986:   Chlorine-bleached paper mills found to produce dioxin.

1988:   First USEPA reassessment of dioxin.

1989:   Study of Seveso population reveals high levels of soft tissue sarcoma.

1989–90:   Monsanto's manipulation of health studies revealed in court.

1990:   Monsanto's flawed studies publicly exposed.

1991:   US (Fingerhut) cancer mortality study of 5,172 workers in twelve trichlorophenol factories reveals elevated cancer levels and high incidence of soft tissue sarcoma.

1991:   German (Manz) cancer mortality study of 1,583 workers reveals elevated cancer levels among long-term employed and high levels of breast cancer among women.

1991:   Second USEPA reassessment of dioxin begins.

1991:   Scientists announce link between hormone-disrupting chemicals and falling sperm counts in human males.

1991:   Second Agent Orange class action begins.

1992:   (North American) Great Lakes Commission calls for ban on persistent toxic substances 'whether or not unassailable scientific proof of acute or chronic damage is universally accepted'.

1993:   American Public Health Association calls for a 'gradual phase-out' of most organochlorines, to be replaced by safer alternatives.

1994:   USEPA release 2,400-page draft report on dioxins.

1997:   International Agency for Cancer Research (IARC) declare dioxin a human carcinogen.

1997:   International cancer mortality study of 21,863 workers exposed to phenoxy herbicides, chlorophenols and dioxins in twelve countries reveals a slight general cancer risk and a high risk to specific cancers, significantly soft tissue sarcoma.

1998:   30 years after the war with the USA, Vietnamese people still exposed to dioxin via their food chain. 'Concentrations of dioxin applied during the Vietnam war era persist in the Vietnamese environment today. Persistent dioxin contamination is present, and is suspected to be related to medical problems being experienced by some Vietnamese born after the war,' Hatfield, Canadian consultants, state in their report. 'Dioxin concentrations in Agent Orange were in the range of a billion times more than that found in some Canadian industrial effluent'.

1998: $200 million US Air Force study on the effects of Agent Orange on exposed military was tampered with. Scientists, who drafted two reports, withheld information on high rates of birth defects and infant deaths among children of Vietnam vets in the first report and altered the second report to give the impression that vets' cancers were not unusual. The data from the first report was finally released in 1992.

1999:   500 tons of animal feed contaminated with approximately 50kg of PCBs and 1g of dioxins distributed to animal farms in Belgium, the Netherlands, France, and Germany.

2000:   Scientists from the USA and Vietnam meet in Singapore to explore the possibility of launching a joint research programme to study the human and environmental health effects resulting from spraying Agent Orange and other herbicides during the Vietnam War.

2003:   US court allows Vietnam veterans to sue Agent Orange manufacturers.

2004:   Vietnamese workers file civil action in US courts against manufacturers of Agent Orange.

Abbreviations and Acronyms

Agent Orange: 50:50 mix 2,4,-D/2,4,5-T
An Foras Forbatha: forerunner to Irish EPA
An Foras Taluntais: Irish Agricultural Research Institute
ASTMS: (British) Association of Scientific, Technical and Managerial
    Staffs
CADI: Citizens Against Dioxin Incineration
CDC: (US) Centers for Disease Control
DDT: Dichloro Diphenyl Trichloroethane
DIRG: Dioxin Incinerator Response Group
DNA: Deoxyribonucleic Acid
DNR: (Missouri) Department of Natural Resources
EC: European Community
EMAS: (British) Employment Medical Advisory Service
EPA: Environmental Protection Agency
EU: European Union
FDA: (US) Food and Drug Administration
FOIA: (US) Freedom of Information Act
GPs: General Practitioners (aka family doctors)
HMIP: (British) Her Majesty's Inspectorate of Pollution
HSE: (British) Health and Safety Executive
IARC: International Agency for Research on Cancer
ICMESA: Industrie Chimiche Meda Societa Anonima
IDA: (Irish) Industrial Development Authority
IJC: International Joint Commission
IPC: Independent Petrochemical Corporation
MAFF: (British) Ministry for Agriculture, Fisheries and Food; now
    Defra
NATO: North Atlantic Treaty Organisation
NEPACCO: North-eastern Pharmaceutical and Chemical Company
NGO: Non-Governmental Organisation
NIOSH: (US) National Institute of Occupational Safety and Health
OCI: (US) Office of Criminal Investigation
OSHA: (US) Occupational Safety and Health Administration
PBB: Polybrominated Biphenyl
PCB: Polychlorinated Biphenyl
PCDD: Polychlorinated Dibenzo-para-dioxin

PCDF: Polychlorinated Dibenzofuran
PVC: Poly vinyl Chloride
REHW: Rachel's Environment and Health Weekly
RTE: Radio Telefis Eireann (Radio Television Ireland)
SLAPP: Strategic Lawsuit Against Public Participation
TBAG: Times Beach Action Group
TCD: Trinity College Dublin
TCDD: 2,3,7,8-tetrachlorodibenzo-p-dioxin
TCP: Trichlorophenol
TD: Member of Irish Parliamentary House
TSCA: (US) Toxic Substances Control Act
UCC: University College Cork
UNICEF: United Nations International Children's Emergency Fund
UNRID: United Nations Research Institute for Social Development
WES: Western Environmental Services
WHO: World Health Organisation

What is Dioxin?

Dioxin is the common name for a family of chemical compounds known as polychlorinated dibenzo-para-dioxins.[1] Chemists use PCDDs for short. There are 75 known PCDDs. Dioxin is also used to describe the 135 polychlorinated dibenzofurans (PCDFs) and some members of the polychlorinated biphenyls (PCBs) family[2] – those that closely resemble dioxin.[3]

Dioxin is released by chemical factories, smelters, all incinerators, processes containing chlorinated compounds (significantly phenols), paper mills and is present in pesticides and wood treatments that have their origins in chlorine chemistry. As a consequence the dioxin family are dispersed through the air and water where they eventually settle in soil and sediment. On land they are ingested by grazing livestock where they lodge in the fat. In water they are taken up by micro-organisms at the beginning of their journey up the aquatic food chain. Curtis C. Travis and Holly Hattemer-Frey estimate that dioxins can bioaccumulate in fish by a factor of 49,000.[4] And because dioxin is swept pole-ward by winds, currents, animal migration and bioaccumulation, the Inuit of Quebec – from the eating of fish, usually cod, and marine mammals, seals, beluga and walrus – have higher levels of the dioxin family than any population on Earth which have not suffered high occupational or environmental exposure.[5] Scientists agree that greater than 90 per cent of human intake of dioxin is through food.[6]

If you eat red meat, fish, poultry and dairy produce, which has been contaminated by emissions from incinerators and other combustion sources, chemical manufacturing and other industrial processes, it is likely that you are carrying dangerous doses of dioxin in your body. In other words all animal food products – everywhere on Earth – are contaminated. But even if you are a vegan, eat biological/organic produce and live the life of a hermit you will still be exposed, because dioxin-like chemicals are dispersed globally by natural migration and by pollution streams.

Arnold Schecter noted in a 1994 study of dioxin levels in US foodstuffs that a vegetarian diet or a diet high in fruit and vegetables 'might have previously unsuspected health advantages for adults along with the more commonly recognised cardiovascular benefits and decreased cancer risk'. But he warned that the dioxin-like PCBs, 'which act in an additive fashion with dioxins and furans' are generally present in considerably higher amounts in the environment and he feared that the food samples studied by his group would have contained twice the dioxin toxicity if PCBs had been measured.[7]

Although the dioxin family is fairly large the potency of each dioxin is different. Some are very toxic, some are moderately toxic and some have little effect. Of the 210 dioxin and furan congeners plus the 209 PCBs only 30 (7 dioxins, 10 furans and 13 PCBs) are regarded as highly toxic and they differ significantly in their potency. 2,3,7,8-tetrachloro dibenzo-para-dioxin (TCDD) is the most toxic – one thousandth of a gram of TCDD can kill a guinea pig. Scientists measure dioxin using the international toxic equivalency factor (I-TEF).[8]

There appears to be little or no dispute among scientists that the dioxin family cause reproductive and developmental problems in animals. The USEPA in its 1994 draft reassessment of dioxin noted that 'relatively speaking, these exposures and effects are observable at very low levels in the laboratory and in the environment when compared with other environmental toxicants'.[9]

Laboratory animals exposed to dioxin before and after birth are most at risk. Their developing immunal, hormonal and developmental systems can suffer irreparable damage, leaving the animal open to attack from bacterial, viral and malignant diseases, and with impaired important hormones.

By very low levels scientists mean thousands of times lower than many other environmental pollutants. In other words the dioxin family produces a wide range of effects at levels that are only detectable with equipment that can measure compounds in parts per trillion.[10] Peter Montague of the Environmental Research Foundation has referred to studies that show that in laboratory mice a single tiny dose of dioxin causes increased deaths when the mice are challenged with an influenza virus.[11]

It is worth emphasising that the effective dose of dioxin is very small: 10 nanograms of dioxin per kilogram of bodyweight (10 ng/kg) harms the mouse immune system enough to increase the death rate from influenza virus. To get 10 ng/kg into perspective, consider that a single 5-grain aspirin tablet taken by a 150-pound adult is a dose of 4.7 million nanograms of aspirin per kilogram of bodyweight (4,761,936 ng/kg). For an adult human to get a dose of aspirin equivalent to the dose of dioxin that harms the mouse immune system, you would have to divide a single aspirin tablet into 470,000 pieces (nearly half a million pieces) and eat only one piece.[12]

We do not know how many humans have died from exposure to dioxin. It is impossible to tell. Dioxin does not enter the body independently from other toxic chemicals. People have died from dioxin exposure but rarely do their death certificates read 'death by dioxin' because they will have died from various specific illnesses. Many modern illnesses are associated with dioxin, some directly, some indirectly, some as a result of a systemic response. All of us are now exposed to dioxin but we are also exposed to hundreds of other highly toxic chemicals.

If we get a particular cancer or an illness that is associated with modern living (alcohol, tobacco, fast food), the role of individual synthetic chemicals is not taken into consideration by the majority of the medical profession. Only those in the medical profession who know what to look for are able to detect a link between a specific chemical and a specific illness, but even this is not clear because dioxin, in particular, does not act in the body in a uniform way. Different chemicals interact in our bodies and cause various illnesses.

This is why the story of dioxin is a cautionary tale. It is a clue to the reason why we are all suffering from a range of cancers and a multitude of illnesses. Four out of five cancers in the western world are caused by environmental factors – by pollutants that get into our body and pollutants we put into our bodies. The environmental factors that are causing modern cancers have twentieth-century industrial sources. Half of the world's cancers occur among people living in industrialised countries, yet only one-fifth of the world's population live in the developed world.[13] The dioxin family is one source we know a lot about. Dioxin is a poison that is an aspect of everyday life. The risk is your exposure, the pathways of exposure and the interaction with other toxic pollutants.[14]

Prologue: The Politics of Truth

By putting business before every other manifestation of life, our mechanical and financial leaders have neglected the chief business of life: namely, growth, reproduction, development, expression. Paying infinite attention to the invention and perfection of incubators, they have forgotten the egg, and its reason for existence.

Lewis Mumford[1]

While we sit gloating in our greatness
Justice is sinking to the bottom of the sea
And it feels like I'm living in the wasteland of the free

Iris Dement[2]

At ten to seven on Wednesday 11 June 2003 paralegal Mark Guy sent an email to family, friends and assorted activists and campaigners. The subject line read: 'WE DID IT!!! Supreme Court sides with Vets in Agent Orange ruling'. In the body of the text Guy wrote, 'We're in the news again. Our little office of 3 versus a mutual fund of chemical giants! (I would recommend divesting your Dow and Monsanto shares now, before it's too late!)' The remainder of the text was a press release that had been sent out two days earlier from the office of Gerson Smoger, an attorney hardly known outside the world of toxic tort litigation and among those who once fought in the jungles of Vietnam where they were poisoned with a deadly chemical designed to defoliate and kill.

The press release read:

(June 9, 2003) Washington, D.C. Today the U.S. Supreme Court announced its decision in the Vietnam veterans' suit, Dow Chemical Co. v Stephenson (02–271), allowing victims of cancers who served in the military during the Vietnam War to continue to pursue their claims against Agent Orange manufacturers despite a 1984 class action settlement. The Supreme Court let stand the 2nd Circuit's decision that the due process rights of Vietnam Veterans were violated by the 1984 class action settlement. The crux of the Vietnam vets' case – by the time the veterans learned they were

1

sick with cancer, all the money from a $180 million dollar class action settlement was long gone. The Supreme Court was forced to decide whether the veterans' cases were ended by that 1984 class action, or whether the vets who first became ill or disabled after all the funds were deleted can still bring suit as a result of their constitutional rights being violated by a settlement they never even knew existed. The Court rejected the arguments of Dow Chemical Co. and Monsanto that the settlement was final, confirming the 2nd Circuit's decision that to bind late injured veterans to the settlement would deny their constitutional rights. According to attorney Gerson Smoger, who first brought the Agent Orange case and argued it before the Supreme Court on behalf of the veterans, 'We are thrilled with today's decision. For the past nine years, we have been working to show that the Agent Orange class action settlement cannot stand when the very victims of Agent Orange are entitled to no compensation from it. Many Vietnam War veterans suffer from devastating illnesses caused by their exposure to Agent Orange and we are gratified that the U.S. Supreme Court has recognised the right of these veterans to sue for the injuries they received when serving our country.'

The release went on to state that 'out of approximately 4.2 million veterans who served in Vietnam, only about 50,000 ever received any compensation from the class action settlements before the money ran out in 1994. This decision opens the way for a number of these veterans to bring suit against the manufacturers who caused their illness.'

All of a sudden it seemed that Agent Orange was back in the news, yet there was a curious lack of interest among the media. The news agencies carried a few paragraphs on the story, that the judges had been deadlocked on the ruling, with only the *Washington Post* acknowledging the historical and political importance of the event with a lead story in its final edition of the following day, stating:

The court's vote was 4 to 4, with Justice John Paul Stevens sitting the case out. He gave no reason for his recusal, but Stevens's son, John Joseph, a Vietnam veteran, died of cancer in 1996 at 47. Under the court's rules, a tie vote results in the automatic affirmation of the lower court's ruling – in this case a decision by the New York-based U.S. Court of Appeals for the 2nd Circuit. It gave veteran Daniel Stephenson, who discovered in 1998 that he had a deadly form of cancer, a chance to argue that he was not adequately represented in the 1985 settlement negotiations.[3]

The *Post* can be forgiven for not checking their facts, giving 1985 as the year of the out of court settlement when they should have written 1984, but of more significance was the simple fact that the newspaper did not mention the word 'dioxin'.

Agent Orange contained 2,3,7,8-TCDD, the most toxic member of the family of chemicals known as dioxin. It is a by-product of chemical processes using chlorine and these include pesticides, plastics, solvents, detergents and cosmetics. Dioxin has been revealed as a human carcinogen – a chemical whose toxicity is so strong it can cause cancer and activate other cancers. It is also a poison that impairs our hormonal, immune, developmental and reproductive systems. It has been associated with heart disease, liver damage, hormonal disruption, reproductive disorders, developmental destruction and neurological impairment. It has been found in human milk.[4] It has been linked to endometriosis but also to diabetes. It has figured in bone and skin diseases and it has been implicated in reduced sperm counts.

This was the reason why Smoger spent ten years of his life fighting to get dioxin back into the courts, and why he now believes that Dow and Monsanto, who manufactured more Agent Orange than anyone else, are in for a rough ride. Smoger, who has written legal and scientific papers on dioxin, must now succeed where attorneys Rex Carr and Jerome Seigfreid failed when they took on Monsanto on behalf of the residents of Sturgeon, Missouri. Evidence introduced in that case, *Kemner* vs. *Monsanto*, showed that the chemical industry knew of dioxin's impact on human health as far back as the 1950s. But Carr and his associate lost the case because they could not prove that their clients had been poisoned by dioxin. 'When we argued the case to the jury [our clients] came into the court room all looking healthy, all looking vital, not a damn thing wrong with any of them,' said Carr, reflecting on a case he believed he could not lose.[5] But lose he did because dioxin seeps into our bodies interacting with our complex biological systems to cause illnesses that do not become apparent until many years have passed.

Smoger and his legal team have been cast in the role of David against the Goliaths of the chemical world, and they don't come much bigger than Dow and Monsanto. Ever since Smoger promised Admiral Elmo Zumwalt, who was Chief of Naval Operations in

Vietnam and chair of the Agent Orange Co-ordinating Council, that he would get Agent Orange back into the courts, his sling-shots have hurt the industry.

Impressed with the way Smoger had handled the case of Alvin Overmann, a trucker from St Louis who died from cancer after being exposed to waste oils contaminated with dioxin, Zumwalt, whose son died from non-Hodgkin's lymphoma – a rare cancer – resulting from exposure to Agent Orange in Vietnam, asked the attorney to join him in his personal mission to raise the profile of exposed veterans. This included lobbying the Veterans Administration to conduct health studies on the effects of Agent Orange and attempting to get the Supreme Court to overturn the Agent Orange settlement, *Ivy* vs. *Diamond Shamrock* (among six other chemical corporates – Dow Chemical, Monsanto, Uniroyal, Hercules, Thompson Chemical, and T. H. Agriculture). 'Originally, it was the Ivy suit. In that suit, it was petitioned to U.S. Supreme Court for review and I wrote an amicus [friend of the court brief, not a party to the suit] brief for the Agent Orange Co-ordinating Council and about 25 veterans service organisations on behalf of the Admiral,' Smoger recalled.[6]

When the Supreme Court refused to consider the Ivy case, Smoger told the Admiral that he would try again and in 1998, he brought another case on behalf of Joe Isaacson, a former crewman at a base from which Agent Orange missions were flown, and followed it with one for Daniel Stephenson, a former helicopter pilot. Federal District Judge Jack Weinstein, the judge who had approved the original Agent Orange class action settlement, dismissed it, so Smoger took it to the US Court of Appeals for the 2nd Circuit, which overturned Judge Weinstein's decision. Dow and Monsanto fought back, taking it to the Supreme Court. On 26 February 2003, Smoger argued the case before the Supreme Court, who ruled in favour of the veterans on 9 June. 'We won three nothing in the 2nd Circuit,' Smoger said. 'So it was a very clear decision that due process was violated.' Veterans that were injured after 1 January 1995 can now consider bringing a lawsuit again. 'The clients I represented are active and we're actively representing quite a number of other people.'

Smoger's success should not be underestimated, but that success – getting to the heart of the matter in the ongoing tragedy that is Agent Orange – will be futile if the chemical industry reacts in its normal fashion, with obfuscation. The publication in July 2003 of the second edition of *Dioxins and Health*, the 952-page bible on dioxin edited by the scientists Arnold Schecter and Thomas Gasiewicz, will give comfort to those who have argued for several decades the case against dioxin. The opening chapter 'Overview: The Dioxin Debate' by Thomas Webster and Barry Commoner is arguably the single most important scientific text ever written about dioxin. Webster and Commoner encapsulate the history of dioxin in a manner not done since 1982 when Alastair Hay, an English toxicologist, wrote *The Chemical Scythe* – so far the only published history of dioxin in book form. Published books on the social impact of dioxin are difficult to find.[7] Even dioxin specialists struggled to publish their work, especially if it questioned the role of industry.[8]

The years between 1977 and 1993 were crucial in the study of dioxin and its effect on human health. Epidemiological studies on chemical workers and exposed communities and workers proved that exposure to dioxin was a direct cause of cancer. Yet industrialists, regulators and some scientists continued to insist that dioxin wasn't such a bad thing if your exposure was low.[9] Industrialists argued that Monsanto, who had lied about its knowledge of dioxin, were bad boys in an otherwise compliant industry – the implication being that they were the only ones who lied.[10] The truth is more interesting. With few exceptions, everyone involved with dioxin – corporates, lobby groups, regulators, media and environmentalists – has tried to cover up their mistakes, and these go back many decades. Why? And why did the cover-ups also include the persecution of scientists and regulators and journalists and activists who have tried to tell the truth?

Part of the reason is the science of dioxin itself. An extremely persistent chemical, it now exists in quantities in the environment at levels capable of extreme and violent damage to living systems it comes in contact with. This damage, however, is subtle. Dioxin is a clandestine poison. It infiltrates the body. If exposure is high it will do its work quickly. If the exposure is low it will make itself familiar with the body's biological mechanisms, settling down to cause a variety of illnesses – many years after the initial exposure. Dioxin does not strike the body down in the way arsenic or cyanide does. The violence dioxin inflicts on the body is internal and not easily identified until the victim is dead and even then sometimes dioxin is not cited as the cause of death. This is what makes dioxin a complex issue. There are no piles of rotting bodies. Instead there is a slow and subtle weakening of the body's functioning systems.

Another part is politics. Alastair Hay was obliged by his university to concentrate on other matters. Despite his vast knowledge of the subject he has been silent for a long time. It has been suggested he was told to shut up or funding for his university department would be stopped. Lennart Hardell, a Swedish oncologist who identified the link between phenoxy herbicides and soft tissue sarcoma along with two colleagues Olav Axelson and Mikael Eriksson, was embroiled in a subterfuge that threatened his credibility as a scientist. He was lambasted by epidemiologist Richard Doll who declared that Hardell's 'work should no longer be cited as scientific evidence'.[11] Cate Jenkins, a US Environmental Protection Agency scientist who naively believed she could regulate dioxin-producing industry, was grounded and for many years was not even listed as having a desk, direct phone line and email address at the EPA. Carol van Strum, an activist and journalist who exposed the politics of pollution in the corridors of power in the USA, became such a threat to manufacturers of chemicals containing dioxin that her life was put in danger.

The final part is probably the most crucial, one which van Strum certainly stumbled upon – profit! In the USA alone the production of chlorophenols for the manufacture of herbicides, significantly 2,4,5-T, wood preservatives like pentachlorophenol, and insecticides like Dichloro Diphenyl Trichloroethane (DDT) were big business for 33 companies – particularly the market leaders Dow and Monsanto. In the 40 years after pesticides were introduced sales rose approximately 12 per cent a year until a slow-down in the late 1980s left the market deflated at $24 billion in 1991![12] The methods used, particularly by US industry, in chlorophenol production created dioxins and the industry was not too keen to change, even though it had known since the late 1950s that dioxin was present and dangerous to its workers. Boehringer and BASF learned that heat and solvents played a part in dioxin formation.[13] Industry was told again in 1973 when Hans Paul Bosshardt warned: 'In the future, to prevent damage, the technical production of chlorinated phenols and formulations will have to be improved so that polychlorinated dibenzo-p-dioxins no longer occur. If this is not possible, the use of these compounds will have to be drastically limited or totally forbidden.'[14] Regulation was to be avoided. The cost was too high.

Dioxin, it could be argued, is a legacy of the twentieth century – a consequence of chlorine chemistry in the production of pesticides, plastics, solvents, detergents, cosmetics and other 'essential' modern products.[15] These products are all around us. If you live in a large industrialised city what do you see beyond the bustle of modern commerce, people moving, working, surviving? Cars, buses, lorries, trains and aeroplanes carrying people as they embark on their rites of passage. All these forms of transport are powered by a combustion process and built with industrial chemicals. What else do you see? Buildings, construction sites, machinery, glass, steel, concrete and treated wood. Look closer. Metals, plastics, electrical wires, pipes, paints, solvents, detergents. Go into the shops. Clothes made from synthetic fibres, fabrics treated with chemicals, electronic appliances made with strong durable plastics, cosmetics made from chemicals, stationery and newspapers made from bleached paper, food grown with the aid of pesticides, tin cans whose lining leaches chemicals into the fish, meat and vegetables they contain. If you purchase any of these items you will carry them home in bags made from plastic. Go into a restaurant, a public house, into the toilet, into the kitchen. Everywhere you look you'll see solvents, lubricants, refrigerants, detergents, soaps, shampoos, deodorants, cosmetics and plastics. Leave the city and go into the countryside, where monocultures predominate – vegetables, cereals, pulses and utility crops, where cattle and sheep graze on intensively farmed land, where farmers have planted chemically-treated seeds and sprayed herbicides, pesticides and fertilisers to increase the yields of their crops.

This technology, however, had its genesis in the eighteenth century when Swedish chemist, Carl Wilheim Scheele isolated chlorine – a pale green gas – from metal salts in 1774. It wasn't a momentous discovery and didn't make much difference to the world of chemistry until the invention of electricity began to reshape the world of industry. Suddenly industry realised it could reduce the costs of manufacturing some of its products. One product that benefited from developments in electrical engineering was caustic soda – which was used in the manufacture of soap and detergents.

As the nineteenth century came to a close the chemical industry discovered they could produce soda and chlorine by passing an electric current through a salt-water solution.[16] The invention of the chlor-alkali electrolytic process revolutionised the chemical industry. But they now had large amounts of elemental chlorine – a by-product that might have gone to waste if Herbert Dow, the founder of the US chemical corporation Dow Chemical, had not made a significant discovery.[17] By combining chlorine with chemicals made from hydrogen and carbon (the organic compounds found universally in plants, animals and humans), Dow introduced the chemical industry to a range of new, highly profitable chemicals – chlorinated hydrocarbons (organochlorines), which are also called halogenated aromatic hydrocarbons.[18] Industry now had to find sources of hydrocarbons. Bituminous coal tar, which was formed during the production of coke, was valuable because it contained a range of aromatic hydrocarbons – benzene, toluene, xylene, naphthalene and anthracene. However, because the chemical industry's demand for coal tar products was growing faster than the production of coke – used primarily as a fuel in steelworks – the need to find other sources of hydrocarbons became imperative. In the USA during the 1920s and 1930s the extraction of mineral oil and natural gas provided chemical companies with that source. The petrochemical industry was born. Since the 1950s mineral oil has become the most important raw material in the chemical industry, along with salt.

Mineral oil – saturated hydrocarbons of different lengths depending on their geographical location – begins as a thick, sticky, volatile liquid. It is the task of the oil refineries to turn it into the various forms used in everyday industrial, commercial and domestic use as gasoline, diesel oil, light and heavy fuel oil and liquid gas. The chemical industry is only interested in the light gasoline – naphtha – which after processing forms the petrochemicals known as benzene, butadiene, ethylene, propylene and toluene, among others. In the years between the beginning of the 1939–45 war and the mid-1950s the chemical industry combined chlorine with these hydrocarbons to create a treasure trove for themselves. The products of the war machine, which had been rushed into production without any thought about their effect on individual species and the ecosphere, suddenly became products of necessity in the post-war world:

- plastics like poly vinyl chloride (PVC)
- organochlorine insecticides like Dichloro Diphenyl Trichloroethane (DDT) – which had actually been manufactured 65 years earlier[19]
- phenoxyacetic herbicides like 2,4,5-T
- wood preservatives like pentachlorophenol
- chlorinated solvents like perchloroethylene
- liquid chlorine for disinfecting and bleaching – cotton for example.

Within a few years the chemical and petrochemical industries grew into giant corporations. Their ability to influence consumer lifestyles through clever and imaginative marketing of their products generated further growth.[20] Suddenly, it seemed, communities and workers all over the planet had become dependent on the products of chlorine chemistry, significantly synthetic chemicals containing chlorine and carbon atoms. Without knowing it. But there was a price to be paid.

1
Awkward Questions:
A Dioxin Spill in the Mid-West

MELYCE CONNELLY

Melyce Connelly, a 22-year-old single mother, believed she had found her modern utopia in Ryan Creek – in the rain forests of coastal Oregon in 1979. Melyce lived in a home and on land that was the product of the mutual aid her neighbours had shared with her. She grew herbs and vegetables and flowers in gardens tended by her own hands. She paid the mortgage and bills with income derived from the sale of the herbs – notably garlic, basil, thyme, rosemary, sage, parsley and shallots. She augmented her income with some part-time teaching.

Melyce's utopia, however, was tainted by modern society. In Ryan Creek the US Forest Service was engaged in a spraying programme of unwanted vegetation. It was a practice that worried Melyce's community who believed the substances used by the federal government agency were affecting their health.[1] The Forest Service promised it would not use toxic herbicides, especially 2,4,5-T – a chemical compound containing dioxin that had just been suspended by the US Environmental Protection Agency (EPA) after more than a decade of wrangling about its toxic effects. This action would cost the agency $20 million, paid to the manufacturers of the herbicide. The use of herbicides like 2,4,5-T had become pervasive. Companies wanting to get rid of vegetation that inhibited the growth of cash crops used 2,4,5-T in large quantities. The herbicide was also used to clear railway embankments and power line routes. Community concern about the risks to health and the impact on the environment was stonewalled, but some people wanted reassurance.

Melyce and some of her neighbours weren't convinced that their water supplies were safe from the herbicide spraying. They met with the district ranger to elicit a guarantee that their spring water sources would not be affected. Three days later a helicopter's noisy chattering woke Melyce from dawn's dreamstate.

It wasn't long after the spraying of Ryan Creek that the first signs of toxic poisoning became apparent. Melyce's chicks and ducklings bore the first assault, dying within days. Her six-month-old son began to suffer persistent bloody diarrhoea. It got worse. Pregnant women miscarried. Young children were hospitalised with various illnesses, including the near-fatal spinal meningitis. When she realised there was a possible connection between the timing of the spraying of the herbicides, the wildlife deaths and the human illnesses, Melyce gathered her dead animals and placed them in her freezer. She would get someone to analyse them to see what they had died from.

Believing the authorities would now take seriously her concern about the health effects from exposure to the toxic herbicides, Melyce co-operated with the EPA scientists who came to study her valley. She gave them her frozen animals, believing them when they said they would do an analysis and come back to her within a few months with the results.

The weeks passed into months, became years while Melyce waited. After four years she finally got an answer. The samples of the herbage, soil and water and her animals had been lost or misplaced or included with other samples. When the EPA did manage to sample water in the Ryan Creek area they discovered that dioxin levels in the sediment upstream from Melyce's home had increased four-fold to the highest ever reported in the Pacific Northwest region of the USA.

On 4 July 1989 Melyce Connelly died. She was diagnosed with brain, lung and breast cancer.[2] She was 32. Her ashes were spread on the gardens she had toiled over to make a living for herself and her family.[3]

We are ruled by Big Business and Big Government as its paid hireling, and we know it. Corporate money is wrecking popular government in the United States. The big corporations and the centimillionaires and billionaires have taken daily control of our work, our pay, our housing, our health, our pension funds, our bank and savings deposits, our public lands, our airwaves, our elections and our very government. It's as if American democracy has been bombed. Will we be able to recover ourselves and overcome the bombers? Or will they continue to divide us and will we continue to divide ourselves, according to our wounds and our alarms, until they have taken the country away from us for good?

Ronnie Dugger[4]

Though you search for the Holy Grail
you're not going to find it
in the chemical world
                    Peter Hammill[5]

For better or worse we're deeper into dioxin than anyone, even
though the public links them more to Dow ... Three lawsuits (Nitro,
Agent Orange, Sturgeon) hold the key ... If we win them all, there
won't be others. If we lose them all, Katy bar the door!
                                        Monsanto memo[6]

In the American mid-west the night of 10 January 1979 was typically
cold. The Missouri countryside was covered with snow that had
settled to a depth of six inches in the lowlands.

A Norfolk and Western freight train was headed westward along
the northern line out of St Louis in eastern Missouri. It was carrying a
tank car on its maiden voyage out of Monsanto's Krummrich factory
in Sauget on the Illinois side of the Mississippi River.[7] The tank car
contained 20,000 gallons of a Monsanto chlorophenol known to the
company as ocp-crude – an intermediate chemical used to make wood
preservatives like pentachlorophenol, a chemical that contained
dioxin. It was en route to its purchaser, Reichold Chemical Company
in Tacoma, Washington.

As the train made its way through the farming community of
Sturgeon, a small town with a population of 787 approximately 25
miles north of Columbia in the heart of Missouri, a coupling axle
broke, derailing the train. The derailment caused a half-inch puncture
along a weld in the tank car. The ocp-crude spilled out along the
track for a distance of about half a mile.[8] It was about 11 o'clock. On
contact with the cold ground the ocp-crude evaporated into a fine
mist. A strong phenolic odour permeated the air and seeped into the
lives of the innocent community of Sturgeon.

Back in Krummrich, Joe Starzyk had been told about the accident.
He called Phil Kirk and at three thirty in the morning the pair made
their way to Sturgeon. 'Upon entering Sturgeon, we noticed a strong
ocp odour. We determined the product was ours. We noticed the odour
about a mile from the scene. Most of the contents had leaked out,'
reported Kirk.[9] The two Monsanto men then went to the command
centre of the Sturgeon Fire Department where they were met by
several journalists who wanted to know what had been spilled and

whether it was hazardous. Kirk told them it was orthochlorophenol and not carbolic acid as some media had reported.

Meanwhile Chemtrek, a company set up by the chemical companies to provide backup for transportation accidents, were now involved, at the behest of Norfolk and Western Railway.[10] Western Environmental Services (WES) of Portland, Oregon had also been brought in by the railway company to clear the track and arrange a clean-up. A decision was taken to evacuate the town.

A television crew made their helicopter available to the Monsanto, railway and environmental people. 'From the air,' reported Kirk, 'we could see a slight orange cast on the snow on the south side of the tracks, for a distance of approximately 1,000 yards.'[11]

Monsanto later noted that their 'clear, immediate concern was whether the high toxic ocp-crude presented a danger to the community and how to avoid contact with the chemical or its fumes'.[12] A local veterinarian advised one of his clients to remove cattle and hogs from the exposed area.

The EPA in Kansas City had sent three of their people to the scene. Air and soil samples were taken. The information that dioxin might be present in the ocp-crude might have remained secret if a curious resident, a student, had not asked EPA officials at a town hall meeting on 8 February whether dioxin was a contaminant of ocp-crude.[13] Some time later an analysis of the tank car contents by Christopher Rappe of the University of Umeå, Sweden, showed 45 ppb of 2,3,7,8-TCDD.[14]

Alarmed by the news about dioxin, 65 residents of Sturgeon, which had been re-occupied on the advice of Monsanto on 12 January, filed lawsuits in Boone County against Monsanto, N&W, GATX Corporation (manufacturers of the tank car that ruptured) and Dresser Industries (manufacturers of the coupling axle that broke and caused the derailment of the tanker). They alleged that 'they suffered personal injuries as a result of exposure to dioxins contained in the spilled chemicals ... that Monsanto were liable for such injuries under strict products liability and wilful and wanton conduct'.[15]

Monsanto had denied there were dioxins in the tank car, as early as the following day after the spill, and continued to deny that they knew of the presence of TCDD.[16] Although the company had dispatched senior officials to the spill site they did not take any responsibility for the clean-up, which was left to WES who had no experience of dealing with highly toxic substances. Monsanto's senior management would have known that the ocp-crude contained dioxin. This was subsequently confirmed by Rappe. According to Rex Carr:

> Monsanto stood by and watched as WES conducted what, in light of the presence of 2,3,7,8-TCDD was a grossly inadequate 'clean-up'. Monsanto watched silently as WES spread the 2,3,7,8-TCDD contaminated material to (the property of William and Frances Kemner), throughout the streets of Sturgeon, and into Sturgeon businesses.
>
> During the clean-up of the spill, the residents walked through and by the spill site, clean-up workers tracked the spilled residue throughout the town, the wind carried debris from the spill throughout the town, ocp-crude-saturated railroad ties were burned (creating additional dioxin), and the smell of the spilled chemical remained in the town for many months.
>
> During and immediately following the spill, the Sturgeon residents experienced frequent headaches, burning and running noses, and sore throats from the prevalent, strong odour of the spilled chemical. In the next few months, the residents began developing unusually high incidences of rare and other illnesses.[17]

During the clean-up the railway workers noticed that the EPA officials were wearing moonsuits. When they asked why, they were told there was dioxin present. The workers also decided to sue. Monsanto settled out of court for $6 million. After the court overturned an award of $53 million for 51 workers against the railway company the issue was also settled out of court. The residents' lawsuit, however, would become a significant chapter in the history of dioxin. Because two of the defendants moved for a change of venue from Boone County on the grounds of adverse publicity, the lawsuit was dismissed. It was refiled in the Circuit Court of St Clair County, Illinois, where the ocp-crude had been manufactured and shipped by Monsanto. On the eve of the trial a settlement of $5 million was agreed with GATX and Dresser. During the trial a settlement of $3,840,000 was agreed with N&W.

The jury eventually reached a split decision. Monsanto won on the issue of actual damages based on liability but lost on actual damage and punitive damages based on the company's wilful and wanton misconduct. The jury awarded William and Frances Kemner $14,500 each for damage to their property and awarded each of the other 63 plaintiffs $1 each for personal injuries. Monsanto were ordered to pay $16,250,000 in punitive damages.

Reading it like this, it appeared that the case was much ado about nothing. Rex Carr, from East St Louis, Illinois, and Jerome Seigfreid, from Mexico, Missouri, had agreed to fight the case for the residents. Carr, as advocate for the plaintiffs, sought to show that Monsanto were aware of the highly toxic properties of their chemicals – that dioxin was present. Proving this became increasingly more difficult as the trial became destined for the history books – as the longest trial in US legal history, starting on 6 February 1984, ending 22 October 1987. And proving that his clients had been harmed eventually defeated him.

The 608 days of evidence the jury endured over three years and six months produced a 91,555-page transcript that was augmented by 6,333 exhibits. A total of 182 witnesses were heard. The jury took eight weeks to make their decision. In the end Monsanto won on appeal and had the damages awarded against them reversed. 'The jury, after three and a half years of trial, found no actual damage but decided to punish the defendant for wrongful acts occurring from 1949 through several years after the incident at Sturgeon, Missouri,' the appeal judge surmised, declaring that 'the punitive damage award must be reversed'.

Carr, a proud attorney who had received the plaudits from his colleagues for the initial success, had lost the case.

> Our proof requires a doctor to say to a reasonable degree of medical certainty – jesus christ, medical certainty? – that dioxin caused that cancer. Not only could we not do that we couldn't even prove that our people were sick.
>
> Our people came back three years later when we argued the case to the jury and they came into the court room all looking healthy, all looking vital, not a damn thing wrong with any of them.[18]

There was nothing Carr could do about this. As the trial progressed Carr learned that dioxin is a subtle and complex poison that does not follow a logical pattern towards a clinical conclusion. Dioxin is characterised by its toxicity. It does not lead directly to dead bodies in the way that war, famine, industrial accidents, fire and traffic, train and plane crashes do. Dioxin seeps into our bodies interacting with our complex biological systems to cause illnesses, which do not become apparent until many years have passed. Carr's clients had been poisoned but it would be years before they would suffer ill-health. 'The jury found, very logically, that my people were not harmed but they also found that Monsanto committed egregious frauds.'[19]

This was the true victory! The jury may have concluded that there was no dioxin on the Kemner property, that there might have been no exposure to dioxin in Sturgeon. But there was plenty of dioxin in Monsanto's factories, in their products and in their workers.

When the trial began it was Carr's task to expose Monsanto's sins – if they had committed any. He believed they had. 'We were seeking punitive damages as well as compensatory damages and that means you have to show that they had some knowledge of what they were doing and had failed to take steps.'[20] This meant that he had to show that Monsanto were aware of the toxicity of dioxin, aware of its presence in their processes, aware of its history. To do that he had to find incriminating evidence. That evidence, Carr was sure, was in Monsanto's files.

> It was hard getting all the documents we needed. The discovery of documents was gradual. They supplied a set of documents that referred to other documents. So I'd go back to the court and say there are other documents. It was so bad at one time that the trial judge ordered the president of Monsanto to sign an affidavit that the production [of documents] had been full and complete, that he personally knew that everything had been done to produce the relevant documents. That's very unusual.[21]

Carr was up against one of America's most powerful corporations. Getting the relevant documents proved relatively easy compared to the trouble he had getting Monsanto management and scientists to admit their complicity.

That complicity was set in motion in August 1948 when Monsanto began a pilot programme to manufacture 2,4,5-T from trichlorophenol (TCP) at its Nitro, West Virginia factory in the USA. On 8 March 1949, six months after full production had begun, an explosion caused by a runaway reaction showered approximately a dozen workers with then unknown toxic substances. Within weeks of the explosion the workers who had been contaminated developed chloracne, a skin disease that is characteristic of dioxin poisoning, and began to complain of nausea, vomiting, headaches, fatigue and metabolic disturbances. Monsanto subsequently revealed that approximately 77 people had been affected by the accident. Subsequent tests of four of the workers revealed that they had severe chloracne. A medical team led by Dr Raymond Suskind examined the workers and found that the men were suffering from debilitating pain, fatigue, insomnia and sexual impotence. In 1953 Suskind took 36 workers (10 who had been present in the building during the explosion and 26 who had occupational exposure) and gave them a thorough medical examination. He reported later that the illnesses suffered by the workers were 'limited to the skin', although his examinations showed that 27 of the 36 workers suffered symptoms of systemic illness as well as skin ailments.[22]

If Monsanto believed this would be the end of the story, they did not reckon on the safety of the trichlorophenol process or the inability of workers, who had been kept ignorant of the perils of chemical manufacture, to cope with the dangerous consequences of this process.

By the end of the 1950s, after a similar accident at Boehringer's trichlorophenol factory in Hamburg, Germany in 1953, scientists had identified one of the toxic substances formed from explosions in TCP factories. It was TCDD. They had also revealed chloracne as a sensitive indicator of high exposure to dioxin.[23] The credit for this discovery goes to Dr Karl Schulz, a dermatologist at the University of Hamburg, George Sorge, a Boehringer chemist, and an un-named research assistant. In 1956 Schulz examined a Boehringer worker with severe chloracne, three years after the explosion. When he researched the literature he discovered that chloracne had first been identified in 1897 by Von Bettman. He learned that it had been characterised as a symptom of exposure to chlorine gas two years later by Dr Karl Herxheimer who called it chloracne after chlorine acne.[24]

But Herxheimer, noted Alastair Hay, was wrong. 'In the ensuing 50 years it was realised that chlorine was not the real cause of the problem, but instead the skin condition was caused by exposure to a variety of chlorine and bromine substituted aromatic compounds,'[25] – the halogens (chlorine, bromine and iodine), which are found in sea salt (sodium chloride) and combined with organic compounds containing a benzene ring, like trichlorophenol and pentachlorophenol. Therefore exposure to the manufacturing processes of trichlorophenol and pentachlorophenol could cause chloracne.

Schulz determined to find out why these compounds caused the disease but when he tested pure 2,4,5-trichlorophenol on the ear of a rabbit, which reacts similarly to human skin when applied with chemicals, there was no effect.[26] Then he tested the commercial 2,4,5-T and within days there was inflammation and reddening of the skin. There was, Schulz realised, something in the commercial chemical products, a contaminant that was the real cause of the disease. It was around this time that George Sorge came to collaborate with Schulz, providing the dermatologist with various compounds. They found nothing.

Then one of those events that make chemistry so interesting in Hollywood films occurred. Ironically, perhaps given the controversy that would surround chemical treatments of wood, this assistant was employed in Professor Sandermann's lab to help evaluate the potential of chlorophenols as wood preservatives. Sandermann and his assistant synthesised 20 grams of TCDD and stored it in a desiccator. As any chemist will tell you it's a bad idea to open a desiccator like you would open a jar of pickles because the powder inside will puff into a rising cloud once the seal is broken. This is exactly what happened when the assistant opened the desiccator containing the dioxin. The assistant, now suffering from chloracne, was sent to Schulz who listened to the story and realised this was the clue both he and Sorge had been searching for. Dioxin, he believed, was the contaminant present in phenoxy compounds. To make sure, Schulz applied some dioxin to his lower left underarm. A few weeks later chloracne developed. The Boehringer workers had been exposed to dioxin!

Sorge went away and did some experiments. He discovered that heat played a part in the formation of dioxin during the trichlorophenol process. The higher the temperature the more dioxin was produced. He told his bosses and Boehringer introduced a low-temperature trichlorophenol process. The producers of trichlorophenol now had a way of reducing the dioxin content in their products.

BASF, another German chemical manufacturer, had also discovered how to reduce the amount of dioxin. By reducing the amount of solvent, BASF discovered that fewer dioxins would be formed. They alerted other trichlorophenol producers in 1956 and 1957 and sold the technical knowledge to Dow. This knowledge certainly stopped the outbreaks of chloracne among the Boehringer workers, but it didn't make the factory a completely dioxin-free zone.[27]

Although Sorge was never able to reveal his role in this discovery, Schulz published in 1957 – 11 years before the Bolsover trichlorophenol explosion and 19 before a similar explosion at Seveso.[28]

What is remarkable is that this information never became common in the literature. 'Although some toxicologists took careful notice of Schulz's 1957 paper, the problem was that no consequences were drawn and no effective distribution of the message was organised. Somehow they were unable, or did not feel called upon, to make proper use of their knowledge in terms of effective warning.'[29] Some commentators have suggested this was because the paper was published in German, but this is a poor reason.

Monsanto senior management gave the impression that they were also ignorant of this and other research on dioxin. When Seveso occurred in 1976 Suskind realised there might be more to the toxicity of 2,4,5-T than he had first imagined. He wrote to Monsanto health director Dr George Roush and suggested a follow-up medical study of their dioxin-contaminated workers. In his reply Roush said the company 'agreed in principle' to a further study of those 'workers who were involved in the chloracne problem in the early 1950s'.[30] Suskind waited for two years and on 9 June 1978 he wrote again to Roush, suggesting a 'systematic retrospective epidemiological study of this group' and enclosed a list of the 37 exposed workers.[31] This never happened.

Instead of examining the 37 workers, Monsanto and Suskind set up three general studies. The first studied 122 workers, the total the company claimed were 'persons with chloracne that could be attributed to the 1949 TCP process accident' who had died between 8 March 1949 and 31 December 1978.[32] The second study featured 884 workers, the entire workforce on the hourly payroll between 1 January 1955 and 31 December 1977 with potential for exposure to TCDD. This study cohort was categorised by those who worked in 2,4,5-T or trichlorophenol production, who were deemed exposed, and all others with potential contact with 2,4,5-T, deemed as non-exposed.[33] The final study was set up to determine the long term health effects of occupational exposure to trichlorophenol in the manufacture of 2,4,5-T. Two groups were chosen, based on work history records that classified workers as exposed or non-exposed. This produced a cohort of 204 workers 'exposed to the process accident as well as those exposed to normal manufacturing processes ... (including) chemical operators and service employees such as pipe fitters and mechanics' and a control group of 163 employees who 'were never associated with the 2,4,5-T process or its materials'.[34]

All these studies were conducted in 1979. When they were finally published the suggestion was that the workers exposed to the 1949 explosion had suffered nothing more serious than chloracne. This was a crucial event in the secret history of dioxin. Monsanto's studies suggested that dioxin was relatively benign, that it did not cause specific illnesses. 'The Monsanto studies, which were published in the scientific literature during 1980–83, have been touted as the most comprehensive studies to date concerning dioxin's human health effects,' was how scientist Pat Costner perceived its relevance.

> Since then, one or more of the studies have played key roles in decisions regarding regulation, liability, and victim's compensation by the US Environmental Protection Agency, the Veterans Administration, environmental and other agencies in Europe, Australia and New Zealand, the scientific community, and the general public.
>
> Despite numerous other studies of workers, veterans and communities indicating strong associations of dioxin exposure with various cancers, heart disease, and reproductive dysfunction, it has become a common phrase that dioxin has never caused a single human death.[35]

This may not be what Monsanto in particular wanted to achieve. Like all corporations they were driven by the profit-desire. Keeping the toxicity of dioxin secret helped management keep their shareholders happy. Monsanto's studies on their exposed workers actually contained the truth about dioxin but the company did not want this and other information they possessed on dioxin to be made public.

In the early to mid 1980s the real truth about dioxin was still hidden from the public domain. Only those who knew the true story or sought the truth realised how toxic dioxin was. The public perception about dioxin was founded on conflicting evidence. Both the specialist and general media made sure of that. Chemical companies like Dow and Monsanto were quick to criticise and damn anyone who dared to present evidence that contradicted their view. The public did not know that health studies had been manipulated and that some chemical companies had top secret agendas.

The initial studies on the exposed Seveso population had been inconclusive. The struggle for compensation and justice by dioxin-exposed workers, communities and army veterans had been compromised by conflicting science and advocacy obfuscation in the courts. Regulatory authorities were content that dioxin did not pose a threat to human health at the levels present in the environment.

The USEPA had, it appeared, set their dioxin levels of safe exposure using the information from the known occupational health studies. The evidence linking dioxin with ill health in humans apparently wasn't conclusive enough. And although some scientists questioned the validity of the Monsanto studies[36] it is likely that the sordid history of dioxin would have remained secret for a considerable time if a train had not gone bump in the night and a small community had not employed Rex Carr to ask awkward questions.

Carr: And doctor, it goes beyond just this case because there are so few studies on human health effects. These two studies that you authored make up a great deal of the world's scientific literature on what are the human health effects of exposure to TCDD, isn't that correct, sir?

Suskind: Correct.

Carr: And it has been relied upon. Your report has been relied upon by government agencies, not just in this country but all over the world, I suppose, correct, sir?

Suskind: I believe so.

Carr: It has been made a major foundation stone in the position that Monsanto and other companies responsible for the manufacture of TCDD have given to the world saying don't worry about what TCDD will do because within a few years, the health effects such as aches and pains and fatigue, all these things, and nervousness, all these things will go away, except in a few cases, isn't that correct, sir?

Suskind: Correct.

Carr: And doctor, if the foundation is flawed, is false, is untrue, then the entire edifice that is built on that foundation is also unworthy of belief and fails, isn't that correct, sir?

Suskind: I don't know what you are talking about, sir.

Carr: Doctor, if the world has perceived and at least half of the literature refers to health effects, the population study, if the world had relied upon something that is untrue, if in fact an overwhelming majority of the workers, 90 percent of the workers or 75 percent of the workers continued to complain of aches and pains and nervousness and fatigue four years after their exposure, contrary to what you said, the edifice upon which that foundation stone is based would also be faulty, wouldn't it, sir?

Suskind: If indeed we had reported it wrong.

Carr: Yes. Now doctor, I expect at this point in time to demonstrate that you have indeed reported it wrong to the world, and that the foundation, the world's concept or view of the health effects of TCDD is not that they disappear in a few years but that they have persisted and that in your examination of 1953 that the overwhelming majority of the 36 workers that you examined at that time continued to complain of aches and pains, fatigue, nervousness, central nervous disorders. And if I demonstrate that, sir, you will agree that you have done a disservice to the world at large, will you not, sir?[37]

Suskind denied that he had done the world a disservice but Carr persisted, going through the medical records of each exposed worker to show that, on re-examination in 1953, the majority continued to complain of the various illnesses. After some stonewalling Suskind admitted that he knew in 1953 that 27 out of 29 of the exposed workers were still ill but wrote in 1980 that, with the exception of a few cases, the illnesses had disappeared.[38]

This was the cornerstone that should have allowed Carr to build the foundation for his case that dioxin is a persistent poison, that dioxin is not an ordinary poison, that dioxin stays in the body causing havoc many years after the initial exposure. Four years after exposure the Nitro workers were still complaining of ill health. This fact alone should have triggered a systematic and thorough analysis of this contaminant of chlorine chemistry by Monsanto's medical team. Instead Carr had to come back to this question a few weeks later on 7 March. 'Didn't you report to the world in three different publications, in three different instances that in your 36 workers all these problems went away except the chloracne and except for in a very few workers these other complaints went away?' Suskind continued to stonewall these questions despite Carr's persistence. Eventually Carr said: 'You told the world that these problems had gone away except in a few cases, isn't that right, sir?'

Suskind: Yes, sir.
Carr: And you wanted the world to rely upon the statements that you made, correct, sir?
Suskind: I made those statements, sir.

Carr: My question goes to the entire world doctor. You do expect
           the entire world to rely upon what you say, don't you
           sir?
Suskind: I hope so.[39]

It was this persistence, however, that eventually wore down Monsanto.
The secrets spilled out.

- Monsanto dumped 30 to 40 pounds of dioxin a day into the
  Mississippi River during the 1970s, knowing that the chemical
  would get into the St Louis food chain via the river.
- Monsanto knew in the mid-1950s how to reduce the amount
  of dioxin being formed during the manufacture of its
  chlorophenols, yet chose not to implement the process until
  1980 so that it could save money.
- Monsanto secretly tested corpses of people who had died in
  accidents and not from illnesses in St Louis for the presence of
  dioxin and found it in every case, admitting that the chemical
  could have come from their Krummrich factory – where they
  manufactured chlorophenols.
- Monsanto had known for half a century that its products
  contained dioxin yet despite the risk to people using these
  products said nothing.
- Monsanto knew that 2,4-D and 2,4,5-T – the chemicals that
  made up Agent Orange – contained high levels of dioxin.
- Monsanto knew about the dioxin content in Lysol, a cleaning
  product made from Santophen – a Monsanto chemical, and
  said nothing, despite the knowledge that Lysol was used on
  children and dogs.
- Monsanto failed to notify and lied to its Krummrich
  factory workers about the presence and danger of dioxin in
  chlorophenols so that it would not have to bear the expense
  of changing its manufacturing processes or the loss of its
  customers.
- Monsanto knew that its business would be hurt if its customers
  learned that dioxin was present in its products, so said
  nothing.
- Shortly after a spill in the Krummrich factory, samples taken
  by the Occupational Safety and Health Administration (OSHA)
  revealed dioxin. Monsanto conducted its own measurements

and discovered higher levels but they told their workers and the media that they had failed to confirm OSHA's findings.

- Monsanto workers were told there were no significant health problems in those exposed to dioxin, other than a skin condition and a reversible liver problem.
- Monsanto workers were never given any health information about dioxin even though the company knew that exposure could cause cancer, liver damage, nerve damage and other injuries.
- Exposed Monsanto workers were not told of the presence of dioxin and were not given protective clothing even though the company was aware of the dangers of dioxin during the manufacture of chlorophenols.
- Monsanto made every effort it could to conceal the presence of dioxin in its manufacturing processes.
- Monsanto told the EPA that it could not test its products for dioxin because dioxin was too toxic to handle in its labs, yet senior management knew that dioxin was being used in its labs.
- Monsanto had no adequate testing programme for the presence of dioxin and only began to implement a more precise dioxin testing method after the Sturgeon spill.
- Monsanto lied to the Canadian government, claiming that its products contained lesser amounts of dioxin than they actually did.
- Monsanto never warned its customers that its products contained dioxin. Management told one customer there was no detectable amount of dioxin in its 2,4-D.
- Monsanto scientists deliberately manipulated the health studies of workers exposed to dioxin as a result of the explosion at their Nitro factory in 1949.[40]

During the three and a half year trial none of this evidence was being reported by the media, which didn't surprise Carr. 'You couldn't possibly get the essence of that trial by just coming in and out an hour or two once or twice a week, you had to be there day after day.'[41]

It was only when he prepared his brief for the appeal in 1989 that this information became public knowledge. All that was needed now was for someone to start collecting the pieces of the puzzle and fit them into place. But that wasn't as easy as it seemed.

2
Heart of Darkness: Phenoxy Herbicides, Agent Orange and the Swedish Doctors

THE EFFECTS OF 2,4,5-T

'There are no provable cases in (Britain) of cancers, miscarriages or birth deformities directly attributable to 2,4,5-T and 2,4-D. But the body of anecdotal evidence continues to grow and the graveyards of Britain bear silent witness to the number of known carcinogens and teratogens that could not be pronounced dangerous until there was overwhelming evidence of their effects,' remark Judith Cook and Chris Kaufman, in their book *Portrait of a Poison*.[1] Here are some case histories uncovered by the National Union of Agricultural and Allied Workers and the authors.

A head gardener in Somerset used 2,4,5-T sprays in 1971 and 1972. His wife gave birth to a still-born child in December 1972. The baby was deformed and had part of its brain missing. Her three previous pregnancies and one later were normal.

A Nottinghamshire forestry worker who used 2,4,5-T said his wife had one premature birth and two babies born under five and a half pounds. One baby was born with only one kidney functioning.

An Essex forestry worker used 2,4,5-T. His first child, a daughter, was born with her upper lip missing, her nose deformed and her upper teeth later came through at all angles. There was no known history in the family of such defects. Hospital specialists assured the worker that he would be safe to add to his family. The chance of a recurrence would be one in a million, he was told. His son was born three years later, with a deformed lip. His daughter was unable to have children.[2]

Scientists can pretend that they can discern 'safe' levels of hundreds of different chemicals, all acting in combination. They can pretend that they can understand all the ill effects of multiple hormone mimickers on each type of cell, each tissue and each organ at every stage of development from conception to birth, through youth and puberty and into maturity, in each of the thousands of affected species. They can pretend to know these things, but they cannot ever actually know them. They are just pretending. Scientists can pretend, but in so doing they perform a great disservice, preventing decision makers from seeing what really needs to be done: we need to abandon the practice of chemical-by-chemical regulation. We need to regulate whole classes of chemicals. And the dangerous classes need to be phased out and banned. Zero discharge. Pollution prevention.

These are the keys to sustainability and survival.

Peter Montague[3]

I do remember my government telling me Agent Orange dioxin would never hurt me or my children.

Tom Baxter[4]

Vietnam has been called the USA's heart of darkness. But it is a pervasive darkness that is beginning to engulf us all. What began as a war against communism ended with a warning about humanity's desire to be gods. This has led us to play with the planet's organic chemistry. This has made us synthesise the compounds that regulate the planet's heart. This has made us attempt to replicate natural hormones. This has made us create so that we may destroy. This is how the innocent history of phenoxy herbicides, of Agent Orange, began.

In 1940 researchers isolated indoleacetic acid – the hormone that regulates growth in plants – as part of a programme to synthesise plant compounds. Phenoxy herbicides have their genesis in this research. Researchers managed to synthesise several plant growth regulating hormones. Among these were 2,4-dichlorophenoxyacetic acid (2,4-D) and 2,4,5-trichlorophenoxyacetic acid (2,4,5-T). A bonding of chlorine and phenol, these compounds have the same molecular structure – 2,4,5-T differing because it contains an extra chlorine atom.

Researchers discovered that tiny amounts of these synthetic plant hormones were capable of stimulating plants. When they increased the dose they learned that these synthetic hormones could also kill. Researchers realised that each compound had different effects on different plants. In combination they formed a lethal weapon against unwanted vegetation. Prompted by the twin desires of the agricultural industry to destroy weeds and the military to use as a biological agent, this research led to the introduction of phenoxy herbicides as weed killers and then as chemical weapons.

Professor E. J. Kraus, head of the Botany Department of the University of Chicago, Illinois, had alerted the military to the existence of these hormone-like substances. Kraus suggested to the military that it might be interested in 'the toxic properties of growth regulating substances for the destruction of crops or the limitation of crop production'.[5] By 1943 Kraus was confident enough about the properties of 2,4-D and 2,4,5-T to recommend them to a US National Academy of Sciences committee on biological warfare.

A year later Kraus moved to the US army's centre for biological warfare at Camp (later Fort) Detrick. But the plan to use 2,4-D and 2,4,5-T to destroy enemy crops was thwarted by peace. The research, however, continued. Kraus oversaw a programme that resulted in the screening of approximately 1,200 compounds. Eventually some of these compounds were tested on tropical vegetation in Puerto Rico and Thailand.[6]

Consequently the chemical industry regarded the discovery of these phenoxy herbicides as the greatest single advance in the science of weed control and one of the most significant in agriculture. In 1947 researchers discovered that 2,4,5-T and 2,4-D affected broad-leaved plants but left cereal crops alone. The chemical industry started its first green revolution. 'After the war,' wrote Thomas Whiteside, 'many of the herbicidal materials that had been developed and tested for biological-warfare use were marketed for civilian purposes and used by farmers and homeowners for killing weeds and controlling brush.'[7]

The herbicides that became the most popular and widely used were the most powerful – 2,4,5-T and 2,4-D. Their sale was swiftly sanctioned by the relevant authorities. Although the USA was the largest market for these phenoxy herbicides they were sold all over the planet. They were used as weed killers but they were also used to defoliate railway embankments, on awkward hedgerows to remove hardy brushwoods, and to control weeds particularly on cereal monocultures. Local authorities, railway and electricity companies, farmers and gardeners all used the various phenoxy herbicides to destroy unwanted vegetation. Between 1945 and 1963, the production of herbicides in the USA rose from 917,000 to 150 million pounds.[8] This total virtually trebled after 1963 with the use of these herbicides in Vietnam.

The spraying began in January 1962. Six chemical mixtures were used. The military named them Orange (2,4-D, 2,4,5-T); White (2,4-D, picloram); Blue (cacodylic acid); Purple (2,4-D, 2,4,5-T); Pink (2,4,5-T) and Green (2,4,5-T). Purple, Pink and Green were used to defoliate mangrove and jungle areas from 1962 to 1965 when they were replaced by Orange and White. Blue was used from 1962 to 1971 to destroy the stable crops of Vietnam – beans, manioc, corn, bananas, tomato and rice. Agent Orange comprised of almost two-thirds of the herbicides sprayed. It was used primarily to defoliate but it was also sprayed on broad-leaved crops. The spraying was done from the air by C-123 planes fitted with 1,000-gallon tanks in what became known as Operation Ranch Hand. Approximately 20,000 missions were flown. A small quantity was hand sprayed around camps, waterways and paths.[9] Between July 1965 and June 1970 11.25 million gallons of Agent Orange were sprayed in Indochina. In April 2003 this figure was revised up to 13.05 million gallons when researchers from Columbia University claimed, after studying more complete data, that 1.8 million gallons had not been accounted for by the US National Academy of Sciences when they published estimates of the extent and distribution of herbicides sprayed.[10] 'Large numbers of Vietnamese civilians appear to have been directly exposed to herbicidal agents, some of which were sprayed at levels at least an order of magnitude greater than for similar US domestic purposes,' the researchers claim. 'Other analyses carried out by us show large numbers of American troops also to have been directly exposed.' The researchers also said that the amount of dioxin contained in the herbicides was double that of the 1974 estimates.[11]

The phenoxy herbicides had become gold dust to the chemical companies. In the USA five chemical companies have dominated the production and market for chlorophenols:

- Dow Chemicals, Midland, Michigan
- Monsanto, Sauget, Illinois
- Reichold Chemicals, Tacoma, Washington
- Vulcan Materials Co., Wichita, Kansas
- Rhodia, Freeport, Texas

In total, however, 33 companies have been involved in the production of chlorophenols and their derivatives, all but four located in the mid-eastern and east coast states.[12] Of these 18 have specialised in the production of 2,4,5-T, 21 in the production of 2,4-D and seven in production of pentachlorophenol. But the market was dominated by two companies – Dow and Monsanto.

Between 1960 and 1968 the production of 2,4,5-T was at its height, peaking at 16 million pounds a year. By 1978 there were 400 formulated pesticide products containing 2,4,5-T. In 1978 it was banned in Sweden. In 1983 it was banned in the USA. For four decades the production of chlorophenols and their derivative products put billions of dollars into the pockets of the chemical industry. They were ready to spend it to defend their products. But they weren't keen on compensation claims that would cost them millions, perhaps more. Claims that might bankrupt them. The industry put itself on a proper war footing. Throughout the 1950s, 1960s and 1970s the chemical industry had been able to defend itself against all attacks. If the battles to continue manufacturing their most lucrative products – 2,4,5-T, 2,4-D, pentachlorophenol – were eventually lost, the war to protect chlorine chemistry was being won.[13] This success was due largely to the industry's guerrilla tactics and its ability to hire mercenaries.

By pouring billions into medical and scientific research and into the science departments of third level colleges the industry held the forward trenches in the battlefield for scientific glory. Many in the scientific community sold their souls to the devil. The price was loyalty. Eventually that became complicity. When the industry or its processes or products were put under attack, counter-insurgency tactics became commonplace. Well timed skirmishes and raids kept the enemy at bay. Conferences, reports, letters, announcements. Subtly the industry attempted to quieten public opinion. They announced:

- There were no risks from exposure to these chemicals.
- There's nothing in the literature to suggest these chemicals are a health risk.
- Levels are too low to affect health.

The media dutifully reported these pronouncements.

It has already been noted that when Schulz revealed dioxin as a contaminant of 2,4,5-T in the mid-1950s how few people noticed or cared about his work. It would be too easy to suggest that Schulz's paper was lost among the literature because it wasn't published in English. This would miss the point. Schulz's work ultimately benefited the German chlorophenol producers. Boehringer were the direct beneficiaries of his research but they decided to share it. Other German manufacturers knew about it and they were in contact with other chlorophenol producers. By the late 1950s every US chlorophenol manufacturer knew about Schulz's work, even if they didn't know who he was. Dow knew about it and Monsanto knew about it too.

Dow decided to use the research and spend the necessary funds to change their chlorophenol processes – to produce less dioxin. Monsanto, on the other hand, didn't want to spend any money. Instead they decided to become the authors of the first known documents on the manipulation of dioxin science.

The chemical industry have been winning this war because they have been able to meet every attack head on and banish their aggressors. They have been able to manipulate the science because it has been easy for them. For decades it has been the industry itself that has researched and published work on the health effects from exposure to chemicals. This work however has been done largely by chemists. Toxicologists, in particular, identify the effect pollutants will have on health. But, as Sandra Steingraber puts it, epidemiologists rely on the body count.[14]

That would be the industry's downfall. When the battle over Agent Orange began in the late 1960s most chemists defended the toxic record of phenoxy herbicides. They knew they had to because they had done research that revealed the extreme toxicity of these chemicals. However, epidemiologists began to notice the impact on human health. And so did mothers like Carol Van Strum.[15]

Among the first doctors to identify problems with phenoxy herbicides was Swedish oncologist Lennart Hardell. After struggling for years on his own, Thomas Whiteside suddenly had allies.

The chemical industry was able to quieten concern about the toxicity of phenoxy herbicides because it had been able to claim that its processes and products were not the direct cause of specific human illnesses – significantly occupational cancer. Those who tried to prove a link between chemicals and human illnesses struggled to present their evidence or had that expertise ridiculed. This is exactly what happened to three Swedish doctors whose research revealed a link. Their tenacity would become a key story in the history of dioxin.

THE SWEDISH DOCTORS' QUEST FOR THE TRUTH

In 1973 a 64-year-old forestry foreman came to Lennart Hardell in the University Hospital at Umeå. The worker had been diagnosed with primary liver cancer. When he died his cancer was revealed as a pancreatic cancer. Hardell learned that the man was from the heavily forested county of Norrbotten in northern Sweden. During the summer months throughout the 1950s and 1960s he sprayed Hormoslyr®16 (a 2:1 mix of 2,4-D and 2,4,5-T) on hardwoods. According to Hardell this combination 'was the most common preparation used for the control of deciduous forests', two-fifths of all Hormoslyr® being used in Norrbotten. 'His relatives claimed that this cancer was due to his spraying. But there was nothing in the medical literature about humans getting cancer from phenoxy herbicides. I wrote to the Swedish EPA and asked them for information on phenoxy herbicides.' The documentation alerted Hardell to dioxin. 'I got interested and realised there could be a problem here.'[17] Hardell contacted a colleague, Christopher Rappe, who provided him with the background chemistry and history of dioxin. Hardell learned that 2,4-D and 2,4,5-T contained a contaminant – TCDD. Rappe told Hardell that the manufacture of phenoxy herbicides varied from country to country. Hardell turned to the chemical industry but they weren't keen to share their information. 'We did not get any help from the chemical industry. They were quite resistant to our research. Basically we had the Rappe work and other chemists saying that pentachlorophenols and trichlorophenols contained dioxins but that's all we had.'[18]

Concern about the effects of the phenoxy herbicides was common in northern Sweden. In Jutis, a small village in Norrbotten, a high incidence of cancer, significantly among young people, was reported. In Torsby, in the county of Varmland, cancers and birth defects were reported. Phenoxy herbicides were suspected.[19] Yet toxicologists and government officials remained unconvinced. The Swedish EPA even announced that the economic benefit from using phenoxy herbicides was more important than trying 'to scientifically elucidate possible remaining uncertainties regarding these chemicals'.

Then in September 1976 Hardell's interest in the toxicity of phenoxy herbicides was sparked again when another forestry worker with cancer was sent to him. This time the cancer was soft tissue sarcoma,[20] a tumour that accounted for 1 per cent of all malignant diseases in Sweden. Over the following months Hardell came across eight more workers who had been exposed to phenoxy herbicides – all with soft tissue sarcoma. Hardell studied the literature for the clues that would tell him more about the association between the phenoxy herbicides and cancer. All he found were more studies that showed a range of illnesses in workers exposed to chlorophenols. One study, by Professor Olav Axelson of Linköping Hospital in mid-eastern Sweden, appeared to confirm Hardell's own findings.[21] Axelson himself had been sceptical about the carcinogenic effects of the phenoxy herbicides. Initially he believed another chemical compound was the cause. 'When I tried to get rid of the phenoxy herbicides in the data by doing a more sophisticated analysis, to my surprise it resulted in the opposite.'

The *Swedish Medical Journal* reawakened Axelson's interest when they asked him to peer-review Hardell's study. 'I told them they should publish and try to get the author to set up a case-control study. I don't know if they ever approached him, but he approached me and asked for some advice how to proceed with a formal study. So I helped him to set up his first study.[22]

Hardell proceeded with a matched case-control study. The studied cases consisted of 21 living and 24 deceased male patients with soft tissue sarcomas, ranging in age from 26 to 80 and admitted to the University Hospital at Umeå. The control group consisted of 204 people who were matched for sex, age, year of death and place of residence. Hardell and his researchers then conducted phone interviews with those who were still living and the next of kin (wife, children or parents, brother or sister) of those who had died. The specific nature of the investigation was not disclosed. A questionnaire sent by mail followed. This consisted of

> a variety of questions about previous and present occupation, different kinds of exposure (especially chemical) in the working environment, smoking habits, etc. Special attention to phenoxyacetic acids or chlorophenols was thereby avoided. The answers were studied and supplemented over the phone by a person not associated with the department, and who did not know whether the interviewed persons were patients or controls. To get as objective information as possible about exposure to phenoxy herbicides, a questionnaire was also sent to the employers of the persons stating forest work, in order to verify their employment and the use of this chemical. Likewise a questionnaire was sent to sawmills and pulp industries about their use of chlorophenols in the production method.

The researchers excluded low levels of exposure (a maximum of one day) and late exposure (five years before diagnosis). When Hardell analysed the results they showed that exposure to phenoxy herbicides gave a six-fold increase in soft tissue sarcoma.[23] This was not what the chemical industry and the Swedish EPA wanted to hear. They argued that there was no problem with phenoxy herbicides.

Hardell released his case study in August 1977. To his surprise the Swedish EPA, the workers' union and employers were upset by his revelations. The employers argued that a ban on use of the phenoxy herbicides in reforestation would reduce the production of trees which in turn would create unemployment among forestry workers. 'They were not specially interested in protecting their workers,' said Hardell. 'When my first case control study came out I went to see the boss of the union. I said, look here, we have results that clearly show there is an increased risk but he wasn't interested in that.' The manufacturers had sent out letters claiming there was no problem with phenoxy herbicides. The Swedish EPA were happy with this. Then Hardell claimed there was. 'They didn't want to listen to this,' he said.[24]

Hardell teamed up with a colleague at Umeå, Mikael Eriksson, and with Axelson. They did another study and found the same results.[25]

The backlash against Hardell and his colleagues wasn't long in coming. The Swedish EPA were the first to respond. In August 1979 Hardell and his colleagues were asked to come down to Stockholm to talk about their results – which confirmed that exposure to phenoxy herbicides and chlorophenols contributed to an increase in soft tissue sarcoma. 'We were asked to deny the existence of any results if some person from the news media contacted us. This was motivated by the fact that spraying was ongoing in forests and these authorities did not want to disturb these operations by creating public alarm.' Hardell said they would not go to the media, but added they would not deny facts if contacted.[26]

The press has really been good to us and backed up our studies and findings. If there had been negative press reaction to what we have been doing it would have been very difficult. We knew we were backed up by the media and by the patients. That gave us some strength. So you must resist the attacks and continue because of the benefit for the patients.

One group had collected cases with cancer and they had collected information on animals but this was rejected by the government because it was not scientifically done. Then we came up with something that was scientifically done.[27]

The media, said Hardell, were quick to make the link. 'At that time there was a discussion between the Swedish EPA and Christopher Rappe – who was saying that there is a danger here. Then our report came out saying that Rappe seems to be right.'[28] But Hardell realised his work was seen as scare mongering. 'There is still a debate in Sweden that if you come out with a risk for a chemical, this is more dangerous to discuss than the risk of health effects because people get worried and get sick. I never got a patient that got cancer from being excited.'[29]

But the facts were not just coming from Sweden.

CORROBORATIVE EVIDENCE

The community of Globe, Arizona, complained of human and animal illnesses after the US Forest Service sprayed 3,680 pounds of silvex and 120 pounds of 2,4,5-T in the Kellner Canyon and Russell Gulch.

In Oregon, the use of 2,4,5-T and silvex by timber companies and the government in forest areas were linked to increased incidences of miscarriage by women living near the spraying areas. Eleven miscarriages were recorded within a month of the spraying. Oregon had been routinely sprayed. Many people complained of illnesses after herbicide spraying. Abortions among cows and deer and the deaths of fish, quail and grouse were reported to be associated with the sprayings. An allergist specialising in environmental medicine reported that complaints of diarrhoea and recurrent boils among the exposed people could have been caused by dioxin.

In north-eastern Minnesota, a family reported that offspring of pigs, chickens and rabbits that had fed in areas sprayed by a US Forest Service helicopter were born deformed, or later developed deformities. For over five months after the spraying the family complained of intense stomach aches, headaches, fever, nausea, diarrhoea and convulsions. An analysis of the family's water supply by the Minnesota health authorities revealed traces of a herbicide that contained 2,4-D and 2,4,5-T.

In Vietnam researchers were beginning to find evidence of ill health among communities who had been exposed to the US military's spraying programme. Numerous deformities in children between the age of 6 and 14 were found. Spontaneous abortions among women in the sprayed areas were common. It was estimated that 25,000 children in south Vietnam contracted birth defects as a consequence of their parents' exposure. The Vietnamese claimed that more than half a million had died or suffered illnesses as a result of Agent Orange.[30]

In New Zealand it was reported that deformities in infants had occurred in three areas of the country and that 2,4,5-T was suspected. Two women who had been exposed to 2,4,5-T during pregnancy gave birth to deformed babies.

In Australia, skin rashes, respiratory problems and higher incidences of birth defects and infant mortality have been associated with 2,4,5-T spraying. In Swedish lapland two infants with congenital malformations were born to women who had been exposed to phenoxy herbicides.

THE CHEMICAL INDUSTRY STRIKES BACK

Much of this evidence was swiftly discounted, by the relevant health authorities and the chemical industry. In virtually all the incidents above, with the notable exception of Oregon, the authorities were able to explain away the various illnesses. The chemical industry explained them all away. The industry also felt confident enough about the toxicity of their products to put a spin on the effects of phenoxy herbicides, and especially on the results of Hardell's studies. 'No one has been able to replicate Dr Hardell's findings,' asserted the authors of an industry document. There is a growing body of literature that does not support Dr Hardell's hypothesis, the authors announced, listing examples:

- New Zealand: No association between the use of these phenoxy herbicides and soft tissue sarcoma has been found in an ongoing case-control study.
- Washington State: No consistent patterns of death due to soft tissue sarcomas were found among occupations related to the use of these herbicides.
- Finland: No soft tissue sarcomas were found among 1,900 Finnish herbicide applicators in a 1982 review. Nor was the death rate for these applicators different from any natural cause in comparison with the Finnish total male population.
- Midland, Michigan: A statistically significant excess of connective soft tissue cancer was found by the EPA among white females in

Midland County (where Dow has production facilities). In its 1983 preliminary report the Michigan Department of Health was unable to link the excess to any environmental factor, including TCDD.[31]

- Sweden: Reports from Stockholm's Karolinska Institute indicate that Swedish farmers, about 15 per cent of whom use the herbicides Hardell probed for, have experienced slightly fewer cases of soft tissue sarcoma than expected, in comparison with the overall Swedish data.[32]

Throughout the 1980s and well into the 1990s the industry continued to put a spin on the research of Hardell and his colleagues – who were being viewed as a significant threat to the chlorine chemical industry.

In 1981 a Dow article titled 'Swedish studies discounted in 2,4,5-T risk assessment' was published in the journal of the American Industrial Hygiene Association. The article quoted Dr Phillip Cole, a professor of epidemiology in the University of Alabama, who said the Swedish studies contained limitations because of the likelihood of observer and recall bias. 'Observer bias is the production, by a staff member, of a difference between cases and controls in the way in which exposure information is obtained.' Recall bias, said Dr Cole, happened when people 'are required to recall events that occurred many years previously'. The article went on to state that Dow toxicologists

believe it is extremely unlikely that 2,4,5-T or any other agent could be responsible for such a broad spectrum of tumours as identified in the Swedish studies. Also, it is inconceivable that the trivial exposures in the Hardell studies could have produced the pronounced effects that Dr Hardell and his colleagues purport to find – especially considering the results of other human epidemiology studies indicating no adverse effects following far greater exposures to 2,4,5-T and TCDD.[33]

In 1990 two US lawyers representing Dow wrote to the *Journal of National Cancer Institute*. Their letter was subtle. 'All of these studies may be flawed by what is potentially a fundamental error in the classification and identification of materials to which the study groups were supposedly exposed.' The lawyers argued that the Swedish doctors had got their chemicals wrong. To make this point they referred to cuprinol. Admitting that in Sweden cuprinol contained pentachlorophenol, in the USA it doesn't, they wrote: 'The variety of materials found in cuprinol products raises a substantial question as to which chemical substances the populations in the Hardell studies were actually exposed.' It was a typical disingenuous assertion from the chemical industry. Hardell and Eriksson, who replied, stood their ground. All fungicides named cuprinol listed in Sweden have contained chlorophenols, they stated. 'The content in cuprinol used in the United States might be of relevance in studies performed there, but is of course of no interest in relation to our studies with persons exposed in Sweden.' It was a retort Hardell and his colleagues were having to produce regularly, to defend their research. By 1990 they were learning this skill because they had walked into a trap. They had allowed the industry to marginalise their work.

By using their resources to refute the Swedish doctors' research, the chemical industry and those associated with them were beginning to refine a strategy that has been constant ever since – that only chemical industry reports and reports peer-reviewed by sympathetic industry scientists are accurate, credible and based on accepted methodology, that everyone else's research is biased, flawed and characterised by poor methodology.

What kept the Swedish doctors going was their belief that the weight of evidence was in their favour, that more and more industry-funded reports were being exposed by independently-funded research. But that, as they were about to find out, was not enough.

Conspiracy theories usually have no basis in reality, because they require an elaborate series of events to coincide perfectly to produce a particular effect. Yet, when the Australian Royal Commission decided to investigate the health effects of Agent Orange and sent an official on a global search for the relevant research and expert witnesses, it is hard not to believe that Hardell and Axelson were being set up.

THE DISCREDITING OF AXELSON AND HARDELL

Hardell refused to travel to Australia. Axelson agreed. Hardell was then put in a position that gave him little choice.

I had moved for one year's sabbatical to Berkeley in San Francisco in 1984. In the Fall of '84 the Australian Royal Commission were travelling from Australia to the US and onto Germany. They said they wanted to come to San Francisco. I said you can come here but I am not going to testify.

Finally there was a lot of pressure from a lawyer for the veterans. He said it's necessary for you to appear before this commission otherwise this will discredit you. It will also give the impression that you cannot stand over your studies.[34]

Hardell was told he had to justify his studies. He gave his testimony to the Australian Royal Commission on 25 and 26 September 1984 in San Francisco. Five months later, his sabbatical over, he was back at the University of Umeå. Among his mail one morning in late February was a letter from David Bayliss, an epidemiologist at the EPA's Carcinogen Assessment Group. Bayliss said he had just received a copy of Hardell's Commission testimony. Bayliss referred to an attached letter from Professor Wendell W. Kilgore at the University of California that claimed that Hardell had 'repudiated' the results of his studies. 'Having read through the transcript I do not get the same impression. Could you clarify this for me?' Bayliss asked. He concluded, 'If you have repudiated the results of your studies, US EPA may have to reconsider its evaluation with respect to the possibility that there may be potential carcinogenic effects due to exposure to 2,4,5-T contaminated with TCDD.'[35] Hardell had not been sent the transcript of his testimony so he did not know what Bayliss was talking about. Eventually he managed to get of a copy of the Australian Royal Commission's published report. At first he couldn't see anything wrong with it.

I started to realise that the figures and facts didn't fit with what we had published. I had to go through every publication page for page and compare what they were writing with what we had written and then make the rebuttals to the Australian Royal Commission. What they did was deliberate. The Australian Royal Commission's report hurt us.[36]

This was the biggest spin of all. Part of the Commission's report 'was almost entirely a verbatim incorporation of a submission ... by Monsanto of Australia'. The Commission, Hardell raged, seemed 'unable to distinguish, or perhaps even, uninterested in distinguishing between the scientific material and the distorted interpretations provided by a chemical company. The Commission's report should have contained a critical appraisal'.

Not only did the report not critically appraise the toxicity of Agent Orange it ignored virtually all of the evidence presented to the Commission by Axelson and Hardell.[37] More significantly, the report included a series of incorrect interpretations of the Swedish studies. And, just to plunge the knives in deeper, the report included a letter from Professor Richard Doll lambasting Hardell.

His conclusions cannot be sustained and in my opinion, his work should no longer be cited as scientific evidence. It is clear, too, from your review of the published evidence relating to 2,4-D and 2,4,5-T (the phenoxy herbicides in question) that there is no reason to suppose that they are carcinogenic in laboratory animals and that even TCDD (dioxin), which has been postulated to be a dangerous contaminant of the herbicides, is at the most, only weakly and inconsistently carcinogenic in animal experiments.

Doll added that he was sorry that the Commission's report should only be published in book form. 'I'm sure, however, that it will be widely quoted and that it will come to be regarded as the definite work.'[38]

Hardell called the letter 'remarkable'. But the damage had been done. 'It's a very tough statement from him. This has gone into the scientific world somehow and people think the Hardell studies are wrong. People still think our papers are controversial, that they are not right. This is because they have not read the literature.'[39]

There is no evidence that Monsanto and the Commission contrived to produce a report that would attempt to destroy the credibility of two experienced medical doctors. Yet almost immediately after the Commission's report was published it started to find its way into the literature and into the letter columns of the scientific media, as the Swedish doctors strived to protect their reputations and credibility.

Disturbingly for Hardell and his colleagues, the Doll letter was frequently quoted. Hardell rallied to protect his reputation. He wrote to Sir Ninian Stephen, the Australian Governor-General, alleging that the Commission had 'arranged a trap for me by asking me to participate in the hearing, thereby being able to misquote me, to interpret my studies in the wrong way, to cite only what is suitable for their purpose and thereby giving an official assignment to the conclusion that my studies are "flawed"'. He also sent copies to the Australian prime minister, the Commissioner, the Veterans Association of Australia, the International Agency for Research on Cancer (a

World Health Organisation body based in Lyon, France), Richard Doll, the *Medical Journal of Australia* and *The Age* newspaper.[40]

Within a few months, the debate about the Swedish studies was in full flow. In the *Medical Journal of Australia* it was all 'a storm in a cup of 2,4,5-T'[41] but it was a storm that would last for three years in the journal and for more than a decade in the wider world. Whilst most of the debate focused on the Swedish doctors' 'flawed' studies one writer, Dr Rodolfo Saracci – chief of IARC's Analytical Epidemiological Unit, made a salient and highly relevant point. If proof beyond all doubt is required, he noted, then no such proof exists. 'But ... on the balance of probabilities, then the studies do suggest, very weakly if one likes, that such an association might exist.'[42]

In September 1986 Olav Axelson and Lennart Hardell got a chance to publicly rebut the Commission at a conference in Los Angeles. The 'distortions and misquotations of basic facts' the Swedish doctors said, make it 'difficult to avoid the impression that a Royal Commission is even consciously lying in order to be able to disregard apparently "inconvenient" results'.[43]

By now the Australian Commission's revised version of the Vietnam War and the effects of Agent Orange had made its way into the literature. Barry O'Keefe, the lawyer who had represented Monsanto at the Commission hearings, contributed a chapter to a book entitled *Agent Orange and Its Associated Dioxin: Assessment of a Controversy* published in 1988.

Hardell again took up the defence of their work, this time in the *American Journal of Industrial Medicine*. 'The danger is obvious,' he wrote, after going through each flawed point made by O'Keefe, 'that if false statements are repeated frequently they might finally come to represent the truth.'[44] In a subsequent letter Hardell stated: 'I notice that in their letter (the editors) are unable to refute any of the "60 items" representing misinterpretations and even falsifications of the research by my colleagues and myself.'[45]

THE SWEDISH DOCTORS PERSEVERE

In 1994 the three doctors were still defending their reputations and making crucial points about ethics in science.

Some ethical principles for scientific publication seem to be needed insofar as there should be some possibility to discuss controversial matters in any journal that publishes scientific material. But obviously, this is not always the case.

Furthermore, published papers should give proper affiliation of the investigators as representatives of environmental groups, university employees, industry paid consultants, and so forth. Sources of funding should be mentioned as well.

They went on to mention Andrew Watterson's comment in the *Lancet* about official risk assessments of hazardous chemicals and a review that found that 135 risk assessment documents revealed a significant industry presence.

So while the chemical industry could manipulate the science, influence risk assessments and get papers favourable to its position into journals and books with ease, Axelson, Eriksson and Hardell struggled to tell their side of the story. The fact that their work was being supported by other studies and by other epidemiologists appeared to matter little to the conservative scientific establishment.[46]

> Our studies have been criticised by different persons including those employed by the chemical industry and its allied experts, who have postulated various ad hoc hypotheses. These ad hoc hypotheses could certainly be easily rejected using information available in our published papers. Rebutting all these statements is, however, an almost impossible task, since it is time consuming and not all editors are willing to give space for rebuttals.[47]

Even if this isn't what the industry intended, it was a sober fact that the Swedish doctors were being increasingly marginalised and their work continuously rubbished.

Undeterred, Hardell, Eriksson and Axelson persevered, eventually proving a link between dioxin exposure and cancer – with the documentation to back up their claims.[48] By the mid-1990s they were adamant that this chemical contaminant was the cause of cancers and other illnesses among workers, military and communities who had come in contact with it in some form or other.[49] It was both a cautious and a pragmatic statement but they had the health studies to back up their claims and repudiate the criticisms of their work.[50] 'I've been convinced all the time that what we are doing is right. I know it. We have worked through every questionnaire. We have scrutinised every exposure. It's not like the US where you give the research to some company. We have done everything ourselves.'[51]

From the research, however, it was clear to Hardell, Eriksson and Axelson that dioxin-like chemicals cause different cancers, even if all the epidemiological data appeared confusing. They noted that 2,4,5-T exposure elevated the risk of one cancer while 2,4-D elevated the risk of another cancer. And they were sure about this. Health studies linked one of these cancers with phenoxy herbicides but not specifically with TCDD. They added that some studies, from the USA, supported the belief that other dioxins are the cause of other cancers.[52] Yet they stressed that both 2,4-D and 2,4,5-T are contaminated with TCDD. It appeared that the dioxin family didn't just cause cancer, it caused different cancers and individual dioxins caused different cancers.

> Based on several of the newer epidemiological studies, as confirming earlier observations, a conclusion for practical purposes could be that some commercially available phenoxy herbicides have been carcinogenic, but probably only under certain circumstances. It may well be that the risk of soft tissue sarcomas is mainly related to chlorinated dibenzodioxins, as especially indicated by one study, whereas the lymphomas[53] might depend more specifically on phenoxy acids, particularly in combinations with other agents, such as other pesticides, solvents, and probably some other chemicals.[54]

VINDICATION!

By the mid-1990s, however, new revelations about dioxin's toxicity put a new spin on the story – a spin the chemical industry struggled to stop, despite their domination of risk assessment policies and their constant revisionism of the science. And the story would keep spinning, as study after study and report after report began to reveal the truth about dioxin – at each step vindicating the Swedish doctors.[55] Finally the truth about dioxin that Thomas Whiteside sought so earnestly in the early 1970s was out in the open.

The collusions and the manipulations about phenoxy herbicides had lasted a quarter of a century when the USEPA produced its draft reassessment on dioxin in 1994 – confirming what was really in the literature.

Whiteside died in 1997. Not many people noticed. Those who did, who knew of his exhaustive research work on phenoxy herbicides, took the time to remember and to celebrate his investigative skills. Although Rachel Carson may take the spotlight for her *Silent Spring*,[56] it was Whiteside's tenacity that made the phenoxy herbicides into a political issue. It's important to note that what Whiteside revealed about phenoxy herbicides and dioxin in 1969 and 1979 was largely in the scientific literature, in the public domain.

'The history of 2,4,5-T is related to preparations for biological warfare, although nobody in the United States government seems to want to admit this, and it was wound up being used for purposes of biological warfare, although nobody in the United States government seems to want to admit this, either,' Whiteside wrote in 1970.

Since 2,4,5-T was developed, the United States government has allowed it to be used on a very large scale on our own fields and countryside without adequate tests of its effects. In South Vietnam – a nation we are attempting to save – for seven full years the American military has sprayed or dumped this biological-warfare material on the countryside, on villages, and on South Vietnamese men and women in staggering amounts. In that time the military has sprayed or dumped on Vietnam 50,000 tons of herbicide, of which 20,000 tons have apparently been straight 2,4,5-T.

In addition, the American military has apparently made incursions into a neutral country, Cambodia, and rained down on an area inhabited by 30,000 civilians a vast quantity of 2,4,5-T. Yet in the quarter of a century since the Department of Defence first developed the biological-warfare uses of this material it has not completed a single series of formal teratological tests on pregnant animals to determine whether it has an effect on their unborn offspring.

Whiteside was one of the first researchers to realise that knowledge of dioxin was known and had been deliberately kept secret by some chemical companies and by the US military. He also realised that the chlorophenol manufacturers knew about the dioxin contamination in the phenoxy herbicides.

Although the chemical companies that manufacture 2,4,5-T have long taken pride in pointing out that 2,4,5-T itself is quite readily decomposable in soil, the crucial matters of how stable the dioxin contamination is and to what extent it is cumulative in animal tissue have apparently been neglected.

Consequently, the fact that dioxin has already been detected in this country (US) in the human food chain – in the livers of chickens and in edible oils – clearly indicates that dioxin should be considered a hazard to humanity. Why, under all these inauspicious circumstances, the production and use here and in Vietnam of 2,4,5-T has not summarily been stopped by the United States government is hard to understand.[57]

The use of Agent Orange and other biological-warfare agents in Vietnam would eventually be stopped but the production and commercial use of 2,4-D and 2,4,5-T would continue – well into the 1980s in some industrialised countries and into the 1990s in the third world.[58] Nearly three decades would pass before it would be considered a human hazard. Despite what Hardell knew in the 1970s it would be another two decades before the phenoxy herbicides would be proven to cause rare cancers like sarcomas and lymphomas.

Although the Swedish doctors' work was vindicated by other studies and announced in the US government's report on Agent Orange and in IARC's report on dioxins and furans, the chemical industry had achieved what it wanted.[59] It had successfully sparked a debate about epidemiological methods and the ethics of science. It did not matter to them how many people contributed to the debate. All that mattered was that a seed of doubt had been planted. Once again the science had been manipulated to allow industry to keep making its profits. Instead of talking about the carcinogenicity of 2,4,5-T, Olav Axelson still has to discuss the methodology of health studies. Hardell still has to justify the results of his work.

People say that chloracne is the hallmark of exposure to TCDD and that this should be taken as a criteria for exposure. None of our forestry workers or agricultural workers who got soft tissue sarcoma had chloracne. I never saw it in a Swedish patient with malignant disease whatsoever yet they were still exposed to TCDD. Chloracne is a sign of very high exposure.

There is also an individual variation to get the chloracne which also means there is an individual variation to get the soft tissue sarcoma. I am quite sure there are combination effects which for example we could show for the malignant lymphomas, that there was a combination from phenoxy herbicides, chlorophenols and organic solvents there was an increased risk. There's also the individual susceptibility.[60]

Yet for years the chemical industry has argued that chloracne is the hallmark of exposure to dioxin. A reason for this, according to Hardell, is the way chemists and epidemiologists work.

> Chemists seem to be very interested to isolate substances to look for the concentrations but it stops there. They don't look to see if it causes harm. They are thinking about industry and what should be done to lower exposure.
>
> Epidemiologists who show the risk are not employed by the chemical industry. Epidemiologists also have contact with the reality because you can see this man who has soft tissue sarcoma or lymphoma and he tells about his exposure. There's an exposure. He gets a disease. There is a fatal outcome. What can we do to prevent the disease? First we have to establish cause of association. So the motivation is quite different. You can see the persons who are hurt.
>
> Now the chemical industry [in the US] has been forced to produce documents that were unknown. From this we can see there was a knowledge of toxicological effects of TCDD, almost ten years before the scientific community knew about it. So for years there was nothing in the literature that said there really is a health problem.
>
> This is an ethical problem. They refused to give consumers knowledge about these toxic products. There could have been a preventative measure. We would also have gained ten years in time, to protect human beings from exposure to dioxins. Cancers could have been prevented.[61]

The story about the phenoxy herbicides and Agent Orange is not over. Compensation claims against the industry will be heard well into the twenty-first century.

The heart of darkness is now absolute.

3
Ignorance is Bliss:
The Poisoning of Missouri

They say that our arguments are all based on emotion. Well, we wouldn't be emotional if the facts didn't lead us to be emotional. When you see those facts, there's no way that you can deny that there is definitely some danger there.

Mary Derrick[1]

Due to its notoriety, dioxin remains a target of those who wish to convince the public that environmental contamination is not a problem. Much of the media coverage of the dioxin debate has consisted of trying to convince the public that their common sense is wrong and that experts know best. In this case, the public's view has been largely correct. Dioxin is a dangerous and unwanted environmental pollutant. Dioxin policy should strive to eliminate the sources and thereby prevent pollution. Rather than telling the public that certain dioxin risks are 'acceptable' – and regarding the resulting opposition as merely hysterical and uninformed – regulators ought to listen to their concerns. The public does not respond according to a one-dimensional measure of risk, but in keeping with a much richer set of criteria. These include, not surprisingly, fairness, democratic choice, and an examination of alternatives.

Thomas Webster and Barry Commoner[2]

Russell Martin Bliss' name will always be remembered in Missouri. It's unlikely that it'll be remembered with any gesture of absolute fondness or words of genuine empathy. Some may even spit out his name with venomous anger. Others will respond with incredulity, forever associating his name with those who attempted to cover up the truth about the events of the early 1970s when his entrepreneurial actions inadvertently revealed another clue in the mystery surrounding the impact of dioxin on human health. Bliss is no hero, however. He is not the villain either, even though he was indirectly responsible for one of the greatest tragedies in America's secret toxic history.

Bliss was a commercial haulier, known and employed in and around St Louis in Missouri for disposing waste motor oils but less well known for carrying chemical and petroleum wastes. It was a vocation he was born to – in 1934 in Overland, Missouri. While Europe warred the six-year-old son of George, who started the business with a hand pump and flatbed truck in 1929, went along for the ride. In 1951, at the age of 16, he started to work for his father. In 1968 Russell bought the business from his father and immediately expanded.

While his father had operated from one truck with a capacity of 1,000 gallons, Bliss started using 3,000-gallon trucks and soon had a fleet of ten trucks. The major part of his business was the collection of discarded motor and lubrication oils from petrol stations, garages, trucking and taxi companies, airports and similar places but he would always agree to haul away chemical wastes.

By 1971 the Bliss Waste Oil Company had approximately 1,800 customers and was collecting 'about 15,000 gallons of oil a day, day in and day out, six days a week'.[3] He sold the majority of this oil to refineries for reprocessing and to industrial fuel merchants, sometimes carrying it directly to them at the close of day, otherwise he stored the oil in six tanks (five numbered B1 to B5) at Frontenac on Conway Road (which had a total capacity of 62,000 gallons).[4]

Some of this waste oil was sold to merchants for treating coal to prevent it freezing during the cold winter months. A small amount of this oil was also used for road oiling to keep dust down. What was left also turned a dollar. During storage the oil would separate leaving a sediment-like sludge at the bottom of the tanks. This sludge couldn't be reprocessed or used for fuel.[5]

The disposal of this waste sludge wasn't a problem to Bliss. Like all smart entrepreneurs he had a solution. This was the waste oil he used to suppress the dust that bedevilled people's lives during dry summer months. Bliss also used this method of dust control on his own land – on the Mid-American Arena at his 12-acre home on the Strecker Road in Ellisville, Missouri and on his farm in Cuba, Missouri. Bliss was an ambitious man and always keen to expand. He placed advertisements in various newspapers, his trucks were commonplace in St Louis. In 1971 this public profile changed his life.

BLISS COLLECTS SOME POISONED OIL

North-eastern Pharmaceutical and Chemical Company (NEPACCO) in Verona, south-west of St Louis, had asked the Independent

Petrochemical Corporation of St Louis (a subsidiary of Charter Oil) to dispose of hexachlorophrene residues from their holding tanks. They wanted to save money and they believed IPC could help them.[6] Gregory Browne, a district manager with IPC, contacted a chemical recycling company who referred him to Bliss. Browne rang the waste haulier. Browne and Bliss have differing recollections of this first conversation. Bliss has claimed that Browne told him he wanted some waste oil removed. Concerned about the quality of the waste oil and the distance he would have to travel to get it, Bliss asked for a sample to be put in the post to see if it was worth his while. A glass bottle was sent. Bliss tested it by pouring some onto a piece of paper to see if it would burn, which it did. He also tasted it. 'It had a bad taste to it, like sulphur, and I thought it had a sulphur content in it.'[7]

Nevertheless Bliss contacted Browne and told him he would haul the oil. Browne's version of this conversation is slightly different. He said he told Bliss it was hazardous waste, recalling that the haulier said he would take the waste to a site that accepted such wastes.[8] Bliss is adamant that he was told nothing about the waste. He said he was simply asked to remove it and only agreed because the amount of oil made it worth his while. 'Most places I went to would have 50 gallons, 100 gallons, 200 gallons. This place had full loads,' he said.

What is sure is that Bliss and one of his drivers, Delbert Eskew, drove a truck with a 3,400-gallon tank to Verona to collect the 'waste oil'. When they got to Verona they met up with Bill Ray, the plant foreman, and were directed to the tanks that held the hexachlorophrene waste. During one of the trips Bliss asked Ray about the waste. He claimed in 1975 that Ray told him that 'it was just oil that was thrown off of their product that they made there'.[9] Bliss has consistently claimed that he was told nothing about the waste.

> I was never told it was a hazardous substance. They may have told me a lot of things but I was never told to use safety gloves, safety goggles, things like that. There was nothing wrote on the tank. There was nothing to lead me to believe there was anything in the oil at all. I never was suspicious because I was down there many times and people were wearing sandals and shoes with open toes in them and cut off shorts and they were walking in that stuff.[10]

Bliss has given confused answers when he has been asked if he knew what they made there. 'I knew they didn't raise chickens there,' he said in 1998. 'I knew it was some kind of a chemical type factory. I had picked up from a lot of places like that.'[11]

At first Bliss agreed to take the waste oil away for nothing but his records indicate he was paid for each load. The oil was very heavy and took a full day to haul, so Bliss asked for five cents a gallon to cover the expenses of the 500-mile round trip. He then asked for ten cents a gallon. The last load he carried was directly for NEPACCO. Between February and October 1971 he hauled away at least 18,500 gallons of waste that was heavily contaminated with dioxin.

What Bliss didn't know and what no one told him was that the manufacture of hexachlorophrene involved trichlorophenol, the same chemical Monsanto had produced in Nitro, Coalite in Bolsover and Roche in Seveso. But even if someone had told him that trichlorophenol produced dioxin as a by-product it probably wouldn't have meant anything to him. No one told him about the extreme toxicity of the waste he had been contracted to handle. Bliss never knew that the hexachlorophrene waste he had taken from the NEPACCO holding tank was contaminated with dioxin at 350 parts per million (ppm).

> I was not suspicious one iota, that anything was wrong with it because I had never heard of something contaminating oil like that. In that day and age it was unheard of and probably, truthfully, in all honesty, if they'd told me it had dioxin in it I wouldn't have known what it was. They could have told me it had liquorice or dioxin, I wouldn't have known the difference.[12]

It took Bliss six trips to haul the dioxin-contaminated waste from Verona to his own storage tanks in Frontenac.[13] He said he put the Verona 'waste oil' in the tank he used most frequently. This tank, B1, was used for the best waste oils and held 18,000 gallons. Confident that the Verona waste was of a good quality, Bliss felt no qualms about mixing it with existing oil in B1. 'It was mixed with a lot of different oils from a lot of different places.'[14] Subsequently he sold some of the oil in B1 to MT Richards, a fuel oil company in Crossville, Illinois and to the Midwest Oil Refining Company in Overland but he also used some of the Verona 'oil' as a dust suppressant.

BLISS SPRAYS THE POISONED OIL ALL OVER MISSOURI

Because Bliss raised horses himself he was acquainted with people in the equestrian business. During May and June 1971 the Bliss Waste Oil Co. was employed to spray oil on horse arenas and stables, a practice he had started on his own arena and on several others in the mid-1960s. Bliss' dust suppressant was also sprayed on truck terminals, trailer parks and unpaved roads in eastern Missouri and on the small shanty town of Times Beach by the Meramec River on the south-western outskirts of St Louis – a job he did at least twice a year from 1971 to 1982, spraying around 40,000 gallons each time.

For reasons that have never been adequately explained by those investigating the consequent pollution, it is not publicly known where Bliss' drivers sprayed their waste oil or where toxic waste hauled by Bliss' firm generally ended up. Bliss provided a seemingly exhaustive list to investigators during the 1970s but it has always been regarded as the tip of the iceberg. Bliss explained:

> They weren't supposed to dump it anywhere except where we had been paid to put it but you've got to understand I had seven or eight people working for me and if they can take it to some side road, to some buddy they know, to oil a road a little bit and dump something that's no good because they're going to have to wait in line to dispose of at a landfill they are gonna do it. That was just a way of life in those years.[15]

Only by circumstance and the persistent probing of activists and reporters has the gradual truth come to light. In 1998, more than a quarter of a century after the Bliss Oil Company sprayed the roads and arenas of eastern Missouri, dioxin sites were still being discovered.

Renate Kimbrough, a pathologist with the CDC found that on 20 May 1971 on the second trip from Verona to Frontenac, Bliss and Eskew were given a ticket for overloading. To reduce the weight they sprayed some of the waste on a road in Bliss' St James farm in Cuba, Missouri.[16] Bliss admitted he had sprayed a road used by his horses but said it was because 'the road was dusty', although he admitted that the overloading was a factor in this decision. 'I remember getting a ticket and I don't remember how I got the truck down in weight, but I guess that's what I did was to unload it at the farm there on the road because I know we wanted to oil that road for a long time and just never got around to it.'[17]

This is a disingenuous response from Bliss if you are sceptical about his motives but it was an event consistent with what he has said and with the behaviour of his drivers who revealed in later years that they dumped toxic waste indiscriminately and in public landfills – and not necessarily because they were overloaded. David Covert, one of

Bliss' drivers, said wastes were hauled to a landfill in the west of the county where the operators were paid off to accept the wastes.[18] On 23 December 1982, in an interview with Illinois EPA officials, Covert talked about picking up ink from a company in St Louis County. 'It smells terrible and I don't think it burns,' said Covert. 'You just haul that stuff into the west county landfill and open the valve and let it run out.'[19]

When Bliss was asked if he knew of 'any occasion when you simply dumped any waste material along the side of the road or by a viaduct or just discarded it', he said waste was only dumped on a piece of ground because he had been paid to dump it there. 'It's possible for the drivers to do anything but I don't know of any offhand that I can think of.'[20]

According to one researcher:

> State and federal officials ... investigated over 375 sites in the St. Louis area based on information that Bliss may have sprayed there. About 45 of these sites were never sampled because the investigation could not substantiate Bliss at the site. Thirty were ruled out without sampling because they appeared to have been sprayed by Bliss after 1972 or 1973, the assumption being that Bliss had used up all of the (dioxin-contaminated) wastes by this time. Over one hundred (other) sites were sampled and dioxin was not discovered.[21]

The EPA have said that over 400 sites were investigated.[22]

WHY WAS BLISS IGNORANT?

Bliss has always stressed that he did not know he had mixed chemical wastes with waste oils. He did not know that he had, inadvertently, generated a lethal, life-threatening concoction by spraying this mixture on arenas, roads and trucking lots. It is hard to believe that Bliss was that ignorant of the chemical wastes he was contracted to get rid off, as if they were benign substances produced naturally and not the products and by-products of chlorine chemistry. Yet it seems he was.

> There's no doubt that I could have been collecting chemical wastes. I could have been getting anything. I had four, five, six trucks out

on the street and they were making anywhere from one to 30 stops a day, six days a week and we had 1,500 to 2,000 stops.[23]

Although Bliss' principle business was waste oils, when asked who his main source for all wastes was he replied, 'I'd say Monsanto' – producers of PCBs, 2,4,5-T and Agent Orange, whose home town was St Louis.[24] It has also been revealed that Bliss collected toxic waste from Union Electric, Wagner Electric, Signet Graphic, Benjamin Moore (Paint Co.), Edwin Cooper, White-Rogers, Jackes-Evans, American Can, General Cable, Carter Carburettor and the Orchard Corp.[25]

It's hard to believe that none of the chemical companies or subsidiaries who employed him thought to ask whether he knew of the toxic nature of the wastes he was carrying. It's also hard to believe that the regulatory authorities never felt it necessary to issue him with some kind of licence to transport and dispose of these deadly wastes. (They didn't because no such regulations were in place in 1971.) It's even harder to believe that the same chemical companies did not provide him with the relevant toxicological data, or that he did not ask for it. 'I just tell them I don't want nothing toxic; that's why I have them put on the tickets non-toxic,' Bliss said.[26]

It's hard to believe because we are looking at this in hindsight. Bliss was an under-educated man who did not know of the existence of dioxin in 1971. 'Who did?' he has asked. Bliss himself still finds it hard to believe that dioxin was known as a deadly chemical in the early 1970s.[27] When he was asked in court if he handled waste chemicals he replied, 'well, all depends on what you consider waste chemicals', and added, 'petroleum products cover a long range from linseed oil to thinners'.[28]

Bliss, it appears, knew nothing about the wastes he was carrying and disposing of. He did not have a proper education. He knew nothing about chemicals. But he wasn't stupid, he was an astute businessman. Today he might be called an environmentalist because he took waste oils and recycled them.

'I didn't know what hazardous waste was in 1971.'[29] When he was asked if he considered dioxin hazardous, he replied: 'I don't think I'm educated or know enough about it to tell you whether it's dangerous or not. They sprayed it all over the soldiers in Vietnam, and they wouldn't do that if they thought it was dangerous, would they?'[30] Bliss claimed he had been deliberately kept ignorant about the extreme toxicity of the NEPACCO waste. The Independent Petrochemical

Company (who had contracted him to haul the hexachlorophrene waste) knew, Bliss asserted, 'damn good and well' that the oil was contaminated.[31]

> I think all the people involved knew what it was. I think there was a cover up at NEPACCO. They were paying other people before me 25 cents a gallon to haul it away. Independent Petrol got paid 25 cents a gallon for every gallon I removed out of there. Let me tell you what they done for it. They put a postage stamp on an invoice and sent it to those people. I did all the work, I took it away. Now if they had come to me and said, 'hey, we've got a client that wants us to haul this stuff away and they are willing to pay us money, we want you to dispose of it – take it to an incinerator or take it to be processed – because there is something wrong with this oil' this wouldn't have happened.[32]

All these statements confuse rather than enlighten. Bliss and his drivers hauled away thousands, if not hundreds of thousands of gallons of deadly toxic wastes. They disposed of them in a manner that today would be regarded as criminal. Yet there is a strong argument that they were deliberately kept ignorant.[33] It wasn't Bliss' role to question the companies who employed him. It was easier to take their word for whatever he was being contracted to carry, sign a docket, and haul the stuff away. 'No questions were asked because what questions are you going to ask about something you know nothing about. I think myself and all the drivers never knew there was anything wrong with anything. Only a fool would try to poison himself,' he said.[34]

However several of Bliss' drivers have contradicted his view of events. One claimed that Bliss also 'dumped raw chemicals' in tanks at his Strecker Road property and that chemical wastes were also stored in two 100,000-gallon tanks at Venice, Illinois.[35] 'One tank had a smelly oil in it and another tank was really smelly stuff,' claimed David Covert, asserting that they contained 'mostly chemicals ... stuff that if you'd smell they'd probably take your breath away from you and knock you out'.[36]

One driver claimed that Bliss stored chemical wastes in tanks B4 and B5, describing them as 'chemical dumpers'. When Bliss' drivers were employed to do a road oil job they would take out the sludge from the motor oil tanks 'until it came to clear oil, then we would mix the chemicals in with that and then we sprayed it on peoples' roads'.[37]

And what of the companies who employed him? What of the managers and the workers who facilitated him when he came to collect the waste? It seems they too were ignorant, knew little about the toxic effects of these wastes or didn't care. But what of senior management, what of the chemists employed by these companies? Did they not know what happened to the by-products and wastes produced by their manipulation of the chemical elements found so abundantly in our ecosphere? If anyone knew about the toxicological effects of these chemical wastes surely it was the chemists. Again, we are told that they too were ignorant or preferred not to know what happened to their toxic wastes.

These are not rhetorical questions. This ignorance of the effects of scientific discovery is not new in the history of technological and scientific enlightenment and progression. To an extent it is understandable and even in a lamentable way forgivable because human nature is not always logical.

In the early 1970s there were no laws or regulations on the transportation and disposal of toxic waste in the USA – or anywhere else it seemed. Bliss was not required to keep records and what he did with the waste was, apparently, his own business. What is not forgivable is the deliberate and secretive manner in which chemists and managers in the companies Bliss collected waste from colluded to keep hidden information about the toxic effects of these wastes.

Of course it wasn't as simple as that. It's often said that ignorance is bliss. In this case it certainly was and it wasn't just the waste haulier who preferred to remain ignorant. The regulatory authorities were also ignorant. It is the job of regulatory authorities to regulate. From the available evidence it appears that the St Louis authorities were genuinely ignorant of the perils of dioxin. They relied on the federal government and its agencies, like the CDC, to tell them what to do. Not everything that was known about dioxin was secret in the early 1970s.

A diligent researcher – as Thomas Whiteside proved – would have found evidence that dioxin wasn't as benign as the chemical industry wanted everyone to believe. If the government agencies were not aware of Schulz's research, for example, it is fair to ask why not. Despite the resources available to them no one in authority followed Whiteside's example. As Bliss and many others have lamented, this was the real reason for the poisoning of Missouri.

'I don't blame Charter Oil, NEPACCO, Russell Bliss,' Bliss astutely summarised nearly 27 years after the events of that toxic summer.

I really truly don't blame anyone except the government. They should have had this stuff regulated. They knew about this stuff years ago. It's the old saying, the horse got out of the barn and then they locked the doors so they started regulating this stuff about 20 years too late. I blame nobody but the federal government and the EPA and the Missouri Department of Natural Resources. If they had it regulated it would have been impossible to happen because now if you haul any oil it has a record from cradle to grave.

They never would have stuck it off on me if there would have been a paper trail. I think some people saw an opportunity to get rid of their garbage the easy way and shove it off on somebody that was not educated in chemicals and all he really knew was waste oils.[38]

THE EFFECT OF BLISS' OIL ON THE PEOPLE OF MISSOURI

One of the first locations to receive Bliss' chemical concoction was the Shenandoah Stables in Moscow Mills, north-west of St Louis. Judy Piatt and Frank Hampel, the owners, had planned a horse show for 30 May 1971 and wanted to control the dust in the arena. One of Bliss' drivers, Gary Lambarth, delivered the unique dust-suppressant in a 1963 International truck to Shenandoah Stables on 26 May, a day after he had collected a load of waste from Verona.

What had started as a gesture for friends in the equestrian business was about to backfire on Bliss.

People would come to my place and say, 'it's not dusty here at all, what do you do?' And I said, I spray it with oil. I was in the oil business and they understood that. They'd say, 'can you spray mine?' I said, if you want me to.

That was the biggest embarrassment because these were my friends. It was a service that I participated in for horse people. The dust would make the horses breath hard. Consequently people called me and asked me to do their arenas. I didn't really like doing it because most of them were out in the country and I didn't want to go out that far. They were hard to drive in because they kept the dirt soft and ploughed and it was hard for my trucks to navigate in that stuff but I did it as a service and a convenience.[39]

Even though he felt obliged to help out his horsey friends, Bliss didn't want his driver to go to Shenandoah, joking that it would be more trouble than it was worth.

> That was one of the few places that I didn't oil. Gary Lambarth oiled it for me. I didn't want him to oil it. I said, don't take the oil out there. Number one we won't get paid for it, number two she'll complain and moan and groan that we've put too much in or not enough.
>
> He said, 'well I'm going out that way and I've got some oil on'.
>
> I said, well if you want to do it okay but I'm against it ...[40]

Between 1,500 and 2,000 gallons of waste oil were sprayed on the arena. Despite Bliss' reservations, serious or not, Lambarth was paid $150 for the job and the cheque was deposited in Bliss' bank. The effect was immediate. The oil Lambarth had brought to Shenandoah was lethal.

The native birds were the first to succumb to the poison, probably taking it into their systems from eating earthworms. Within three days the arena was littered with hundreds of dead birds. 'There literally were bushel baskets full of those dead wild birds,' recalled Patrick Phillips – who would conduct an epidemiological investigation into the animal deaths for the state the following year.[41]

The horses, cats and dogs were next. Four days after the equestrian arena had been sprayed, the first horse began to writhe in agony. It was dead three weeks later. By June, 29 horses, eleven cats and four dogs had died. More horses died in the subsequent months. Mares lost their foals.

On 21 August, Judy Piatt admitted her six-year-old daughter to St Louis Children's Hospital. The girl, who played daily inside the arena during June and July, had suffered flu-like symptoms and diarrhoea. She became listless. When she tried to urinate she was wracked with pain. The doctors took a look at her and discovered that her bladder was badly inflamed. She was in agony and remained that way for months, losing 50 per cent of her body weight during the course of her illness.[42] The little girl's ten-year-old sister had also been in the arena during that summer but her activity, riding horses a few times a week, did not bring her in contact with the contaminated soil. Yet she too succumbed to headaches, nosebleeds, occasional abdominal pain and diarrhoea.

The children weren't the only ones affected. Hampel, who had acted as a ringmaster at the show four days after the spraying, suffered a severe headache and was nauseous while in the arena. Piatt herself got severe headaches, was overcome with nausea and suffered from diarrhoea – even though she only worked in the office.

Elsewhere in Missouri similar tales were being told. Bliss had used his dust suppressant on three other equestrian arenas. When comparisons about the dioxin contamination were made with Seveso some years later, the results revealed that the dioxin levels at Shenandoah were 7.5 to 13 times greater; at Timberline two to five times; Bubbling Springs 7.6 times; Minker, 55 to 90 times and Stout as much as two times greater.

Thus the story was the same, birds falling from the sky, cats and dogs losing their will to live and horses falling by the score. In one arena 25 horses died. In another seven died after exposure to the contaminated soil. Two three-year-old boys who had been playing in this arena developed chloracne that took a year to subside.

Piatt's local vet James Evans, who had been summoned to treat the horses, realised the soil was the key to the illnesses. He collected some soil samples, went home and shortly after began to develop chloracne that, like the children, lasted for a year.[43]

What had happened at Shenandoah was beyond the scope of the practising local vet. Piatt, realising like the vet that the soil was the key to the problem, scooped some of her contaminated arena into a Miracle Whip jar. It would become a crucial piece in a jigsaw that would come to represent a picture of toxic poisoning in eastern Missouri.

The CDC were invited in by the Missouri state epidemiologist. The CDC's Dr Robert Koehler led the investigation. Blood samples from affected animals and some soil were brought to the CDC headquarters in Atlanta. At first the CDC identified the poisoning with exposure to PCBs and chlorinated insecticides but they could not isolate the toxic compound responsible.[44]

The investigators had hit a wall and nothing happened for two years until the summer of 1973 when events took a strange turn. A student at the CDC lab in Atlanta was asked to run chemical tests on soil samples from Shenandoah. The test revealed the presence of trichlorophenol.[45] The CDC needed to confirm these results. They contacted Dr Arthur Case at the University of Missouri's veterinarian school in Columbia where the state investigation into the Shenandoah poisonings had been continuing, albeit at a slow pace.[46] For a reason never explained, Piatt's Miracle Whip jar had been brought to the veterinary lab and left there. When Case was asked by the CDC for a new batch of soil samples he sent them the soil (2.4 pounds of it) in Piatt's jar.

An initial test of the soil in the jar showed trichlorophenol. Renate Kimbrough, who was given the task of identifying the toxic contaminant, was thwarted in the continuing investigation. The bureaucracy of the CDC prevented them from testing for dioxin and obtaining lab animals for experimentation. After several months of stonewalling Kimbrough and her colleagues used the 'rabbit ear' test to determine the toxic contaminant in the soil. The affected rabbits died within a week, scaring 'the dickens out of the people at CDC,'[47] who decided to run the soil through a final test, using the gas chromatography method. On 30 July 1974 – three years and two months after Lambarth had sprayed the Shenandoah arena – the CDC revealed 30 parts per million (ppm) of dioxin; 5,000ppm of 2,4,5-T, and, interestingly, 1,350 to 1,590ppm of PCBs in the contaminated soil.[48]

In September 1971, after they had filed lawsuits against Bliss, Piatt and Hampel began tailing Bliss drivers on their daily routes. Their surveillance continued for more than a year. During that time, the pair sometimes disguised themselves, Hampel donning a woman's wig, Piatt wearing a man's cowboy hat. The undercover work paid off. The pair observed Bliss' drivers wantonly dumping waste into ditches, creeks, rivers, roadsides and fields.[49] On one occasion, Piatt watched a Bliss driver pick up a load at the Monsanto facility in St Peters, Missouri and dump it in a Mississippi River slough. On another instance, she witnessed chemical wastes being dumped at Times Beach! She also said PCBs had been found in Bliss' storage tanks.[50]

She also said she telephoned 13 waste producers in the St Louis area, pretended to be a secretary and asked for a recommendation on who could get rid of some 'bad stuff'. All 13 suggested the Bliss Waste Oil Co!

Piatt eventually compiled an 18-page report. She cited 16 different companies whose waste had been dumped by Bliss drivers. Piatt's list also included 31 locations that had been sprayed. She submitted the report to the EPA in Washington, DC, the CDC in Atlanta, the Missouri Department of Natural Resources (DNR) and the Missouri Department of Health in Jefferson City.[51] But it wasn't until the summer of 1974 when the CDC revealed the dioxin that action was finally taken. Officials from the CDC and the Missouri Department of

Health visited Piatt. They advised her and her family to seek further medical evaluation. Even though she had sent copies of her report to them in 1972 she gave them new copies.

Piatt's soil contained dioxin and 2,4,5-T but it also showed a high amount of PCBs – revealing another twist in this toxic tale. The first researchers on the job accurately guessed that the toxic substances in the soil had come from industrial waste. Bliss was contacted for a list of his waste sources but there was no evidence that any of the waste he carried contained dioxin.[52]

The investigators had identified the toxic compounds that had killed the animals and made Piatt's children ill. They now faced the more arduous task of locating the source of the contamination. Bliss had been ruled out for the time being, despite Piatt's investigation into his methods. Patrick Phillips of the Department of Health had asked Bliss where he had picked up chemical wastes. The haulier named seven companies but none, Phillips learned, were involved in processes that produced dioxin. Phillips suspected the dioxin must have come from someone in the production of 2,4,5-T or Agent Orange. He decided to contact the US Defense Department for the names of companies that had produced Agent Orange in the St Louis area. Four companies were named: Monsanto, Thompson Hayward Inc., Thompson Chemicals Corp. and Hoffman Taff Inc. All claimed they had not used Bliss' company but officials with Hoffman Taff (who had been bought by Syntex) fingered NEPACCO at Verona. Somehow the PCBs were forgotten about.

The investigation led them conveniently back to Bliss. 'He said that yes, he had remembered since the last time he talked to us that he had hauled waste from Verona,' said Phillips. 'There was no information from Mr Bliss that led us to the original source of waste in Verona.' Approaching Hoffman Taff for information, Phillips added, had been 'serendipitous'.[53]

Bliss' ignorance is understandable, given his methods. What is not is how the authorities reacted. According to C. D. Stelzer, an award-winning investigative reporter with the *Riverfront Times* in St Louis, there was mystery afoot.

> After the CDC announced its find, dioxin became the buzzword that grabbed headlines, spurred by its links to Agent Orange and the Vietnam War. The resulting clamour allowed the additional discovery of highly-toxic polychlorinated biphenyls in the same soil to escape the media's attention. When CDC officials began

investigating at Shenandoah Stables, they suspected either PCBs or nerve gas ... After finding dioxin, however, health officials turned their attention toward Agent Orange.[54]

Linda James also questioned the methods of investigation, the coincidences and events that led the investigators to the NEPACCO waste.

> The sickness of one little girl, two 'amateur sleuths' trying to find out what killed their horses, an accidental hit in a laboratory analysis, a hunch about Agent Orange producers, a calendar on a wall, a tip from a disgruntled employee – so began the investigation of dioxin in Missouri.
>
> Were it not for these 'key' accidents, the true extent of the Missouri dioxin problem may have never been known. Although government agencies were involved at the site where the material was generated and at the site where the material was deposited, they were off on different tangents, one trying to solve a pollution problem in a stream and spring, the other dealing with the symptoms, but not the cause of the problem.[55]

It would take the passing of more than a quarter of a century and the controversy over the disposal of the waste before minds would be focused again on who knew what in the early 1970s. Monsanto, the US military, the EPA, the DNR, the CDC and other government agencies made a potent mix.

In July 1974 the CDC confirmed the dioxin contamination. In March 1975 the CDC advised the EPA to remove the dioxin-contaminated soil to minimise further exposure. The CDC also informed the State of Missouri. Instead of instigating a thorough investigation, the EPA moved into procrastination mode. Because the sites they had tested revealed levels below what was required for them to take action, the EPA made a 'discretionary decision' not to inform the residents of Times Beach that dioxin had been discovered in their town.

Unbelievably the CDC told state authorities that dioxin had an estimated half-life of one year and no one questioned them on this, even though the knowledge existed that dioxin was a persistent compound.

In 1976 the State of Missouri was supposed to take further samples from the contaminated sites. Like the EPA they did nothing.

In December 1982 the CDC's assertion about dioxin was proved dramatically false when the river flooded and carried the dioxin-contaminated soils into the homes and workplaces of the 2,242 inhabitants of Times Beach.[56]

It would be the beginning of a nightmare for the residents of Times Beach, the continuation of what many people believed was a deliberate cover-up to protect St Louis' rich and powerful.

NIGHTMARE AT TIMES BEACH

Marilyn Leistner was the alderman of Times Beach when the revelations about dioxin levels in the town were made. She often wonders whether the authorities would have told them about the dioxin if a local reporter had not seen the list of contaminated sites and contacted the Times Beach city clerk for a quote.

'The day they printed it, the EPA wanted to look at our records. And that's when we found the ordinance giving Bliss permission to spray at will for the whole year,' said Leistner many years later, reliving her shock at the knowledge that the authorities had known about the dioxin contamination since the early 1970s and had done and said nothing. 'It's just amazing that your government could do something to jeopardise you physically, economically, psychologically and socially and not tell you about it.'[57]

The poisoning of Times Beach was now in the open. For the first time the people who lived in Times Beach learned that Bliss had sprayed dioxin on their town as well as on the horse arenas and dirt roads of eastern Missouri. Still the EPA dragged its heels, claiming that it would take them up to a year to initiate a test programme of the town. This didn't impress Leistner and her colleagues in the Times Beach Town Hall. 'We hired Enviro-Dyne Engineers to do testing. EPA said even if we do test we can't get the tests back in six months to a year. We had a lab that promised us a turnaround of two to three weeks. EPA couldn't believe it,' said Leistner.[58]

Then came the flood, which many in the community decided was divine intervention. 'You know why dioxin and flooding hit Times Beach, don't you?' Leistner asked a reporter many years later, answering the question herself. 'It was because the aldermen voted to allow strip dancing at one of the bars. That's what some of the people thought. God was punishing us.'[59] The community of Times Beach was being punished alright but it had nothing to do with the nefarious lifestyles of those who ran and frequented the town's 13 bars and the fact that the community had no churches. The 801 families that made up the community of Times Beach had become victims of a mindset seduced by technological progress and selfish desire.

The evacuation of Times Beach took place during Marilyn Leistner's tenure as mayor. She had been elected on 7 June 1983. That summer the evacuation began after the people of Times Beach agreed to sell their homes to the federal government. The state paid $35 million for 801 residents properties and 30 businesses. For more than ten years Times Beach was a ghost town, guarded initially by state troopers and visited only by curious sightseers – who were warned to stay outside the fences that enclosed its deserted roads, homes and offices.

Marilyn Leistner now lives in Eureka, a few miles from Times Beach. But she will never forget the place that has become synonymous with dioxin contamination. She and her family now carry the emotional and biological scars of the decision to allow Bliss to spray his lethal concoction on the dirt roads of Times Beach every year between 1971 and 1982.

About 1,500 residents of Times Beach have received $45 million in legal settlements but nothing will ever compensate for the damage to their health. This damage has been significant. Women suffered miscarriages. Several children were born with serious birth defects, some with spina bifida. There have been many cases of leukaemia, both in children and adults. Some children suffered varied and rare types of seizures. Children and adults have had liver problems, allergies, giant hives, severe acne, kidney and bladder problems, thyroid disorders and bone tumours. Hyperactive children with an array of learning disabilities have been common. An alarming number of women in their twenties and thirties have had hysterectomies.

Marilyn's own family suffered many disturbing illnesses. Her first husband was one of three cases of porphyria cutane tarda (a rare blood disorder associated with dioxin poisoning) within the community. One of her three daughters suffered with giant hives all over her body, rashes and severe acne. Her hands blistered, the scars of which doctors have told her will be with her for the rest of her life. Another daughter became sterile and developed a hyper thyroid condition. Her other daughter had a rare seizure disorder. Marilyn's second husband had kidney and bladder problems and a severe black-head type of acne. Marilyn herself had no feeling in her left hand and was diagnosed with severe peripheral neuropathy. She had a hysterectomy in 1980.

The tragedy of Times Beach will never be adequately resolved until the absolute truth is known about the poisoning of Missouri and until people who knew what was happening are able to speak freely. In 1983, Fred Lafser, then-director of the Missouri Department of Natural Resources told the *Riverfront Times* in St Louis that 'most of our hazardous waste problems (in Missouri) can be traced back to him (Bliss) – including problems with PCBs, solvents and inks, you name it'.

This is a convenient response, if not entirely true. What happened in Times Beach is now a historical fact, how it happened is not. Bliss was not just a haulier of waste oils, he also carried toxic chemical wastes. He has admitted this openly. He has admitted that he carried chemicals wastes, that he hauled transformer oils (PCBs), that he took away solvents and inks. Accepting the contract to carry the Verona hexachlorophrene waste was not an isolated job, it was part of his business. But Bliss was not the only player in the toxic games that were being played in Missouri in the early 1970s. Those who have studied this sordid history of dioxin have repeatedly asked questions about the poisoning of Missouri and are still waiting for answers.

When PCBs were discovered (in the Shenandoah soil, in Bliss' tanks, in Times Beach), why didn't the authorities go looking for the source? Why wasn't the information that Bliss provided at the various trials followed up? Why did the investigation into the dioxin-contaminated sites ignore the clear evidence that other chemical wastes were involved.

Why do the dioxins found in the Verona tanks differ from the dioxins found in the many contaminated sites in and around St Louis?

'We're still waiting for answers to these questions,' said Fred Striley, a community activist who fought the authorities to reveal the truth about the poisoning of Missouri.[60] 'Not all sites sprayed by Russell Bliss have been tested. Sites that have been tested that were not contaminated with dioxin but may have been contaminated with other toxic chemicals were not included in the Times Beach clean-up. EPA concluded that 27 sites required clean up action.'[61]

WHY DID THE AUTHORITIES NOT ACT?

It may never be known how much senior USEPA officials knew about the toxic contamination of Missouri. What is known is that the EPA and the chemical industry make companionable bedfellows.

Since the formation of the agency in 1971 officials with the EPA have found their way with comparative ease onto the management teams and corporate boards of the chemical and toxic waste industries. William Ruckelshaus was the first administrator of the EPA between 1971 and 1973 when Bliss was distributing toxic waste all over Missouri. In the mid-1980s Ruckelshaus returned to the EPA. He would have been familiar with the poisoning of Missouri and the attempts to identify sites and clean them up. Ruckelshaus eventually became the chairman and chief executive officer of Browning Ferris Industries – one of the largest waste management companies in the world. He also served on the board of Monsanto.

Leo Thomas was EPA administrator from 1985 to 1989 after a period as Ruckelshaus' deputy when he oversaw the clean-up of Missouri. In 1993 Thomas became senior vice president of Georgia Pacific Corporation – a paper-pulp company. But it was the roles of Anne Gorsuch, who was appointed administrator of the EPA in 1981, and Rita Lavelle, who ran the Superfund toxic waste clean-up programme, which deserve the most scrutiny. Both were called to a congressional hearing to answer why the clean-up of toxic waste sites in Missouri and Arkansas had not commenced. Gorsuch avoided testimony while it was alleged that Lavelle had shredded documents relating to the sites. A lawyer by profession, Gorsuch went back to her old job, eventually representing Syntex in claims against the company by victims of Bliss' folly.

It is the same story with the politicians and ruling elites of Missouri. In 1983 Hugh Kaufman, an EPA official, appeared on the Phil Donahue TV talk show and alleged that US Senator John Danforth had received a list of potential dioxin sites in Missouri, while state attorney general, and had failed to do anything about it.

During that period Kaufman was the EPA's chief hazardous waste investigator. His inquiries led him to suspect that Bliss had connections to the 'power-elite culture' in Missouri, a belief Kaufman has continued to hold, that the political and social climate in Missouri compares to a banana republic. 'You've got an elite club, and the disposal boys are a part of that club.'[62]

This to an extent is also true but whether Bliss was a member of some kind of secret club is debatable. Some observers have pointed to Bliss' association with Charles Shaw, the criminal defence lawyer who represented him in court, as evidence of a special collusion. Shaw was a World War II veteran (the film *The Great Escape* starring Steve McQueen was based on his exploits) and associated with the anti-communist American Security Council.[63] Bliss' connection with Shaw was horses. 'He was a lifetime friend. I taught his children how to ride horses. He had horses and I had oiled his ring. I always talked to him about legal stuff. He never made any money out of it and for years he never charged me anything,' said Bliss.[64]

By 1983, the USEPA had identified at least 100 sites thought to be contaminated by dioxin, yet wouldn't release the names of the sites. Even more remarkably only 21 of the 100 sites had been sampled. 'The feeling is why go look for more problems when we do not have the staff to solve what we know about?' Fred Lafser of the DNR told the media.

An internal EPA memo revealed the agency's attitude when it became obvious that Times Beach would have to be evacuated and cleaned up. Instead of identifying every contaminated site, the EPA set 'a level of concern' for dioxin at one part per billion that meant they could ignore contaminated sites below this level. This decision, according to the memo, was 'based on cost and need for immediate action, not total health protection' and 'allows immediate action for agency and good press. Buys time: allows time for reassessment of agency risk analysis methods and policies ... Allows preparation of public for possible change in policy. Intermediate cost option ... easily implemented, sampling is relatively inexpensive and easy.'[65]

Something strange was going on.

EPA SOLUTION SPARKS COMMUNITY ACTION

Steve Taylor, an activist with Earth First! (the direct action ecological movement), had grown up tending horses. He knew about the dioxin-contaminated land. When the EPA decided in 1990, in its wisdom, that the solution to Missouri's toxic waste problem was to incinerate it, Taylor decided to utilise his direct action skills. He didn't trust the EPA. He didn't believe in the infallibility of the incineration process. And he didn't think anybody would oppose the incinerator. He decided to do it himself. When it was learned that Syntex, the chemical corporation, which had been implicated and deemed liable in the poisoning of Missouri, had been given the contract to dispose of the dioxin-contaminated soil, Taylor reacted.

I knew there was a big spin on the 'lack of toxicity' of dioxin. I knew from personal experience that EPA was covering up information. They were going along with the corrupt CDC, who had falsified evidence on the toxicity of dioxin and Vietnam veterans situation.[66] This was probably the heart of the beast when it came to the conspiracy of the attempts to detoxify dioxin – the cover-up.[67]

In 1993, with some friends, he formed the Times Beach Action Group (TBAG) to oppose Syntex's proposed incinerator in the flood plain of the Meramec downwind of St Louis county. C. D. Stelzer described the site of the incinerator thus: 'The Meramec River forms an oxbow from which the town of Crescent most likely takes its name. On the opposite bank, towering limestone palisades have been sculpted over aeons by the spring-fed waters that push this Ozark landscape to within 20 miles of St. Louis.'[68]

TBAG set out to 'uncover the dioxin cover-up, and the way citizens have been mistreated', believing that many people had never been compensated for dioxin exposure.

Taylor was not alone in believing that only the community would fight the plan to burn the contaminated soil. Mary Derrick had moved into Crescent, a scenic community on a forested hill a mile from Times Beach in September 1993. Just over a year later, in November 1994, she learned about the proposal to truck contaminated waste from 27 sites around Missouri to the proposed incinerator. She approached her neighbour Ann Dollarhide and together they sought some answers from the authorities. After a round of 'unanswered questions and nonsensical answers' from EPA and state officials, Derrick and Dollarhide got in contact with the growing network that was emerging to oppose the incinerator. They found these activists a wealth of information.

Ann and I realised that we needed to wake up what appeared to be a very complacent Crescent. People in Crescent were tired and worn out from the whole Times Beach affair. They had seen in earlier years of opposition that the government was going to do what it was going to do (and) there was not a thing they could do about it.

Ann and I felt that with so much at stake this was a battle well worth fighting. We felt it would be irresponsible to do otherwise. We knew that the voice of the people would be the greatest weapon we had in keeping the incinerator out of the community. Out of the convictions of our heart, Citizens Against Dioxin Incineration (CADI) was born.

We took our message door to door, handing out folders of literature. CADI joined efforts with two other existing opposition groups: (Striley's) Dioxin Incinerator Response Group (DIRG) and (Taylor's) Times Beach Action Group (TBAG). Together we drew from a pool of skills, talents and connections. We became a force to be reckoned with.

As a coalition of dedication and solidarity, the three groups worked hard and accomplished much. Historical and current documents were researched continuously. Obscure but relevant documents were unearthed, analysed and brought to the attention of government agencies and the public. We monitored the project as close as we possibly could, holding the agencies accountable for misleading the public.[69]

By June 1995, when the construction of the incinerator began, the opposition embraced a network of individuals and groups that included TBAG, CADI, the DIRG, Gateway Greens Alliance, the Times Beach Legal Defense Coalition and the Student Environmental Action Coalition. 'We feel there's a lot of secrets,' said Taylor. 'That this whole incineration project was about preserving secrets and protecting commercial interests more than protecting public health.'[70] He is adamant that the history of dioxin poisoning in Missouri will never be completed until the role of the US military and the chemical industry, particularly Monsanto, is revealed.

During the 1950s the US Army Chemical Corps were engaged in a search for 'materials of unusual toxicity'. This led them to Monsanto for information on the toxicity of 2,4,5-T but following an exchange of documents and samples the army decided they had 'no further interest in this by-product of the 2,4,5-T plant operation'.[71] According to C. D. Stelzer, 'the context of the letters indicates the Army was investigating the possibility of using the substance as a chemical weapon not a herbicide'.[72]

The poisoning of Missouri has also been shrouded in secrecy since the day it began. Much more so than in Bolsover or Seveso or even Nitro, the story of the dioxin contamination at Times Beach and other places in Missouri has induced a strange illness in all those implicated in the investigation. Some call this disease lethargy, others call it apathy. It might even be incompetence.

Whatever it is called there's no argument that it is malignant and reduces all those inflicted to a state of paranoia and inertia. When community activists realised they would have to conduct their own investigation, they found this disease rampant among those who worked for the EPA and the Missouri state authorities – the people entrusted with their health and safety. Instead of ensuring the well-being of communities these bureaucrats perceived the communities as a threat. Tim Schmitt, of the TBAG, realised that the authorities were actually engaged in a public relations exercise to cover up the truth. As the community groups began to reveal the secrets and lies surrounding the contamination of Missouri, significantly the role of the EPA, 'the agency responded with greater secrecy, bureaucratic procrastination and questionable science,' leading many people to ask if Times Beach in particular was a genuine clean-up or the 'clean-up of an image'.[73] According to William Sanjour, EPA papers over environmental problems with 'slick PR' while showing contempt for the victims of environmental pollution.[74] 'How could my government endanger my health?' was Marilyn Leistner's response.[75]

Fred Striley reached an obvious conclusion.

It is the opinion of citizens' groups who have engaged in the process of trying to determine the truth about what was happening at Times Beach, that the companies and the regulatory agencies have consistently behaved in such a manner as to cloud and obfuscate the truth. They have engaged in public relations campaigns to mislead the public; they have taken legal action to prevent evidence from being heard in court; they have refused to answer questions; and they have pretended they were answering questions when they were talking around the question.

All the while, the incineration process moved inexorably forward under the guise of regulatory oversight. This is now all part of the history of the Times Beach site. Although the incineration project is completed, it may be generations before its full impact is understood.[76]

WAS BLISS THE ONLY VILLAIN?

Russell Bliss is perceived by some as the sole villain in the poisoning of Missouri because it was his actions that led to the dioxin contamination of several hundred sites, even though the toxic waste he mixed with waste oil and sprayed all over the place originated in the processes of the chemical industry. He says:

I don't really like pointing my finger at anybody but I really do believe the government should have done something about this long before they did. If this stuff is so hazardous, so dangerous why did they wait so many years before cleaning it up? So how would an uneducated truck driver like me know anything about this? If I had known what was in [the Verona waste] I would have taken it to a landfill because landfills then were taking anything.[77]

In 1983 Larry Gooden, another dealer in waste oils, testified that Bliss was not ignorant at all. Gooden, who had been given immunity from prosecution in exchange for his testimony against Bliss in a tax evasion trial, alleged that he had received up to $4,000 a year in cash from Bliss for toxic waste between 1973 and 1976. While he was manager of Reidy Terminal Inc. – whose operations included the recovery of oil, chemicals and other material from tankers – Gooden received seven cents a gallon from Bliss for the waste. 'Russell Bliss knew that the material he was picking up was a hazardous material with waste oil in it or blended oils in it and that once the materials left Reidy Terminal I didn't know – want to know why, when or what was done with it,' said Gooden in his testimony.

The wastes, according to Gooden, included benzene, toluene, methanols, phenols, acids and caustics. It was a good arrangement for Gooden whose company usually had to pay between 10 and 20 cents a gallon to dispose of the oil and other hazardous material from the slop tanks at Reidy Terminal.

This is where the story becomes murky. In a refrain from Bliss' innocent claims that he never knew what was in the waste from Verona he stressed that the slop waste he received from Gooden was not toxic and that he had subsequently sold it to his customers. One of those customers, Bliss alleged, was a company owned by Gooden.

In 1977, Gooden, in partnership with Lorraine H. 'Pat' Kiesel – owner of Kiesel Co., formed KG Venture, an oil brokerage firm. During 1977 and 1978 KG Venture bought oil from Bliss, mixed it with high-grade fuel oil and resold it to the Kiesel company.

Gooden confirmed this but he challenged Bliss' assertion that the waste in the slop tanks at Reidy Terminal was pumped directly into Gooden's KG Venture tanks by Bliss' men. Gooden claimed that he would never have allowed hazardous waste to be mixed with fuel oil. Gooden also alleged that Bliss preferred to keep their transactions secret, by paying in cash, keeping no records.[78] But tax evasion is a common practice in the USA, as common as traffic offences.

We may never know whether Russell Bliss took a fall for those who needed to get rid of Missouri's secret toxic waste. What we do know is that the investigations into his actions revealed a hidden side to Missouri society, touching the raw nerves of those who controlled the means of production and manipulated economic and political life. We also know that Bliss' folly alerted the military and those with an obsessive desire to protect US national security, to the extent that decisions were taken at a high level in government to instigate a cover-up.[79]

A series of elaborate mechanisms were put in place to achieve this. The consequence was a web that embraced state and federal authorities, regulatory bodies, scientific and academic institutions, politicians, the media plus the military and the chemical industry. The controversy over Agent Orange had focused a few minds but such an elaborate web was destined to show signs of wear and tear. It was only a matter of time before the truth began to emerge.

From the beginning of the century St Louis was a toxic city producing everything from phenols to PCBs to solvents and ultimately dioxins. A lot of these chemicals ended up in Times Beach because they ended up in Bliss' tanks, where they settled into the sludge, ultimately to become the concoction that the Bliss Oil Company sprayed in eastern Missouri. Tests conducted in Times Beach in 1982 detected not only dioxin and PCBs, but ethyl benzene, acetone, toluene, xylene and other hazardous substances.

Bliss and his drivers picked up toxic waste from chemical factories all over St Louis. He claimed these chemical wastes were disposed of at a landfill in east St Louis. But Bliss was not the only haulier of toxic wastes. He is, however, the only one that anything is known about.

More than anyone else Monsanto have been responsible for putting these chemicals into the St Louis environment. The company manufactured among the deadliest chemicals known, particularly PCBs, yet they have cleverly avoided scrutiny. Instead a small waste haulier by the name of Bliss has been blamed for Missouri's toxic tragedy. Monsanto knew what PCBs were, Bliss did not. He thought PCBs were 'the prettiest oil you ever seen' and never once thought that PCBs might be the most toxic oil you ever seen.

When you open a transformer that oil is like brand new. I would have bet my bottom dollar that transformer oil was as pure as pure could be. We had to test all the oil we sold to oil refineries. They would put it into a centrifuge to see how much sludge and how much water was in it. Transformer oil would shake out nothing. It was premium oil. I used to sell it to refineries. They would give me 12, 13, 14 cents a gallon for transformer oil.[80]

That was the most Bliss ever got paid for any of the waste oil he sold on.

On 2 May 1991 Bliss' wife Evelyn died from breast cancer. She was 57. She used to ride horses on their own Mid-American Arena, which her husband had sprayed with waste oil. After she died Bliss thought the dioxin might have had something to do with it and considered legal action but he was persuaded out of it. He had been married to Evelyn for 41 years. She bore him two sons, Jerry Russell and George Cash – who was born in 1972. He buried her in a small plot on the farm he sprayed with dioxin in 1971. In 1998 at the age of 63 Bliss said:

This has been a catastrophe in my life. The only thing that has helped me through this is that I had a wonderful family. I had the worst publicity. It just went on and on in the papers and the tv. I got no help from anyone but my friends. People are very scared of the unknown.[81]

A very active man, he started to suffer from a shortage of breath during 1997. 'I can't figure out why. I go to the doctor. He says you're 63, you can't run three miles like you used to.'

Bliss said he began to fit the pieces of this particular toxic puzzle into place in the 1980s. Some of his conclusions are difficult to refute, significantly about those who benefited. 'People have been making money out of this dioxin thing since it started. I probably made $600. Everybody who touched this dioxin thing made large sums of money. One lawyer friend of mine handled one case and his cut was almost a million dollars.'

Rex Carr, whose diligent detective work revealed Monsanto's dioxin fraud, does not blame Bliss for Missouri's toxic tragedy. 'He was also a victim.'[82] Anyone who cares to take the time to understand what happened is likely to come to the same conclusion. 'Why would I take the worst oil that I've ever got my hands on and spray it on my farm at St James [in Cuba, Missouri], my farm in Ellisville, Missouri, where my son lives and where my family lived at that time, plus property in the city where I kept my oil tanks – I sprayed there?'[83]

In 1998 Bliss lived on $674 a month, social security. In the winter of 1997 he had made another settlement with the federal government 'for the damages they say I caused'. He has one question: 'Why don't they get it from the chemical company that created the dioxin?'

Unfortunately that is a question that cannot be answered adequately because it is not known who created the dioxin sprayed by Bliss. The history tells us that the tank at Verona may have contained residues from the time when Hoffman Taff produced 2,4,5-T. The history also reveals that the waste Bliss hauled away was contaminated with dioxin as a result of NEPACCO's hexachlorophrene production. But Bliss, by his own admission, carried other chemical wastes, including PCBs. He may have hauled them from Union Electric but they were manufactured by the chemical industry, significantly by Monsanto at their Sauget factory in east St Louis.

Sadly for Bliss he never made these connections until the late 1980s. Throughout the 1970s and 1980s the chemical companies implicated in the poisoning of Missouri were forced into legal settlements. But it is Russell Martin Bliss who has shouldered all the public blame. 'My father told me once, you're too ambitious, it's gonna get you in trouble. Maybe he was right.'[84]

Bliss was a victim of society – a society that protects the rich and powerful, a society that punishes the weak.

I would walk down the street and people would point at me. Aren't you Russell Bliss, they would say. I don't want to talk about dioxin, I'd say. They'd say, could you just answer one question and they'd have some crazy question. I'd say, before I answer your question I'd just like to tell you that I'm the guy who sprayed roads and arenas at the same time as Uncle Sam sprayed our boys in Vietnam.[85]

4
Toxic Shock:
Deep Rumbling Sounds

WORKER X

Worker X was employed at the Boehringer chemical factory in Hamburg-Moorfleet. Born on 16 April 1916 worker X started at Boehringer on 19 May 1952. In February 1953 he was transferred to their chlorophenol plant. His job was to remove with a shovel 2,4,5-T in flake form from open drums and move them to autoclaves. In November 1954 worker X contracted chloracne, bronchitis and conjunctivitis. Although Boehringer acknowledged his illness they refused to pay compensation. Worker X went back to work. A series of court cases followed. Boehringer agreed to pay DM10,000 ($5,950). Worker X contested this in court in 1984. On 12 April 1985 worker X died. He was diagnosed with oesophageal carcinoma. Professor Christopher Rappe was asked to test worker X's fatty tissue for dioxin. He discovered 87ppt of 2,3,7,8-TCDD and 1,000ppt of hexachlorodibenzodioxin. The subsequent court ruling on 4 April 1989 stated that worker X's illness and consequent death were caused by dioxin. They awarded in his favour.[1]

For too long the chemical industry has denied the harmful effects of dioxins. Nowhere has this travesty of bad science and injustice been more perpetrated than at Seveso.

Fabrizio Fabbri, Greenpeace Italy[2]

In my personal opinion the risk of dangers of dioxins are heavily over estimated. We know about the fears and the prophesies but the real dangers of dioxins, what do we have, which events and incidents? Seveso?

Gerhard Stolpa, Bayer scientist[3]

You don't need a weatherman to know which way the wind blows.

Bob Dylan[4]

73

Coalite duty chemist Eric Burrows left two young children behind when he became one of the first fatal victims of the chemical disasters that would begin to etch the word dioxin into the public consciousness. He was almost 40 when he died. He had worked at Coalite's Bolsover factory in Derbyshire, England for 20 years and lived locally until the evening of 23 April 1968.

It's not known exactly where Burrows was working or what he was doing when an explosion sent him and Coalite's trichlorophenol unit into space. All that is known is that he was inside the building at the time of the explosion. The blast came an hour after midnight just as the men in the building were preparing for a meal break. They were making their way to the entrance. This may have saved their lives. Six process workers were hurt. John Gerrard got a shoulder injury from the falling masonry; David Bostock and Robert (Bob) Martin were treated in hospital. Bostock returned to the factory to collect his belongings and intended to return to work. Three other process workers belonging to a different shift – Dennis Goss, Leslie McGregor and John Faulder – were also taken to hospital where they were treated for shock and sent home.[5]

The works fire team fought the fire caused by the explosion until firemen from Chesterfield and Bolsover arrived to fight the blaze for six hours. Burrows was only discovered after a roll call by night shift supervisor Richard Stafford. Some of the men had just escaped from the building. Though dazed and confused and in shock, they went back in with a stretcher. 'We found him buried under debris about 15 yards from the entrance. His pulse was feeble and one of the men thought he was dead.'[6]

The explosion smashed every window in the three-storey building and blew large sections of masonry out of the top floor walls. Inside the plant was a blackened mass of twisted metal, an image that Chesterfield's Senior Fire Officer found disturbing. 'The plant looks as if it has been hit by a bomb. I have not seen such destruction since the war.'[7]

MAKING HERBICIDE 2,4,5-T

Coalite began manufacturing trichlorophenol in August 1965. Coalite, like most producers, used their trichlorophenol as the precursor for the production of the herbicide, 2,4,5-T. Industrie Chimiche Meda Societa Anonima (ICMESA) at Meda, near Milan in Italy were the notable exception, using the phenolic mixture to make the bactericide hexachlorophrene.[8] Coalite produced their trichlorophenol in an autoclave, reacting 1,2,4,5-tetrachlorobenzene with caustic soda in the presence of two solvents – ethylene glycol and orthochlorobenzene.[9] The orthochlorobenzene solvent was used to prevent blocking of the condenser by solid molecules of trichlorobenzene. These two solvents played a significant part in the accident and the consequent production of dioxin. The Coalite management had decided to reduce by half the amount of glycol it had previously used, to cut costs.[10]

A trial run went ahead on 22 April. As usual the autoclave was heated by oil to a temperature of 180°C. This would start the reaction to produce the trichlorophenol. On completion the vessel's contents were cooled to 140°C and transferred. The following evening this process got out of control. The place went up, showering everything with dioxin – which was abundantly produced as a result of the exothermic reaction.[11]

Over the following months more and more of the Coalite workforce came in contact with dioxin simply because they were employed during the clean-up. 'We were asked if we would like to help with the clean-up,' a worker recalled, 'and everybody agreed.' Chloracne is the initial consequence of high-level exposure to dioxin. Over the following weeks and months at least 90 workers developed the disease, including the four-year-old son of one worker, Anthony Spillane. The son was still affected many years later. It's not known what the long term effects of his particular exposure to dioxin have been.

Although George May – the local GP and company doctor – and several other researchers did some research into the effect of dioxin on the workers immediately after the accident (May publishing his findings in a medical journal) Coalite managed to keep the whole episode out of the public eye, until 10 July 1976 when the ICMESA trichlorophenol factory at Meda near Milan in northern Italy exploded.[12]

SEVESO

The accident at the ICMESA/Hoffman La Roche factory 13 miles north of Milan on Saturday morning 10 July 1976 was, not surprisingly given the similarity of the processes, just like Coalite's eight years earlier.

The explosion took place in a reactor that was being used to produce 2,4,5-trichlorophenol by combining tetrachlorobenzene with sodium hydroxide in an ethylene-glycol solvent. This reaction and a subsequent distillation process to remove the ethylene-glycol solvent took place each day. However at the end of the last shift of the week, in the early hours of that particular Saturday morning, the process was deferred until the beginning of the next work week. Everything was switched off. The temperature gauge of the reactor read 158°C. It'll cool gradually the technicians told themselves as they took off their coats. They weren't concerned. Everyone went home. It was just after 6.00a.m.

Just over six and a half hours later at 12.37p.m., as the neighbouring communities of Meda and Seveso went about making lunch, the chemical mixture in the reactor, instead of cooling down, gradually overheated and exploded. The force of the explosion blew out a safety disk at the top of the reactor and sent the boiling chemical mixture up a venting pipe into the sultry summer Italian air. The explosion, one resident recalled, was like a 'deep rumbling sound'. From the vent a white plume, containing 2,900kg of organic matter, reached 50 metres into the atmosphere.

Within minutes the plume had formed into a white cloud. Less than two hours later some of it began to descend and settle on the southern part of the community at Meda and on most of the adjacent community of Seveso.[13] Dispersed by light north-westerlies the thinning cloud drifted southwards over the communities of Cesano Maderno and Desio, eventually settling on vegetation, pastures and homes, affecting about a quarter of a million people.

When the cloud dissipated completely it had settled heavily into the soil and onto the vegetation of nearly 1,000 acres of land that consisted of horticulture plots, fields of crops and cattle and dwellings that housed about 5,000 people – artisans from southern Italy, particularly Sicily, and their large families.[14]

At the time most people were indoors preparing lunch although there were some outside, especially children playing.

I was outside eating under a small trellis in front of my house. At half past twelve, I heard a loud whistle, then we saw a cloud rise in the sky. It looked like an ice-cream cone.

Then this cone dropped some particles and the wind blew them toward our house. At that moment we escaped inside the house, because it seemed like a fog coming towards us. We thought immediately about some acid, about something that could harm us. After about ten minutes, we went outside and found the ground completely wet. Just after that, we saw the leaves of the flowers, the roses, all spotted, as if an acid had fallen from above.

But at that time we didn't pay much attention to it because there was always some cloud, some leak. And although there was a terrible smell, we didn't worry about it; we ate, we collected vegetables and flowers from the garden, as if nothing had happened.[15]

Those exposed to the cloud, significantly those closest to the factory, were immediately affected, suffering nausea and skin irritation that developed into sores on their exposed faces, legs and arms. Gradually they began to develop other symptoms – headaches, dizziness and diarrhoea. Within a few days the small animals in the area – rabbits, mice, chickens and cats – became sick and eventually died. Birds that had been engulfed in the cloud while they flew through it or while they were perched in the trees also died.

Shortly after the explosion one of ICMESA's chemists arrived at the factory and inspected the reactor. Afterwards he went to the homes nearest the factory and told people not to eat vegetables from their gardens.

The next day the mayor of Seveso, Francesco Rocca, received a phone call from a doctor in the area who told him that the plant manager and one of his assistants were looking for the local health officer but couldn't locate him; could they talk to the mayor instead. Rocca invited them to his home. ICMESA's Director of Production Paolo Paoletti told Rocca that it would be a good idea to advise people in the area not to eat fruit from their trees.

Two days after the explosion ICMESA's manager Herwig von Zwehl contacted Rocca and the Seveso health officer, Francesco Uberti. In a subsequent letter to Uberti the ICMESA manager explained that trichlorophenol was produced in the reactor and that the vapour from the explosion was chlorinated phenols. 'They said nothing about dioxin or TCDD,' Rocca told a reporter later.[16] All von Zwehl told Uberti was that the company was 'not in a position to evaluate the substances present in the vapour or to predict their exact effects, but knowing the final product is used in manufacturing herbicides, we have advised householders in the vicinity not to eat garden produce'.[17] At the time this was, as several commentators stressed, an ignorant response.

Rocca then got in contact with his counterpart at Meda, Fabrizio Melgrati, who in turn told the local police. Both mayors asked the Seveso Health Office to inspect the ICMESA reactor. The health officers who visited the factory reported back to the two mayors, that vegetation in the area was wilting.

ICMESA[18] was owned by a Swiss corporation called Givaudan – a supplier of cosmetics and hexachlorophrene – which was itself a subsidiary of Hoffman La Roche. It was apparent fairly immediately to Roche that they needed to deal with the disaster. But this only came about because Givaudan's technical director and chief chemist Dr Jorg Sambeth found himself unsure what to do and turned to Roche for help. While the ICMESA management had led Uberti to believe that there wasn't a problem, Givaudan's hierarchy, who had been told about the explosion on 11 July, reacted with some gravitas. Sambeth ordered ICMESA to seal off the reactor. He requested samples from inside the reactor and from outside the factory. These were sent to Givaudan's laboratories at Dubendorf in Switzerland.

The Dubendorf technicians were used to receiving samples from ICMESA. It was part of their job to regularly check the trichlorophenol produced at ICMESA for contaminants like dioxin. Realising the significance of the latest batch of samples the director of the lab, Dr Bruno Vaterlaus, decided to get them analysed immediately because their condition meant that the process would take longer. He told Sambeth that they wouldn't be ready for several days, not before 15 July. The two men agreed that a visit to Seveso would be productive. It was more than that.

Sambeth and Vaterlaus spent Wednesday, 14 July 1976 inspecting the burnt-out remains of the ICMESA reactor. As they walked around, Sambeth began to get worried about the toxic substances that had been released in the cloud. The following day those worries were confirmed when the results from the lab revealed high levels of dioxin. Sambeth told von Zwehl to warn the Italian authorities that Seveso and its environs had been contaminated with a highly toxic substance. Six days after the explosion the truth about the content of the toxic cloud was known, but not the extent.

Sambeth travelled to Basle in Switzerland to meet Roche's clinical research director, Dr Giuseppi Reggiani, in the hope that the parent company would row in behind Givaudan in the investigation that was now imperative. But Reggiani knew less than Sambeth about dioxin. He even admitted that prior to the meeting with Sambeth he had never heard of this toxic by-product of chlorine chemistry.[19]

Nevertheless Reggiani took the investigation very seriously, immediately contacting doctors and health officials in Seveso, organising a search for literature on dioxin, and corresponding with industry doctors and scientists who had knowledge of dioxin. However Reggiani was unable to move fast enough to defuse what was rapidly becoming a disaster for Roche, Givaudan and in particular ICMESA – the three chemical companies who were implicated by the explosion on 10 July. The knives were out.

THE CONSEQUENCES

The animals had, as noted earlier, been the first to die. Virtually all of Seveso's entire domestic population of 81,000 animals was wiped out. The majority – about 80,000 – were poultry, rabbits and other small animals raised on family-sized farms for household consumption. The rabbits went first, about 2,062, immediately after the explosion. Between 10 July and the end of the month 2,294 autopsies were carried out on animals (mostly poultry and rabbits) from 1,200 farms in the area.

This was the first indication that the land had been heavily contaminated. Larger animals also suffered and many had to be slaughtered when the extent of poisoning in their bodies was discovered. These included 349 cattle, 233 pigs, 49 horses, 49 goats and 21 sheep.

There are no mortality figures for the wildlife of Meda, Seveso and the surrounding areas. In the immediate years after the explosion toxic levels in the bodies of field mice were comparable to that of the soil. There was strong evidence of bioaccumulation. Earthworms, hares, snakes, toads and mice all contained dioxin many years after the explosion.[20]

Rocca, who had been told by the ICMESA management that things were really fine, was alarmed. The mayor of Seveso had learned about the animal deaths on the Wednesday. He contacted Malgrati and together the following day they released a statement banning the consumption of local fruit and vegetables. Seveso, they announced, was polluted.

The children were next to suffer. Although most families were indoors when the explosion occurred and remained there throughout lunch a number of children were playing outside and had been engulfed by the toxic cloud. By Friday, 16 July, 19 children, who had developed what appeared to be skin rashes, were taken into a local hospital.

Reggiani had been told about the children by Dr Ernesto Bergamaschini, ICMESA's company doctor. The Roche man told him they should be hospitalised. This was already apparent to local doctors and they were admitted to the Mariano Comense hospital near Seveso. But Reggiani was worried about the condition of the children and he suggested that the most serious cases be moved to a hospital with intensive care facilities. These were four children with swollen faces. Immediately after their transfer, to the Niguarda hospital in Milan, the doctors who treated them began to talk about Agent Orange. Was dioxin present here? they asked Reggiani when he visited the hospital on the Sunday. 'It's possible,' he replied. Reggiani also gave the Niguarda medical staff copies of the dioxin literature he had compiled.

Back in Seveso the air had been replaced with anger, confusion and frustration. With animals dying and children hospitalised the community weren't in the mood for official platitudes. And neither were the workers. While Mayor Malgrati was preparing the orders to pronounce the factory and the area around it polluted, the destruction of all vegetable, fruit and animal produce from the contaminated area and the closure of the factory, the ICMESA workers, incensed that they had not been told anything about the explosion by management, downed tools on Friday, 15 July. Von Zwehl told them he knew little more than they did yet had he not just been informed by Sambeth about the contents of the cloud?

The next day Malgrati's order about local produce was released. On the Sunday the order for the closure of the factory was given. And on the Wednesday, Desio magistrate Salvatore Adamo – who had placed the ICMESA factory under the jurisdiction of the court primarily to prevent any tampering of the damaged reactor – had von Zwehl and Paoletti arrested. They were to be charged with causing a culpable disaster. And the media, which had only learned about the explosion when the children were hospitalised, were now scrambling all over Seveso.

Suddenly Roche and Givaudan were in the public eye and under pressure yet Reggiani managed to present a calm figure, albeit from the far removed offices of his company, in Basle. While ICMESA's management were being arrested, Reggiani was contacting chemical companies who had experienced accidents with trichlorophenol. These included Dow in the USA, Coalite in England, Philips-Duphar in the Netherlands, BASF in Germany and Chemie Linz in Austria. Given what we now know about dioxin exposure and the reactions of the chemical industry to the impact of this class of chemicals on human health, it is perhaps surprising to learn that they all told Reggiani the same thing – evacuate the population of Seveso at once!

THE REACTION

There is still some confusion over when the Italian authorities were told that the toxic cloud contained dioxin (specifically 2,3,7,8-TCDD). Sambeth knew six days after the explosion. It is now generally accepted that dioxin was not publicly revealed as the primary contaminant in the soil, herbage and animals until Tuesday 20 July – the same day Reggiani was phoning around the world requesting information on dioxin – ten days after the explosion. Vaterlaus had produced a map detailing 36 locations that revealed dioxin contamination. On that Tuesday evening he passed it over to two Italian health officials.

Italy is famed for its bureaucratic stonewalling and official obfuscation yet, with hindsight, it is hard to see what else might have been done amidst all the confusion. For virtually everyone who became involved, the poisoning of Seveso was a learning process. Whether the ICMESA management lied or not is irrelevant, the deaths of so many animals and the hospitalisation of the children was an indication that something very serious had occurred.

Both Rocca and Melgrati had acted swiftly, as did Adamo. Reggiani had provided information and support. Much of this activity happened while the community was still bewildered and shocked – before the hysteria naturally began. The weeks immediately after the explosion would see clashes between local and regional authorities, and between Reggiani and the Lombardy minister for health, Dr Vittorio Rivolta – who decided on Friday, 23 July, after consultation with academics and scientists from Milan and Rome, not to evacuate Seveso. No one, it seemed, was able to answer his question: is dioxin harmful to the residents of Seveso?

Reggiani, however, was adamant that Seveso be evacuated and told Rivolta so. Seveso had been contaminated with the deadliest dioxin known. Everyone he had spoken to about dioxin contamination told him that the community had to be evacuated. Rivolta relented and said he would call another meeting for the following day, but, he scolded Reggiani, I want proof.

So Guy Waldvogel, Givaudan's managing director, the two scientists Vaterlaus and Sambeth, and Reggiani met in Lugano, by the lakeside, in Italian-speaking Switzerland and composed a letter to Rivolta, arguing their case for the evacuation. A new map with details of dioxin contamination of soil and vegetation at 44 locations was also drawn. The following day Rivolta ordered the evacuation.

On Monday 26 July – 16 days after the explosion – the evacuation began with 170 people from Seveso and 55 from Meda departing their homes. A week later 511 people joined them, making a total of 736 people from 160 houses. These people had lived in the areas of Meda and Seveso that had the highest concentrations of dioxin. It covered 269 acres and ran south, south-east from the factory for approximately three kilometers following the motorway to Milan, just as the toxic cloud had done. It would become known as Zone A – the area of highest contamination.

The Italian authorities' reluctance to evacuate people from their homes was also exacerbated by the problem of how to accommodate 736 people. Hotels near Seveso and Milan were chosen but this temporary accommodation was cramped and unsatisfactory. People were also told to take the minimum of clothes and possessions with them. Everyone took as much as they could carry. Initially to protect their homes an order was given to seal off Zone A, but after a while the authorities gave up trying to prevent people re-entering their homes and agreed to allow ten persons to enter on weekdays and 20 on Sundays. This brought amusement. 'So dioxin is twice as dangerous on weekdays as it is on Sundays,' they laughed.[21] But it wasn't a laughing matter. People had been forced to leave their homes and their emotional attachments behind. They had, like refugees from a war zone, become victims. They had become toxic refugees.

It is often said that the two most emotional and stressful experiences anyone can suffer is the loss of a home and the loss of a loved one. The residents of Meda and Seveso had lost the first and believed they were in danger of losing the second. 'The fear of unknown health damage was matched with a strong feeling of lack of protection,' Professor Pier Alberto Bertazzi told health conference delegates twelve years later when the full extent of the social, emotional, economic, political and cultural impact of the tragedy of Seveso became known.[22]

Mayor Rocca among others was quick to realise what was happening in the immediate aftermath. His ignorance of the chemicals that had engulfed his community didn't however affect his political mind. As news of the disaster spread, at each stage prompting sensationalist responses from people who mostly didn't know what they were talking about, Rocca, naively perhaps, considered his social obligations.

> The citizens of this area, even those directly affected themselves, do not constitute any danger for others. I beg of you, do not add to our misfortune by isolating us from the rest of the world. It must be explained also that it is not dangerous to enter this region to buy our products. I am terrified by the thought that you may create a depressed area of unemployment due to an irrational fear of what has happened. A strong impression is arising that a sanitary cordon, psychological and physical, is being drawn around Seveso and environs.[23]

More than 50 small firms were forced to abandon their workplaces, machinery and products. The hardest hit were the handicraft and furniture makers who had a fine reputation all over Italy and beyond for their products. Not only was Seveso under siege by the media, scientists and bureaucrats it was under the public gaze. Suddenly there was a problem with the people of Seveso. Discrimination became commonplace, Bertazzi noted, 'as if they carried some mysterious and noxious contagion'. Moral and religious values became sacrosanct, particularly on the issue of abortion as many of the exposed women who were pregnant feared abnormal births. And insecurity among the people augmented the high levels of stress they were suffering.

The Italian authorities, with these factors to consider, were reluctant to evacuate anyone else. Nearly 5,000 people lived in the area that was regarded as moderately contaminated, classified as Zone B. Attached to the eastern and southern borders of Zone A, this 669-acre area, which was mostly agricultural, took in part of eastern Seveso and continued further south through Cesano Maderno, curving eastwards into Desio. The authorities had to make a tough decision, whether to leave the inhabitants of Zone B exposed to dioxin or to displace them as well.

The solution lay in the response measures the authorities were drawing up for the exposed communities – which included nearly 38,000 people in total, although as many as 250,000 people had been exposed to the toxic cloud.

A third zone, which engulfed southern Meda, central and eastern Seveso, central and eastern Cesano Maderno, eastern Bovisio and western Desio – comprising 3,575 acres and containing 31,800 people, had been designated an 'area of respect' because dioxin had been found in low levels in these areas. This became known as Zone R.

The task facing the authorities was to minimise further contact with the contaminated soil, vegetation and animals. People were told not to eat fruit or vegetables from the contaminated areas. An order was given to destroy all the domestic animals in the affected areas. Further crop planting was prohibited. People were told to wash regularly and the Lombardy Health authorities advised against sexual intercourse. The health authorities insisted that children under twelve and women in the early stages of pregnancy be kept away from the contaminated areas. This proved relatively easy for the women but more difficult for the children. School hours were increased to keep them off contaminated land but parents found it hard to keep an eye on their children all the time. Nevertheless these inconveniences were tolerated, although many people ignored these rules when it suited them.

What was now becoming obvious to people, particularly those from Zone A who were languishing in hotels, was the reality that their lives would never be the same again. Givaudan had been told by the authorities to decontaminate Zone A and make it habitable. A workforce of 250 was brought in to remove the top layers of the contaminated soil, strip contaminated vegetation and clean the affected houses. The contaminated top soil and vegetation was moved to an area close to the factory while it was decided what to do with it. Incineration was suggested and a plan was drawn up to erect an incinerator on the site of the factory for the disposal of the contaminated soil and vegetation, but it never got off the drawing board. The people of Seveso said no, travelling into Milan in May 1977 to protest about the proposed incinerator. It was never built.

A few months later some people were allowed back into their homes in the southern part of Zone A. The authorities told them they had to wash continually and not to grow any vegetables or raise animals. These were the lucky ones. Some people never got their homes and belongings back. They lost their lives.

The first death left a deep scar among the community because it was a young woman of 35 who succumbed on 29 July 1976. Her death certificate made no mention of dioxin.

At the start of the Seveso accident no one among the Italian authorities or in ICMESA appeared to know anything about dioxin. But Givaudan, ICMESA's immediate parent, did. Givaudan, which had been set up in 1898, got into hexachlorophrene production in the

1940s at its home factory in Switzerland and at its US base in Clifton, New Jersey. In 1963 Givaudan was bought by Hoffman La Roche and in 1969 Givaudan took control of the ICMESA factory in Meda. The ICMESA factory was converted to manufacture trichlorophenol that was then shipped to Switzerland and the USA where it was used to make hexachlorophrene.[24]

When Thomas Whiteside began investigating 2,4,5-T, Agent Orange and dioxin, his research led him to Seveso a year after the accident. After securing an interview with Guy Waldvogel, Givaudan's managing director, Whiteside learned that the company had decided to go into trichlorophenol production on its own because it was concerned about the quantity of dioxin in the trichlorophenol that was being supplied to it from other chemical companies.

Waldvogel told Whiteside that the dioxin content of the trichlorophenol manufactured at ICMESA was regularly monitored. Whiteside confirmed this in a visit to Givaudan's lab in Dubendorf where he met Dr Peter Schudel, the company's vice-director of research. 'He spoke with pride of the precautions taken at the Swiss laboratories in the handling of dioxin,' Whiteside reported. 'Only male workers were employed in the analytical work; they worked in an isolated building and were regularly subjected to intensive medical examinations.' But, Whiteside discovered,

> at Givaudan's Italian plant the safety standards have been another story. The workers there were given no meticulous medical checkups such as were given workers in Givaudan's Swiss labs, and from what they have been reported as telling their union representatives and the press, not only were they not instructed by the ICMESA management concerning the true toxic properties of dioxin but they had no idea of its existence.

Givaudan, therefore, not only knew about dioxin, they also were aware that the toxic cloud that escaped from the ICMESA factory on 10 July probably contained dioxin. Why, Whiteside asked Waldvogel, did the managements of both companies not inform the authorities and the local people of this? Waldvogel argued that they had spoken about the possibility of highly toxic by-products in the cloud. And he stressed, would the situation have been different if we had mentioned the presence of dioxin?[25]

THE STUDIES

It might, but this is something we'll never know. All we know is that the primary concern about health was being taken very seriously. The medical surveillance programmes that were set up in the aftermath of the explosion aimed to ascertain any immediate adverse ill-health, to provide the necessary medical services and resources, and to identify the future epidemiological needs of the exposed population.[26] But the initial health studies were confusing, primarily because in 1976 medical technology had not advanced sufficiently to allow accurate measurements of the family of dioxins but also because data collection had not taken place following initial exposure. According to Bertazzi 'people with specific expertise in epidemiology should therefore be part of the response team from the very beginning'.[27]

Chloracne had been identified in 193 people (170 under 15) following an extensive screening of thousands of children.[28] Some brain damage of non-acute nature was shown in people who had been heavily exposed to the dioxin cloud.[29] Tests to determine whether there had been any birth defects in aborted foetuses were considered inconclusive,[30] despite anecdotal evidence about miscarriages. 'Any doctor who is honest in this area will admit the increase in miscarriages is considerable. They are happening between the third and fifth month of pregnancy and the mothers are crying everywhere.'[31]

Children born between 1977 and 1982 were examined for birth defects but the results failed to show any increase above accepted levels.[32] Yet immediately after the accident, in 1977 and 1978, local doctors argued that birth defects had increased alarmingly.[33] Starting in 1976 more than 4,500 blood tests were done on 373 children aged between six and ten at the time of accident, but any effects were seen as minimal and short-term.[34]

A follow-up study of the 193 chloracne cases was set up with comparisons to an unexposed control group. The chloracne had disappeared in all but one and some high cholesterol levels were measured.[35] What the studies on chloracne did reveal, and this was significant, was the correlation between frequency of the disease and high exposure.[36]

There was, however, a warning. On 22 February 1977 district nurse Maria Bortaccio was admitted to hospital. She had developed chloracne, hepatitis and a swollen liver. She also complained of lethargy and nausea. Her symptoms were consistent with dioxin poisoning and a local doctor diagnosed dioxin contamination. Eventually she was sent home. Over the spring and summer her pains persisted until, in September, she was readmitted to hospital and operated on for gallstones. Immediately after the operation her kidneys failed. On 6 October 1977 she died.

The following year, on 13 April 1978, Dr Tom Margerison questioned an area health officer about her death. Dioxin, Dr Margerison was told, was not the cause of death. She had, the health officer insisted, a history of kidney disease that dated back before the 10 July explosion. Dr Margerison decided to seek confirmation of this. He spoke to Maria Bortaccio's local doctor and checked hospital records. The health officer had lied![37]

As these studies were completed it was evident to the doctors and presumably the authorities that a long term investigation on the health of the exposed population was imperative but, because of the immense cost, infeasible. The dioxin that had been released from ICMESA comprised 90 per cent of the deadliest member of the family – 2,3,7,8-TCDD.

This told scientists that they were dealing with a contaminant with a legendary persistence. When the Seveso TCCD was examined they discovered 'it was a poorly water-soluble compound with a strong tendency to be absorbed in soil and water sediment, and with a significant potential for bioaccumulation'.[38] This implied that the contamination would be stable and long-lasting. It also meant the toxic chemical was fat soluble. There would be long term human exposure. So a decision was made to go ahead with the long term investigations but to restrict future study to cancer and cause of death, according to Bertazzi, 'the only end-points for which a valid study were judged to be feasible'.[39]

This still presented the scientists with a vast and difficult task because, as Bertazzi has stressed on several occasions, determining long term effects 'requires comprehensive and reliable information systems'.[40]

When Bertazzi and his colleagues began their investigation into cause of death and cancer occurrence among the exposed population in 1983 the first problem they faced was identifying an accurate, coherent and complete population data base. It is Bertazzi's assertion that the 'most suitable end points for long term surveillance studies are cancer cases and reproductive outcomes'[41] but without an adequate data base this can prove impossible. It was decided that a long term study of reproductive effects was not feasible. Bertazzi and his colleagues instead took on the onerous task of determining cause of death and cancer incidence.

This would become even more crucial a year later when the short term surveillance programmes were discontinued, the International Steering Committee concluding 'that chloracne represented the only health outcome clearly attributable to the accidental exposure of TCDD'. But, as Bertazzi pointed out, no conclusion could be reached at that time regarding long term effects.[42]

Bertazzi and his colleagues solved the problem of identifying the exposed population by using a practical epidemiological method. To avoid any kind of bias they opted for a study population – known in epidemiological terms as a cohort. They choose 'all persons ever resident in one of the 11 towns within the accident scenario, at any time from the date of accident onwards (including new borns and immigrants), irrespective of their current residence'[43] and they made the cut-off point for admission into the study cohort 31 December 1986 – on the basis that 'no potential for exposure was deemed to exist anymore for newcomers into the area after that date'.[44]

While the health studies continued in Italy, the Seveso disaster virtually forgotten until it became a European Community synonym for chemical accidents,[45] events were unfolding in other parts of the world. As the first results of the Seveso investigation began to leak out, dioxin was becoming known as the most studied chemical in history. It appeared it wasn't as benign as the chemical industry had been making out. It was instead one of the most complex toxic chemicals ever studied. Its effects were widespread and not easily identified. The Seveso studies were beginning to reveal this and more. This was a confirmation that something truly wicked had been stalking the lives of industrialised communities for decades. This was already known:

- from accidents at trichlorophenol factories in America, Austria, Czechoslovakia,[46] England, France, Germany, Italy, Japan, the Netherlands and Russia,[47]
- from the poisoning of Missouri by an innocent waste oil haulier,
- from the effect the use of the herbicide 2,4,5-T and its production was having on workers,
- from the strange deaths of beautiful birds,
- from the laboratory experiments on tiny animals.

But it wasn't really known. It wasn't in the public domain. The truth had been obscured. Sometimes truth has a way of coming out and the consequences of Seveso were being felt all over the world, not least of all in Bolsover.

COALITE'S SECRET HISTORY

The regional paper, the *Sheffield Star*, were quick to realise the significance – of what became known as the Seveso disaster – to the Coalite workers and embarked on a remarkable campaign of investigative journalism. It was remarkable because of its thoroughness and focus. It also showed what reporters could achieve if they were allowed time and resources.

It didn't impress Coalite's management who naively believed they had successfully kept the lid on the tragedy that had killed Eric Burrows and exposed a large proportion of its workforce to the deadly effects of dioxin. On 13 August – a month after Seveso – the management took out quarter-page ads in the national British media – significantly the influential *Times*, *Telegraph* and *Guardian* – saying everything was really hunky dory.

It wasn't and Coalite must have suspected that they were about to become embroiled in a controversy that would continue to haunt the company for more years than they could ever have imagined. A few months later, on 14 October, the managing director Charles Needham announced that the plant would close. But a can of worms – significantly the controversy over the secret location of the dioxin-contaminated rubble from the 1968 explosion – had been opened. And for the first time, there was genuine concern about the workers' health.

Both Needham and his assistant P. R. Marshall tried to justify the reasons for the closure of the trichlorophenol factory, which had been rebuilt in 1969, citing social and financial factors. 'No one reason was overwhelming. It was the totality. And the desire to be good neighbours with people in the neighbourhood and the local authorities,' Marshall said two years later.[48]

The local feeling about the company's decision to close the plant was very different. The disturbing information that had been coming out of Italy about the Seveso disaster and the *Star*'s adept coverage focused the minds of many people on what were the crucial issues – notably health and safety. It was the workforce who made Coalite think more carefully. The refusal of 150 Coalite workers to work in the trichlorophenol plant contributed to this decision, but it was the knowledge that the plant was being run at a loss plus the growing controversy about the herbicide 2,4,5-T that finally made the management realise there was going to be no future for them in trichlorophenol. So they shut it down.

STUDYING THE HEALTH OF THE WORKERS

The news from Seveso had done more than concentrate minds on the subject of dioxin. It had forced those in authority to do something. The British Health and Safety Executive (HSE) told the Coalite management in the harshest terms it could muster under its limited powers to organise for the health of the affected workers to be tested. George May was assigned to the task and he brought in several people to help him with the research, including two doctors, Eric Blank and Anthony Ward, from Sheffield University and 41-year-old Dr Jenny Martin, then consultant chemical pathologist at Chesterfield Royal – the region's largest hospital and one with considerable experience of respiratory diseases – and a lecturer in occupational health.

Although Coalite was a large employer in the area they were dwarfed by the coal-mining industry. Of the 395,000 miners employed in Britain in 1968, 21,000 worked in Derbyshire pits and they knew all about occupational illness. This is perhaps why Coalite suddenly got cold feet about the research and decided that it didn't want the results published. Whatever the reasoning behind their decision the Coalite management wasn't taking any chances.

May had selected 121 people for participation in the research. He included 41 process workers who were known to have been exposed to dioxin. But the company managed to make sure that some clerical workers were included in the control group. Despite this obvious devaluation before the research had begun, the medical team May had assembled went about their work and the results were not what Coalite wanted to hear.

Dr Blank, who had been asked to assess any chromosome damage, reported that he could see no change in chromosomal activity.[49] Dr Ward, who looked at the immune systems of the group, revealed that the exposed workers' 'short term immunological memory' had been impaired. Dr Martin, who took blood samples to measure blood fat and liver function, was more emphatic. Her results showed the workers who had been exposed to dioxin had suffered liver function damage and had elevated levels of cholesterol and fat proteins. This information showed Dr Martin conclusively that dioxin was present in the bodies of the exposed workers. What she didn't realise was how significant this information was to Coalite.[50]

But she was beginning to understand. The Coalite management's manipulation of the control group didn't impress Martin, when it was explained to her after she had completed her research. She decided immediately to do another study. So she took the blood chemistry of eight workers suffering from chloracne, comparing the results with a matched control group of workers – who had not been exposed but worked in the factory and not in the offices. Once again she noted increased cholesterol and fat protein levels. In February 1979 her results were published in a letter to the medical journal, the *Lancet*.[51]

Then Martin's home was broken into and the material used to prepare the study was stolen – nothing else. She didn't have any duplicates. The entire study was devalued. She would no longer be able to refer to the specific medical reports of the exposed workers. The response from the local police was also interesting. 'A key hidden under a stone was used to get into the house,' they told the media after the break-in. 'Nothing else was stolen. It is very odd.' No one has ever been arrested or charged for what was obviously not a routine burglary. Martin still believes that several people – she's sure there was more than one – broke into her house to place a bug on her phone and inadvertently discovered the Coalite workers' documents by mistake. They were on the top of a pile that was fairly visible to anyone entering the house.[52]

One of the trade unions at Coalite, the Association of Scientific, Technical and Managerial Staffs (ASTMS), had been given an abbreviated version of her first study that somehow managed to conflict with Martin's original draft. The shorter version somehow managed to miss the higher cholesterol and fat protein levels in the exposed workers. Something strange was going on.

The HSE had now got seriously involved – largely because the local Member of Parliament, Dennis Skinner, was like a dog with a bone and wouldn't give up on the health effects of the occupational exposure to dioxin. At first the HSE attempted to obtain full medical reports on the poisoned workers. Coalite refused, until Alastair Hay, a specialist on dioxin who was lecturing on chemical pathology at the University of Leeds, revealed in the science journal *Nature* the existence of Martin's research in March 1980.[53]

A few weeks later Coalite, now chastised, handed HSE all the medical reports from Martin, Blank and Ward. The HSE's Employment Medical Advisory Service (EMAS) subsequently issued its own evaluation of the Coalite documents, criticising the company for preparing a report that was virtually worthless. But the HSE authors must have privately pleased the Coalite management because they said they could find no illnesses among the process workers that were related to dioxin! What didn't please Coalite was HSE's suggestion that the exposed workers be tested every three to five years. This didn't suit Coalite, they wanted to resolve the issue once and for all. Within a few months of the publication of the HSE EMAS report Coalite offered to re-examine the men. Then May claimed that not all could be located or were prepared to participate in a further study. Only 29 of the original group of 41 were re-examined. But not everyone agreed with May's version of events.

Dennis Goss has always insisted that no concerted attempt was made to contact the men.[54] The *Star* had more luck, claiming on 27 June 1980 that it had managed to contact most of the process workers originally exposed to the dioxin from the explosion and learned that several men had heart problems – which Dr Martin's results indicated, that higher cholesterol and fat protein levels can lead to heart disease.[55]

The HSE had by this stage decided to do its own study and believe it or not this study wasn't published until 1995 – the government agency revealing after 15 years that there wasn't really a problem![56]

It's hard to believe looking back at the events that shaped this secret history of dioxin that it is possible for anyone to say there isn't a problem with these chemicals. What happened at Bolsover and subsequently at Seveso were more than events in the story about dioxin, they were confirmations that industrialists, scientists, doctors, politicians, bureaucrats and journalists were as ignorant as the workers and communities who were exposed to this deadly chemical.

The industrialists who ran the trichlorophenol factories at Bolsover and Seveso used that ignorance as a political weapon to pretend they were genuinely concerned about their workers and the neighbouring populations. Even some of the medical people involved attempted to use the knowledge they were learning about dioxin's health effects.

It was obvious to anyone who cared to notice that blatant career moves were being made. As Martin put it, there were a few who wanted to run with the fox and with the hounds. It was the same at

Seveso where the Roche[57] management reached for the opportunity to be seen as a benevolent company that cared and wanted to do the best it could for those who had been exposed to dioxin and wanted to present itself to the wider community as the chemical company who would reveal all there was to know about dioxin.

Martin's observations about the Coalite management were not unique to that company. They acted, she stressed, in the way any top company management would. Both the management of Coalite and Roche were the same, 'like cells in an organism' she emphasised, noting, in the mid-1990s when the truth about dioxin became known, that chemical industry management had not changed.[58] She is also very critical of her own profession, how it responded to the events in Coalite and how some people attempted to build reputations. Martin thinks she was naive at the time. It is only with hindsight that she realises how the circumstances of the time contrived with human nature to produce an effect that didn't do justice to those involved in the various medical studies, significantly George May who was completely out of his depth.

> I think at the beginning, [May] probably thought the problem was a load of nothing, and then it started to become clear. The information from these studies really showed that there was more to this dioxin problem than had originally been thought, and I think [May] was presented with a situation that looked far less reassuring as time went by.

May had got himself into a dilemma. He wanted to do more tests on the workers but didn't have the funding. Coalite were obviously not interested. Martin had done some independent work of her own on dioxin exposure and was sympathetic. 'So I said to him, well you need to do this and that and he said "don't worry, leave it with me, I've got a source, I can't reveal it yet". He was all very mysterious and in fact for some considerable time he didn't reveal where his source of income was from.'[59]

May's dilemma was that as a doctor he wanted to get to the truth but his employers wanted him to cover up the truth and were determined to make sure that any studies on the workers would reveal nothing of significance. What had made a reputation-making opportunity into a nightmare for May was the fall-out from Seveso and the simple fact that the man who was to head Roche's investigation into the

ICMESA explosion regarded the Englishman as an expert on dioxin exposure.

George May's source was Dr Giuseppi Reggiani of Hoffman La Roche! Reggiani regarded May as a dioxin expert. When he discovered that the Seveso disaster had re-opened old wounds in Bolsover and that May was struggling to make his name as a local GP and company doctor he offered to fund some research.

Jenny Martin believed that May was torn between wanting to make a name for himself in medical history and his loyalty to his employers. The workforce of Coalite Chemical Works in Bolsover in Derbyshire presented May with the chance to prove that science is good as well as evil. If he had devoted his mind to it he could have taken that can of worms, dumped it into a bowl in his laboratory and started dissecting the unspeakable beast the chemical industry, in its pathetic ignorance, had produced and didn't care about. May was in a position to reveal the inner truths about Frankenstein,[60] that the science is both creative and destructive, good and evil. It was obvious that the medical profession around him in Chesterfield and Sheffield were prepared to give him support.

And it would have been possible for him to contact the numerous doctors all over the globe who were trying to unravel the thread that was leading them, inexplicably, to dioxin, as they sought to understand the illnesses their patients suffered from.

- He might have wondered about the Yusho poisoning in the far east where contaminated rice oil had wrought terrible harm on two unsuspecting communities.
- He might, if he had looked hard enough, even discovered the work of Schulz and Sorge.
- He might, if he had asked quietly and discreetly enough, discovered that many lab scientists who had worked with dioxin had developed chloracne.
- He might easily have stumbled upon the reports of the researchers who sought answers about the illnesses that had killed wildlife and horses, and poisoned children in Missouri.
- He might have noticed the early work of Olav Axelson and Lennart Hardell on phenoxy herbicides.

May choose a different route and it would be unfair now to blame him because, as we have seen, dioxin is a complex subject. Privately he may have wanted to extend his research. The circumstances to do that were not in his favour. The chapters on the secret history of dioxin in Bolsover were put on the back burner.

DIOXIN MAKES A RETURN TO DERBYSHIRE

Apart from the stories that are told and heard in industrialised communities, that history remained unchronicled again until 1990 when scientists from the Ministry for Agriculture, Fisheries and Food (MAFF, now Defra) in London revealed high dioxin levels in milk from two farms close to the Coalite factory. In June the following year the British government banned milk from the farms. It was suggested that the source of the dioxin was an incinerator. The finger was pointed at Coalite but they claimed publicly that they didn't have one. Coalite not only had an incinerator, they had a licence to burn 5,000 tonnes per year of liquid chlorinated residues. Why they tried to conceal this is a mystery in itself. The company have said this was a misunderstanding.[61]

In August Her Majesty's Inspectorate of Pollution (HMIP) tested the emissions from Coalite's incinerator and found high concentrations of dioxin, but interestingly not high enough to cause the high milk and soil concentrations in the area. In November the government ordered the incinerator to be closed down while Coalite admitted that a fire in 1986 at their factory might have been the source of the local dioxins!

Suddenly the secret history was being told again. The pollution from Coalite had permeated the Bolsover community for so long that they had become accustomed to it. They had become accustomed so much that suddenly people began to associate events in their lives with the pollution and never stopped talking about it. They didn't do this in public, it was done in guarded conversations, in hushed voices, in casual remarks between friends. When it was done in public it was in the creative spirit that comes from a few drinks, sardonic and sarcastic. Eventually the stories began to live lives of their own and soon everybody knew – especially the workers. 'We've lived with this stigma, this 2,3,7,8-TCDD for more than 30 years. We had the explosion in 1968, the fire in 1986 and then the contaminated land in 1991. It frightens you to death.'[62]

Because everyone knew that Bolsover had been poisoned with dioxin it was easier to talk about the concerns of the community. Outsiders came to talk and to publicise the insidious tragedy that was unfolding in Bolsover. Various green groups became involved. The

Women's Environmental Network wrote a report. Greenpeace did one. A community group headed by Coalite workers was formed.[63] Coalite was put under pressure. Eventually the workers demanded blood tests and the company conceded by offering tests that were regarded as inadequate. 'It's the fat cells you need to determine the effects of dioxin and unless you take a pint of blood you won't get enough,' Ann Link of WEN said when she learned that the company had tested only for liver function.[64] 'You can look for the biological effects which is what we did,' said Jenny Martin when she heard about the tests.

> You need much larger amounts of blood than Coalite appears to have taken, and they must be taken under controlled conditions. You need more blood for the wide range of tests because you need to measure a range of effects. It's the combination that pins it to dioxin because it's a potent multi-system toxin. I have a sense of déjà vu about all this. The [company] doesn't seem to have learned any lessons from the 1968 investigation.[65]

Subsequently Greenpeace paid for tests done by Vyvyan Howard of the Fetal Pathology Department of Liverpool University. Joe Holland, a process operator since 1975, was one of the workers tested. Before agreeing to be tested he said:

> No one wants to know they have dioxin poisoning. Ignorance has been bliss, and it breeds contempt, but there is a resolve among the workers that they want the blood tests. We don't want casual information. We want definite information on the long term exposure of these chemicals. The [company] have a workforce here that are as naive as they were when they started. They haven't said, 'you're working in a chemical plant and these are the possible health risks'. If they said 82 per cent of us would get cancer how many would still take the job?[66]

The results told the workers what they did not want to know. Their factory and their bodies had been contaminated with high levels of dioxin.[67]

The Bolsover story differs from the Seveso story in only one fact. One happened in 1968, the other eight years later. Although it could be argued that more people suffered in Seveso, because there was more dioxin (2,900kg against 390kg at Bolsover), that would miss the point about dioxin – that it is a persistent, insidious multi-systemic toxin.

THE TWENTIETH-CENTURY FACTOR

Dioxin is a complex toxic substance, capable of causing a multitude of reactions in the body. It does not appear to matter what the dose is. If it is low it appears to cause one particular illness. If it is high it appears to cause a different one. It can also react in conjunction with other chemicals. It can alter the chemical balance of the body. But there is also another factor, when it comes to studying the effect dioxin has on human health.

It is a built-in factor, a twentieth-century factor you could call it, present every time an epidemiological study is set up with a control group. So we are told that the statistical increase in breast cancer is only 0.5 per cent above the relative risk factor. What do they mean by this? A control group is usually taken from a similar area to the exposed group. The simple difference is that the control group has not been exposed. This means health professionals can allow for other environmental and social factors – such as the background levels of pollution, diet, weight, lifestyle (smoking, drinking, etc.), workplace. This is assuming a general homogenisation of personal lifestyles, workplace and environment, but it also allows for the illnesses and causes of death that are peculiar to that area.

When Bertazzi and his colleagues began their research they obtained the cancer registry prior to the explosion, so when they completed their first study covering the years 1976 to 1986, they were able to compare the results. They found that the incidence for all cancers was the same for the exposed population (30,703) as it was for the surrounding un-exposed population (167,391).[68] The knowledge, known since 1978, that dioxin caused cancer in laboratory animals was conclusive, but the evidence that dioxin causes cancer in humans wasn't being revealed by the Seveso study; at least not after a short observation period that would not have been sufficient for most cancers to develop.

It has been revealed that other dioxins were present in the contaminated soil but they had not come from ICMESA. They had come from another source, which has never been identified. Thus background levels of pollution were already high enough to cause illness.

This is one of the problems facing epidemiologists, that it is virtually impossible to find a contemporary control group that has not been exposed to environmental pollutants. To do this scientists would need to go back in time to a period when polluting industry did not exist in the area. Epidemiologists do not have time machines so they must rely on contemporary data, which is unreliable. The knowledge that breast cancer is a consequence of twentieth-century living is not regarded as relevant. All that matters is that the risk factor is not significant. In the twentieth century it was accepted that some people would die from cancer.[69]

The Seveso studies of the exposed population revealed higher incidences of unusual illnesses, including cancers linked to dioxin poisoning, yet Bertazzi felt it was not possible to associate 'any of the unusual cancer mortality findings with exposure to TCDD in 1976'.[70] So what caused them and why does he make this claim? The analysis of three groups of workers occupationally exposed to TCDD by Kenny Crump, Richard Canady and Manolis Kogevinas may provide part of the answer. The USEPA has based its lifetime risk of cancer mortality from exposure to dioxin on data from Fingerhut's 1991 study of 5,172 workers from twelve US chemical plants (and Steenland's 1999 follow-up), Flesch-Janys' 1998 study of 1,189 workers at a chemical plant in Hamburg, Germany and the Ott and Zober study of 243 workers exposed to TCDD as a result of the 1953 accident at BASF's trichlorophenol plant in Ludwigshafen, Germany.[71] Following criticism of the EPA risk assessment,[72] Crump and colleagues did a new analysis of the data and came to the conclusion that a 'statistically significant (p = 0.02) trend was found in total cancer mortality with increasing dioxin exposure'. Crump and colleagues state that their 'analysis argues for careful consideration of the upper ranges of long-term average exposures for dioxins'. Whatever way some scientists want to put it there was an increase in specific cancers in Seveso, attributable to TCDD. Marcella Warner's group examined the association between individual serum TCDD levels and breast cancer risk in 981 Seveso women, who were infants to 40 years old in 1976, and found a significant relation.[73]

WHY SEVESO SPELLED THE END FOR DIOXIN

However, Seveso – more than any other dioxin 'accident' – has revealed much about this toxic by-product of chlorine chemistry. It confirmed much of what was known. But the research also revealed patterns scientists knew little about. Researchers looked at a control group of people born between nine months after the explosion to December 1984 to exposed parents in Zone A. The seven and a half year period corresponds with the half-life of TCCD in adults. Their results showed an excess of females (26M v 48F) but after this period the sex ratio stabilised (60M v 64F).[74] It would be a good few more years before scientists would reveal the role of the dioxin family in hormonal development.

Other researchers, who measured dioxin levels in 62 people from Zones A and B and 59 people in the surrounding area 20 years after the explosion, found elevated levels of TCDD in women in Zone B and in the non-involved area. In Zone B they found that TCDD levels were higher in elderly people.[75]

This is the significance of Seveso. It exposed a very large number of people to dioxin. It produced the highest levels of dioxin recorded over a wide area:[76]

- Seveso population: up to 56,000 parts per trillion
- Missouri general population: 5.9ppt
- US ground troops in Vietnam: 45ppt
- Antipodean phenoxy herbicide sprayers: 131ppt
- Operation Ranch Hand airborne sprayers in Vietnam: 618ppt
- US chlorophenol process workers: 3,400ppt[77]

Some observers have therefore noted that the Seveso studies may provide a truer indication of pure dioxin exposure. Swedish epidemiologist Olav Axelson has suggested this relevance.

> For dioxins, rather than phenoxy herbicides and chlorophenols, assessment of exposure is even more difficult. Dioxin contamination may well have varied from batch to batch and between producers and countries. Another explanation for the lack of effect in some studies may simply be small numbers, a consequence of the rarity of the soft tissue sarcomas. Small numbers mean inconclusive studies rather than no effect.

And he goes on to emphasise this.

> Judging from studies in the US and Canada, it seems as if non-Hodgkin's lymphoma might be associated with exposure to 2,4-D or perhaps some other contaminating dioxins than TCDD. Not

exclusively so, however, since an excess is seen among those with a long residence in Zone R of the Seveso area.

At Seveso, the production of 2,4,5-trichlorophenol was the source of the emitted TCDD. Risk of soft tissue sarcomas seems to be related to dose of TCDD exposure in the Swedish studies. There is also some effect from phenoxy herbicides and chlorophenols without any clear contamination from TCDD. Other dioxins may have occurred in these chemicals however.[78]

The contribution of Seveso to the dioxin debate may also disentangle the arguments about bias and confounding. To show that multiple injuries are caused by multiple, systemic chemical substances in a society that pollutes itself. 'In view of the close association of dioxins and other chemicals,' Axelson stressed, 'it is more relevant to look upon the entire complex of exposures as risky rather than to discuss confounding from various indiscernible component exposures'.[79]

This makes Bolsover and Seveso blips on the screen. They are only two of the many places where workers and communities have suffered chemical poisoning in western countries as a result of industrial incompetence and governmental ignorance.

5
The EPA:
A Regulatory Sleazefest

THE EFFECTS OF PENTACHLOROPHENOL

Maternity hospitals are generally regarded as happy places because they are associated with new birth. In the late 1960s a St Louis maternity unit became a house of horror for young mothers after nine babies between the ages of six and 14 days were rushed to St Louis Children's Hospital. The babies were sweating excessively, their heart rate was increased, they had difficulty breathing and their livers were enlarged. Two of the nine babies died soon after admittance to the hospital. An investigation to determine the cause of the babies' illnesses revealed that the expectant mothers had been lying between sheets that had been laundered using a product, which contained pentachlorophenol. Despite rinsing the chemical was still present in the sheets. It penetrated the mothers' bodies and crossed the placenta barrier, infecting the unborn children.[1]

> We're failing to deal with dioxin not because of any lack of information about its dangers to human health, but because of political and economic considerations.
>
> Dr Samuel Epstein[2]

> If all you are worried about is dioxin, the levels of dioxin by itself are probably not that high. But when you look at the sum total of what is out there, that is where the body burdens may be high enough – so you might say we are having a response.
>
> Linda Birnbaum[3]

Monsanto's secrets were toxic time bombs. But it wasn't until Cate Jenkins, a scientist with the EPA, got hold of them that they assumed a political significance and exposed Monsanto's supposed ignorance about dioxin. Once again the tenacity of a scientist would play a key role in the truth about dioxin, revealing in this case the incompetence of the regulatory process. At last someone in authority was collecting the pieces of the puzzle and starting to make them fit.

Jenkins had become an irritable thorn in the flesh of the chemical industry when Carr set about Monsanto in the St Clair County Circuit Court in 1985.[4] A chemist by trade and an artist by vocation, Jenkins didn't fit the mould in the EPA. After she completed her PhD in 1976 she forged a career for herself with both a pragmatic and imaginative initiative. She co-founded the Art Hazards Project in New York city. 'It was basically an educational project in industrial hygiene for artists at various schools, informing them about the hazards and safe handling of chemicals like benzene, asbestos, and other really toxic materials that artists used routinely, in those days often without realising the dangers.'[5]

A scientist with an eye for detail and the manner of a studious, inoffensive scholar, Jenkins joined the EPA in 1979 after a period of politicisation working for the International Chemical Workers Union. A report she had written on the organic dyes used by artists had alerted the union to her potential as someone who might be able to deal with the problems they were facing over occupational exposure to chemicals in the workplace. Gradually she educated the workers and the workers educated management, in some factories forcing companies to stop using toxic dyes in their products. The EPA appeared to like what she was doing and took her on as a dye expert. Her expertise soon took her into other areas. She did some of the early work on alar – the pesticide used on apples.[6]

In 1980 she was assigned to wood treatment wastes and immediately concerned herself with workers' safety and protection. But Jenkins had been marked down as a troublemaker by industry. She had antagonised the chemical industry with her work on dyes. It wasn't long before the timber–paper–wood treatment industry saw her as a 'key obstacle to their goal of weakening wood treatment waste regulation'.[7] Jenkins' research on the wood treatment industry revealed that the primary wood treating chemicals – creosote, arsenate and pentachlorophenol – were highly toxic and contaminated with several poisonous compounds. Jenkins discovered that pentachlorophenol, in particular, was contaminated with dioxins. This wasn't a unique revelation she came to by herself.

The EPA had known since the early 1970s that dioxin was a contaminant of pentachlorophenol.[8] The agency had noted a 1975 report, which revealed that workers who had handled pentachlorophenol had contracted chloracne.[9] Anyone searching the literature on occupational exposure to pentachlorophenol and trichlorophenol would also have realised that industry knew about the toxic effects as far back as 1951 when a report noted chloracne in German workers employed in the manufacture of these chemicals – even if the presence of dioxin wasn't known, as we have seen, until the mid-1950s. The evidence appeared conclusive to Jenkins and she began to prepare the necessary documentation to regulate dioxin levels in pentachlorophenol. Then she hit a wall.

Jenkins had started working on the wood treatment industry regulations during the Jimmy Carter administration in 1980. The EPA had successfully managed to slap a ban on the use of the highly lucrative 2,4,5-T the year before. The industry, still smarting from this insult, wasn't keen to see another ban on another profit-generating chemical. At the time the use of pentachlorophenol as a wood preservative made it the second most widely used pesticide in the USA. In the late 1970s three chemical companies – Dow, Reichold and Vulcan – annually produced 79 million pounds of pentachlorophenol.[10] In 1978 the EPA called on industry to prove that the benefits of pentachlorophenol outweighed its risks to human health, issuing the necessary notice.[11] These were the same regulations that had resulted in the ban of 2,4,5-T.

In 1981 former Hollywood actor Ronald Reagan came to power in the USA, his administration bringing a free market principle to the production of chemicals like pentachlorophenol. But while industry gathered its forces and began to rearrange its offensive positions (Dow ceased production of pentachlorophenol in 1981 after attempting to manufacture the chemical with lower levels of dioxin) the EPA began to drag its feet.

Regulating pentachlorophenol wasn't as simple as it appeared. Ironically it was the battle over dioxin's toxicity and the fact that dioxin was being pumped into the environment from numerous sources that left the EPA with a dilemma. They didn't know how to regulate it without getting it in the neck from all sections of industry. Carol Van Strum and Paul Merrell, two activists, summed this up: 'The fundamental question of whether pentachlorophenol should be produced or used at all was forgotten, however, when the political controversy over dioxin expanded far beyond pentachlorophenol or other chlorophenolic pesticides.'[12]

The chemical industry, fighting back with a vengeance to protect its profits, intensified its lobbying of state politicians and regulatory officials to such an extent that a public interest group, the Natural

Resources Defense Council, subsequently took the EPA to court to highlight these abuses and conflicts of interest.[13]

The Reagan administration had appointed pro-industry people to the top EPA posts. According to Merrell and Van Strum

> secret negotiations with the wood treatment industry became routine, dominated by industry's fear of expensive pollution regulation and potential tort liability for injuries to employees and the public. From 1981 to 1983 the wood treatment industry and EPA held numerous closed-door meetings for the purpose of 'negotiating' the terms under which EPA would continue the registration of Penta.[14]

These meetings had their desired effect. By the summer of 1982 the EPA succumbed to the pressure and prepared to terminate the notice on pentachlorophenol. All that was left was the manipulation of science. Industry wanted to make sure that the new regulations contained no loopholes that would leave it open to liability in the future. All the EPA had to do was draw up a cosy risk assessment programme.

Then a ghost some EPA senior officials thought they had exorcised reappeared to haunt them. While the EPA was banning 2,4,5-T and preparing to ban pentachlorophenol, the spectre of dioxin was manifesting itself in many guises all over the planet but its presence in the Great Lakes, which were under the jurisdiction of both the USA and Canada, caused alarm.[15] Investigators had revealed levels of TCDD at 10 parts per trillion in the Great Lakes. This would have exposed one in a hundred people eating a single meal a week of Great Lakes fish to the risk of cancer. The Canadians wanted to know the source of the dioxin.

While the EPA hierarchy might have been unsure about the source they knew that the announcement of such levels would cause trouble. For a start the US Food and Drug Administration (FDA) would have needed to declare a ban on Great Lakes fish, so the EPA said nothing. Instead the FDA recommended that people limit their consumption of Great Lakes fish to two meals per month. The regional EPA office responsible for the Great Lakes didn't see it this way. They had prepared an investigation into the source of the dioxin and named Dow, who had been manufacturing 2,4,5-T and pentachlorophenol, as the culprit. In their draft report the EPA regional office recommended that consumption of Great Lakes fish, caught in the vicinity of Dow's Michigan plant, 'be prohibited'.

CORRUPTING THE REGULATORS

Then another of those strange things happened. When the report was published all the damaging information about Dow had been deleted. The EPA hierarchy had not been too pleased with the efforts of their regional colleagues and told them so. Deputy Administrator John Hernandez, who was subsequently implicated in this scandal along with senior EPA official John Todhunter, instructed EPA officials in the inter-departmental Chlorinated Dioxins Work Group to persuade their colleagues in the Great Lakes region to delete all references in the report to Dow, to any discussions about the health risks of eating dioxin-contaminated fish and to other studies on dioxin's toxicity – specifically 2,4,5-T induced miscarriages in Oregon and the affects of exposure to Agent Orange. So determined was Hernandez to ensure that fair play was done by industry he invited Dow to review and edit the regional EPA report.[16]

The EPA was rife with corruption in the early 1980s, so much that it didn't escape public and political scrutiny. This was also around the time that EPA Administrator Anne Gorsuch and her assistant Rita Lavelle had been abusing Superfund money. Congress demanded answers. Gorsuch withheld documents that would have implicated her in a Superfund scandal, got done for contempt and subsequently resigned. Lavelle got six months in jail for perjury.[17] Hernandez followed soon after, accused over complicity with Dow and his refusal to initiate a clean-up of toxic contamination around lead smelters in Dallas, Texas.[18]

However, despite the upheaval in the EPA and the congressional, court and media revelations, the wood treatment industry was slowly getting what it wanted. It was business as usual in the EPA headquarters. William Ruckelshaus replaced Gorsuch for his second term as EPA Administrator following his first appointment during the Richard Nixon administration in the early 1970s just after the EPA had been formed. And Ruckelshaus, who had spent the intervening years as an executive with the timber company Weyerhaeuser, was ready not only to allow the continued registration of pentachlorophenol but to reinstate the registration for 2,4,5-T.

This was where Carol Van Strum's and Paul Merrell's persistence began to pay off. Co-founder of the Oregon-based Citizens Against

Toxic Sprays in 1976, Van Strum, along with Merrell, her partner, had been researching the effects of herbicide spraying on rural communities, campaigning vigorously for proper regulation, plus justice and compensation for victims of dioxin poisoning for many years. Using the Freedom of Information Act they had succeeded in revealing information on the EPA's dioxin regulation programme. In the summer of 1983 the EPA's unpublished study into miscarriages in western Oregon found its way into their possession. It was the final nail in the coffin containing the trichlorophenol industry.

The consequent publicity and congressional inquiry brought Van Strum and Merrell a significant victory. On 14 October 1983 the EPA cancelled all 2,4,5-T registrations[19] – 14 years after it had been revealed that Dow knew about dioxin's birth deforming effects.[20]

JENKINS CLASHES WITH MONSANTO

Then the wall hit back. Only Cate Jenkins stood in the way of the wood treatment industries and they weren't long getting rid of her.[21]

> I was already on industry's blacklist because of my work on dyes with the unions. But it wasn't until 1985–86 when we were about to complete a good, strong regulatory package, that I began having real problems with industry interference. The first sign of real trouble came from within, with direct interference from the Reagan Administration.[22]

Jenkins knew too much about dioxin's toxicity but her bosses threw her off the project on the regulation of the wood treatment industry in September 1987 just in time for her to catch the falling star of Monsanto and hurl it into the cosmos. Jenkins, however, didn't really need Monsanto. She needed her job back and fought the EPA hard, eventually getting a position in the Office of Solid Waste and Emergency Response. Jenkins was now like a dog with a bone. She had found a tastier morsel and wasn't going to let go. She now had dioxin in her teeth and wanted to savour what she was seeing – the manipulation of science to show that this deadly poison wasn't so bad after all. She went at it with a vengeance only someone who has been spurned has the energy to sustain. Memos, with extensive documentation attached, were sent to the appropriate people in the EPA.

The Kemner trial revelations about Monsanto's dioxin studies were so serious that Jenkins felt the EPA had to take action. It was her belief that the EPA had used Monsanto's manipulated data to set the health standards for dioxin. In February 1990 she asked the EPA's Science Advisory Board to re-evaluate the standards for dioxin and to approach all the data on dioxin with a new perspective. Monsanto, she alleged, had deliberately manipulated their health studies on the exposed workforce at Nitro. Studies by Zack and Gaffey and by Raymond Suskind and Victor Hertzberg were fraudulent, Jenkins alleged to Raymond Loehr, who chaired the Executive Committee of the Science Advisory Board.[23] She attached Carr's brief to the memo.

The story of Monsanto's alleged fraud was now in the open. Alastair Hay, the English toxicologist and author, was quickly onto the story. 'Is anybody else writing up this information for publication?' Hay asked Carr. 'If not, I would be keen to do so as it is vital that the information be published more widely.'[24] Hay, who had been aware of the trial and knew of its outcome, was genuinely concerned that the story would be buried. It wasn't, surprisingly.

The corporate spin doctors were dizzy. Peter Montague was among the first to pick up the story in the USA after an EPA official William Sanjour sent him a copy of Jenkins' memo. On 7 March he ran a story entitled 'Dioxins and Cancer: Fraudulent Stories' in *Rachel's Hazardous Waste News*.[25]

The story was now in the public and political domain. A month later Jenkins wrote to Carr. He replied a few days later, enclosing 'a considerable amount of material' including excerpts of the Kemner transcript and trial exhibits. Nearly a decade after Monsanto had told the world that there wasn't a problem with their products and that their workers were fine, the truth was out.[26] Jenkins made use of Carr's information. The EPA, she was sure, had to act.

In August 1990, EPA's Office of Criminal Investigation (OCI) wrote a seven-page memo recommending that a 'full field criminal investigation be initiated by OCI'. The OCI alleged that Monsanto had engaged in a deliberate course of conduct designed to convince its employees and the world that dioxin is harmless. The OCI declared that 'a potential conspiracy, between Monsanto and its officers and employees, exists or has existed to defraud the USEPA' noting that the company had provided misleading information to the EPA, failed to disclose all pertinent TSCA [Toxic Substances Control Act] related information to the EPA, issued false statements in notices and reports to the EPA and had used the allegedly fraudulent research to erroneously convince the EPA and the scientific community that dioxin is less harmful to health and the environment.[27]

Exactly eight months after Jenkins had sent her memo to the Science Advisory Board she received a memo instructing her to assist the EPA's National Enforcement Investigation Center 'in a full criminal investigation of these Monsanto studies'.[28] On November 14 she met with John West, Special Agent in Charge of the Office of Criminal Investigations (OCI) and Kevin Guarino, Special Agent in the Office of Criminal Investigations National Enforcement Investigations Center (NEIC). The following day Jenkins started to prepare the documentation to support criminal charges. She sent the OCI and the NEIC a memo that she also released to the environmental groups working on dioxin, Vietnam veterans organisations, to numerous politicians and to Axelson, Eriksson and Hardell among others.[29]

Jenkins alleged that 'Monsanto covered up the dioxin contamination of a wide range of its products. Monsanto either failed to report contamination, substituted false information purporting to show no contamination, or submitted samples to the government for analysis that had been specifically prepared so that dioxin contamination did not exist.'[30] She knew, however, that the EPA would still have to prove fraud.

> You stated that pursuing a criminal investigation against Monsanto would require a prior determination of the significance of the fraud. In order for proceedings to be initiated by EPA, the fraud would need to have affected the regulatory process at EPA, and Monsanto would need to have knowingly submitted the falsified data and health studies to EPA in order to affect the regulatory process.

This would become a crucial element in the investigation against Monsanto. Greenpeace, realising this, prepared a petition calling for an investigation, effectively mandating the EPA to take action.[31] They supported their petition with an 800-page report by their scientists Joe Thornton and Pat Costner that detailed Monsanto's alleged fraud.[32] Monsanto called the allegations 'bald faced lies'.[33] Jenkins followed her November memo with another in January, asserting that 'it would be a terrible miscarriage of justice' if the EPA did not re-examine the real carcinogenic effects of dioxin and let Monsanto's alleged fraud 'languish'.[34]

STUDIES REVEAL HIDDEN TRUTH

A watershed had been reached. After decades of clever manipulation of health studies and the obfuscation of the truth about dioxin, the three years between 1989 and 1991 changed everything.

Scientists like Axelson, Eriksson and Hardell, who had been vilified for their work on occupational exposure to the phenoxy herbicides, were vindicated.

Pier Alberto Bertazzi's on-going study of the Seveso population showed an increase in soft tissue sarcoma and non-Hodgkin's lymphoma – the two rare cancers identified by the Swedish doctors.[35]

Richard Clapp led a team of seven independent scientists in a review of the dioxin literature. Their results also showed a link between Agent Orange and ten cancers (including those identified by Hardell, Eriksson and Axelson) but also neurological effects, reproductive problems, immunological abnormalities and liver damage.[36]

BASF's health studies were revealed by an independent scientist, employed by exposed workers seeking compensation, to be flawed. The workers' expert, Friedemann Rohleder, found evidence that the company's study had included 20 clerical staff who had not been exposed. When Rohleder re-analysed the data without the clerical workers he discovered significant increases in two groups of cancers – of the respiratory organs and of the digestive tract.[37]

The US National Institute of Occupational Safety and Health (NIOSH), which estimated that approximately 11 million workers were exposed to occupational carcinogens, released its 13-year study of 5,172 chemical workers in twelve chlorophenol manufacturing plants including Monsanto's Nitro facility.[38] The company's alleged fraud was compounded.

Whereas Dr Suskind and his colleagues had not found any increase in cancers, rare or common, Marilyn Fingerhut's study for NIOSH revealed a cancer rate 46 per cent above normal and three cases of soft tissue sarcoma – two at the Nitro plant. Dr George Roush, Monsanto's Medical Director, had admitted in court that the workers with soft tissue sarcoma and malignant lymphoma had been excluded from their studies. It didn't stop there.

Later in the year a similar study of 1,184 male and 399 female German chemical workers revealed a rate 39 per cent above normal but the German study also revealed that the cancer rates were 82 per cent for workers employed for 20 years or more. Breast cancer among the women was twice as high as normal.[39]

Amidst all this the CDC was accused of manipulating the science in their Agent Orange exposure study and the Veterans Association faced a similar charge on their health study of malignant lymphomas in US military exposed to Agent Orange.[40]

BACKLASH

Meanwhile, with Monsanto on the rack, the industry backlash was coming. The chemical and wood treatment industries had been joined in the mid-1980s by the pulp and paper industry in the battle to get the EPA to detoxify dioxin. Represented by the Chlorine Institute – a trade association with a mandate from its members in the chlorine chemistry business – industry got down to some serious lobbying.

A conference on dioxin at the Banbury Center was instigated by the Chlorine Institute. The industry, according to the Institute's Head of Communications Joe Walker, believed that the meeting could be 'beneficial to our interests, particularly our interest in the paper industry'.[41] What Walker really meant was that the pulp and paper industry desperately needed to detoxify dioxin to deal with the increasing amount of litigation it was facing over dioxin contamination from its mills.

The Chlorine Institute then stood back and let Banbury officials organise the meeting and select the participants, requesting only that their consultant Michael Gallo attend as an observer for the Institute. The meeting, which was held in October 1990, was attended by 38 dioxin specialists. The EPA had come on board as co-sponsor and the invitations stated that it was a collaborative government–industry conference, yet none of the participants appeared to realise this. There was no general consensus among the scientists who disagreed on many points. Some felt that the latest data on dioxin merited a fresh assessment by the EPA and even suggested that the agency had over-estimated the risks from exposure. Ellen Silbergeld, a toxicologist at the University of Maryland, rejected this notion. That was the kind of meeting it was. Everyone went home. The manipulation of the media began.

Confident that it could present the conference in a favourable light for industry, the Chlorine Institute employed a public relations company, Edelman Medical Communications to prepare a press pack. The package contained a press release from the Chlorine Institute, statements from three scientists and a background paper by George Carlo who had also attended the meeting as another observer for the Institute. The press release had been carefully drafted and dioxin had been carefully detoxified. The Institute announced that a consensus had been reached on several key issues, specifically that a threshold level for dioxin existed, below which these chemicals posed no general risk to human health. Carlo, in his paper, announced that the meeting had 'reinforced the notion that dioxin is much less toxic to humans than originally thought'.

The media were slow to pick up on the story and most didn't bother with it until the new year.

Meanwhile the industry intensified its lobbying. On 23 January 1991, four chief executive officers of paper companies visited EPA Administrator William Reilly. 'We were also encouraged by what we perceived as your willingness to have the agency move expeditiously to re-examine the potency of dioxin and chloroform in light of the important new information that has been submitted with respect to those chemicals,' the executives said in a five-page letter from the American Paper Institute a few days later, thanking him for the meeting.[42] The executives went on to inform Reilly in an unsigned two-page addendum that there was now a 'prevailing view that low-level dioxin exposures do not pose a serious health threat' and 'despite this new reality, EPA has taken no tangible or timely steps to revisit its health criteria for dioxin, and has even failed to temper the agency's zeal in acting on the worst risk estimates ... '.[43]

As Reilly was entertaining the paper industry executives, the Chlorine Institute's press package found its way onto the desk of Ellen Silbergeld, who freaked when she saw the contents. 'I did not expect to be manipulated by industry and government spokespeople (who are not dioxin researchers, incidentally),' she raged in a letter to the Banbury Center Director Jan Witkowski, furious that she had been 'made into a supporter of their political views on dioxins and risk assessment'. Copying the letter to the media and all the participants of the meeting Silbergeld said she had given the main conference paper on a 'scientific basis for dioxin risk assessment' and did not feel that 'this complex topic can be reduced to a simplistic press release'.[44]

The response was immediate. The scientific media gave it extensive coverage and Silbergeld even found allies among people who disagreed with her stance on dioxin. 'I don't think it is fair to represent consensus when none was really sought,' the CDC's Vernon Houk told *Science* magazine.[45]

Dioxin was starting to become a hot subject again. In April, 1991, the EPA's second reassessment of dioxin was set in motion. The following month Houk told Tom Uhlenbrock, a reporter with the *St Louis Post Dispatch*, that the Times Beach evacuation was a mistake. Associated Press ran Uhlenbrock's story and it was picked up by several media across America. Then it resurfaced in August when *New York Times* reporter Keith Schneider ran it as a news story and it exploded onto the front pages of America's print media. 'The *Times* piece was picked up and treated as if it were breaking news,' said Vicki Monk in her analysis of Schneider's journalism.

> At least 20 major newspapers reprinted the *Times* story, while other dailies followed up with their own similar reports and editorials that lambasted scientists for sowing panic and encouraging the government to waste money on dioxin clean-ups (like Times Beach). The favourite news bite for many reporters was Schneider's contention, attributed to 'some experts', that exposure to dioxin was no more harmful than a week of sunbathing. But when they repeated it, most erroneously attributed the statement to scientists.

Now whether all this revisionism had anything to do with potential regulatory action as a result of the USEPA's reassessment of dioxin or with the pulp paper industry's desperate need to see dioxin detoxified is hard to know.

Uhlenbrock has said that Houk's comment was news and he reported it as such. Schneider has said that he was reporting the views of the scientists sceptical about dioxin's perceived high toxicity. Peter Montague, a scientist who produces a weekly news sheet on toxic pollution and health issues, commented that Schneider had caved in to ignorance or pressure. 'Either he is intentionally misleading his readers or he is fundamentally ignorant of the topics he is writing on.'

It was Monk's belief that 'covering an issue like the health risks of dioxin ... requires a good deal of time and effort to seek out the most knowledgeable scientists, weigh competing views, and sift through complex data,' and that 'the coverage of dioxin is a glaring example of the danger of blindly accepting facts as reported by any other news organisation – even if it is the *New York Times*'.[46]

Reilly even told Schneider how he expected the reassessment to turn out. 'I don't want to prejudge the issue,' he said, 'but we are seeing new information on dioxin that suggests a lower risk assessment for dioxin should be applied.'[47]

'However,' as Peter Montague stressed after the reassessment had entered the public domain,

> the scientific reassessment did not turn out as Reilly and the paper industry supposed it would. EPA scientists evidently took their mandate seriously. They designed a reassessment process that involved original laboratory research, many meetings with non-government scientists, at least two public hearings, and many drafts of the nine-volume reassessment document, which was peer-reviewed prior to release. Eight of the nine volumes were written by non-governmental scientists. EPA had never before involved such a large number of non-agency scientists in its work. It managed to solicit and include the viewpoints of industry, academia, government, and the general public.[48]

JENKINS PAYS THE PRICE

Jenkins, meanwhile, had become a hero. And a villain. Her 15 November memo to the Science Advisory Board, which she had sent to interested groups and individuals, provided Vietnam veterans with new evidence to confront the US Congress for proper compensation. But the EPA weren't happy with Jenkins' whistle blowing antics. They grounded her. She complained to the Department of Labor who agreed that she was being illegally harassed. The EPA appealed to the courts but the judge ruled in Jenkin's favour. The EPA turned to the Secretary of Labor and finally the harassment ended when he too found in Jenkins' favour and she was reinstated and her legal fees paid.

Then, inexplicably, the EPA dropped their investigation into Monsanto. Almost two years after it had instigated the investigation, on 7 August 1992, the Office of Criminal Investigation announced that the investigation was closed. 'The submission of allegedly fraudulent studies to the EPA were determined to be immaterial to the regulatory process. Further, allegations made in the Kemner litigation appear to be beyond the statute of limitations.' What the OCI had discovered was that because some of the alleged criminal activities were more than five years old the company could not be prosecuted. The OCI also claimed that the government had not relied on the Monsanto studies to set dioxin regulations.

But it didn't rest there. Two years later, on 20 July 1994, William Sanjour sent a 30-page memo to his supervisor, David Bussard describing the history of the two-year investigation of Monsanto by the OCI, claiming that 'the investigation itself and the basis for closing the investigation were fraudulent'. Sanjour's memo was the result of a Freedom of Information Act (FOIA) request for all documents related to the investigation. 'One gets the impression, on reviewing the record, that as soon as the criminal investigation began, a whole bunch of wet blankets were thrown over it,' Sanjour told Bussard, noting that the investigation centred on criminal fraud. 'In August 1992, EPA quietly closed the criminal investigation without ever determining or even attempting to determine if the Monsanto studies were valid or invalid, let alone fraudulent.'[49]

This was the crucial point. As Peter Montague put it: 'A finding of criminal fraud would have required first a finding that Monsanto's studies were scientifically flawed. Only an analysis by government scientists could have reached such a conclusion, and no EPA scientists were engaged in EPA's Monsanto investigation. This left the criminal investigation essentially crippled.'[50]

Sanjour summarised:

When Jenkins made her allegations, and when the veterans groups made known the full implication of those allegations, a government with a decent respect for the welfare of its armed forces would have publicly ordered a full and impartial investigation with all the resources and support necessary and let the chips fall where they may. Instead, our top government officials were silent or even worse, they let it be known that they despised the messenger and had nothing but friendly feelings for the accused. The United States government gave no support or encouragement to a scientific, civil, or criminal investigation of Monsanto.[51]

GLOBAL DIOXIN STUDY

The USEPA has consistently adopted a Jekyll and Hyde attitude towards dioxin. While Jenkins was familiarising herself with this class of chemicals, senior officials with the EPA were involved in an international 'pilot' study on dioxin.[52] Set up to correlate global research on dioxin, the study was initiated in 1985 under the auspices of the North Atlantic Treaty Organisation (NATO), involving nine countries with the World Health Organisation taking observer status. The three-year study cost $142.4 million. It brought together 282 research projects and was concluded in 1988. Anyone reading this study, which carefully avoided making specific judgements on the toxicity of dioxin, would have been left with a strong feeling about the dangers of dioxin and the need for adequate regulation.

Anyone reading it in conjunction with all the EPA's own documents on dioxin plus the wealth of scientific publications and papers on dioxin would have found it difficult not to conclude that dioxins are a lethal class of chemical compounds. So was no one doing this in the late 1980s? Was no one reading all the documentation on dioxin and coming to a logical conclusion? Was no one capable of realising that dioxin was no longer a scientific problem, that – in 1991 while industry was pushing its own agenda and nation-states were procrastinating – it had become intensely political?

After years of agenda setting by industry and governmental obfuscation on the science of dioxin, it was now obvious to those scientists who were not being corrupted by industry or seduced by state grants that a new perspective was needed. In the summer of 1991, while the detoxification of dioxin was beginning in earnest, Ellen and Paul Connett were preparing the first of the citizens' conferences on dioxin involving independent free-thinking scientists, researchers and activists.

THE USEPA MAKES A DECISION

The science of dioxin was no longer for sale. A year later, on 9 October, Erich Bretthauer, EPA's Assistant Administrator for Research and Development and one of the authors of the NATO report, sent a memo to Reilly setting out what the agency actually knew about dioxin. He made seven specific points:

1. To understand the risks of dioxin we should consider a broad range of health effects, not just cancer.
2. Dioxin has been observed to cause certain non-cancer effects in animals by disrupting the body's endocrine system. These endocrine effects include reproduction, behaviour of offspring, and changes in the immune system. Some data suggest that these effects may be occurring in people at body burden levels that can result from exposures at, or near, current background.

3. Recent studies indicate that dioxin causes cancer in humans; these studies need to be evaluated further and then EPA needs to form a new official position about the cancer hazard to humans.
4. Additional compounds besides dioxin (for example, some types of PCBs) have dioxin-like effects and should be included in EPA's reassessment of the hazards of dioxin.
5. There is insufficient data to develop a model that will allow us to predict the cancer hazards to humans from low-level exposure to dioxin. During the next three to five months, government studies may provide the needed data.
6. The available data seem to indicate that dioxin will cause cancer in humans in proportion to the exposure – high doses will cause many cancers, lower doses will cause fewer cancers, and the only dose that is risk-free is zero.
7. Risks from existing background levels of dioxin in the general population need to be 'carefully considered'.[53]

The scene was set for the EPA's reassessment of dioxin, even if their administrator was sure it would be a foregone conclusion. Throughout the 1990s the science of dioxin became much clearer. The EPA gradually released draft reports of its reassessment while the continuing studies into exposed workers and communities began to reveal the tragic truth about dioxin. Responding to Pier Bertazzi's 1993 study on cancer among the Seveso population (which showed an increase in cancers), Linda Birnbaum, director of environmental toxicology at the EPA and co-ordinator of the reassessment, said 'the weight of the evidence is becoming overwhelming'.[54]

And so it was. When the EPA finally released its 2,400-page draft on dioxin in 1994 the evidence appeared irrefutable, yet that's what industry has continued to do, refute the evidence. 'Dioxin,' Peter Montague asserted in October 1995, 'is an astonishingly versatile and potent poison. EPA, and the corporations that release dioxin into the environment, have waffled and fudged for 20 years or more.'[55]

The politics of pollution, however, have determined that industry shall not lose, because commerce, as any economist will tell you, is about balancing the books. Profit and loss. Someone gains and someone pains. The gains to the chemical industry have been vast but the pains have been suffered largely by workers, soldiers and the communities who live in the midst of polluting factories.

6
Tears in the Valleys:
Incinerator Stories

In large communities it is called rumour but in small communities
it is knowing. You cannot hide real events and call them by another
name, because men are not fools and if you give them the evidence
of their ears and eyes, and even with a minimum of intelligence,
they can piece together all the facts.

Walter Macken[1]

The silver-haired woman is standing in the sitting room of her modest
home, a large two-storey farmhouse built in the perfunctory tradition
of those few Irish families who somehow managed to acquire land
when most of it was owned by the English, acknowledging the
location of her family domain in the picturesque Suir Valley in South
Tipperary.

'This is the valley of tears,' she says quietly. She is solemn, though
it is possible to detect a trace of emotion in her voice. 'Our story was
true, you see. We were very pleased that in the end we got, I suppose
you could say, justice. But at what price? That is something none of
us can say.'[2] Mary Hanrahan has the manner of a matriarch. This is
not tradition. It is the consequence of a tragedy that has virtually
destroyed her son and his family. For without Mary, her son John
might never have endured the ordeal that could have easily wiped
out many another man.

It is a cold December afternoon, dry and crisp without a hint
of rain. The day is bright, patches of hazy blue can be seen in the
winter sky. The Hanrahans should be elated. They have just received
an out-of-court settlement against the US chemical corporation,
Merck, Sharp and Dohme, after a twelve-year battle to prove that
emissions from the company's Ballydine factory – just beyond the
hill and over the railway – were responsible for the death of 225 of
the Hanrahan's farm animals. It is 1990 and the war between the
Hanrahans and Merck should be over, but it isn't. Significantly the
Hanrahan's were unable to prove that their own illnesses were the
consequence of Merck's activities. This is a crucial element in this

story, because the animals were not the only ones affected by Merck's toxic emissions.

It's probably fair to say that no one in Ireland had ever heard of dioxin until the Hanrahans took on Merck. And even now it is not known what the extent of the dioxin contamination was around Ballydine. What is known is that people have illnesses associated with dioxin poisoning. So Mary Hanrahan is both right and wrong. There has been a price and it is possible to say what it is. The Hanrahans and their neighbours are slowly paying it, irreparable damage to their health. The Supreme Court's ruling means nothing, because the Hanrahans know in their hearts what caused their illnesses and those of their neighbours.

Seline Hanrahan, John's wife, has endometriosis, which has been identified with dioxin contamination.[3] The rise in cancers in the area around Ballydine has increased dramatically, to the extent that no longer do the people of the valley shrug their shoulders in bemusement. Now they know. They know what has caused their illnesses.

Those who have studied the Hanrahan case believe that Merck got off lightly, estimating the total cost to the company at around €6.25 million ($7.31m). No one in Merck will comment on how much they spent fighting the Hanrahan family but for a company that records its profits in billions it was a small price to pay. We don't even know how much the Hanrahans received in compensation because Merck insisted that the terms of the settlement remain secret. Barristers in Dublin's Four Courts have claimed that the Hanrahans got less than €1.25 million ($1.46m).[4]

POLLUTION ON THE WIND

The Hanrahans' ordeal began on a cool August Sunday in 1978.[5] John Hanrahan, in the ritualistic manner of all farmers, was up with the dawn to tend to his animals. He immediately noticed that one of the farm dogs was weeping. There was a sweet sickly smell in the air. Wandering around his farm, which was cloaked in a thin fog, he saw other animals coughing and weeping.

For 18 months the farmers complained to Merck and to the local authority until, in February 1980, South Tipperary Council commissioned Dr Ian Jamieson of An Foras Forbatha to do a €2,500 ($2,930) study on air pollution around the area of the factory. Dr Jamieson completed his report in October 1980. He found no evidence of serious air pollution and he noted that acid vapour emissions were within EC limits. He did, however, make a recommendation:

> It is most important that the council should be aware of emissions of air pollutants from factory processes in order to confirm that these comply with the levels originally estimated. It may be that prior to this investigation the council has had no information.
>
> In particular, it is necessary to ensure that the process gas scrubbing system continues to function properly and it is recommended that Merck Sharp and Dohme be requested to provide continuous records of emissions measured at the stack, together with the gas velocity at the stack, etc.[6]

It wasn't until 6 November 1981 that Byron L. Rowe, General Manager of Merck, wrote to James O'Callaghan, the county engineer, with the relevant information. This showed that between 'May and early June 1980' emissions from the factory violated the permitted levels. Rowe said this was because of 'severe mechanical problems' but 'repairs were made as quickly as possible'.[7] Merck had broken their planning permission levels by four times the permitted amounts; South Tipperary County Council, nevertheless, took no action against the company.

The first problems with pollution in the area had occurred in 1978 and were perceived as minor. From 1980 animals began to die of a strange wasting disease, cattle miscarried, twin births and deformities increased and milk yields dropped. The problems were not confined to the Hanrahans; other farmers complained. Metal was seen to rust and corrode in the farmyards and houses closest to the factory. The tops of trees were pointed in the opposite direction from Merck.

The farmers believed the Yanks were the problem and that was a problem in itself. Merck, Sharp and Dohme was and still is the largest employer in the area and the earlier experience of bitterness, divisiveness and intimidation associated with the farmers' opposition to Schering Plough, another American chemical company who had wanted and failed to locate in South Tipperary, stopped many from speaking out. Yet the problems were real and investigations were called for.

On two occasions over the winter following the first Jamieson report, the county council met with local residents to discuss the problem and the implications for the area. At a meeting on 20 February 1981, it was suggested that a special committee be set up of technical experts in the pollution, agricultural, medical and veterinary areas to sort out the problem. (The first cattle deaths had just occurred at the Hanrahans' farm.) The county manager, T. Rice, agreed with the idea of a committee. It was felt that such an independent body would solve or go close to solving the problem. It was never set up.

In November 1981 Dr Jamieson informed the council that the findings of his second report, which he had begun the previous April, seemed to confirm what he had found in his first report. He suggested a further report be done using different methods. Trinity College were brought into the investigation.

In the meantime Dr Jamieson's second report recommended that as a matter of urgency the animal health problems on the Hanrahans' farm be fully investigated by veterinary and other appropriate authorities, and that the monitoring of emissions from the factory continue. He also stated that complaints be properly recorded and monitored by the council and subjected to serious investigation. 'Until an explanation for the health problems is found the possibility that some serious toxic substance, from whatever source, is responsible should not be ignored.'

When the report from Trinity's Botany Department appeared both the council and Merck were alarmed, but not just about its findings, which stated that there was 'clear evidence' that the surrounding countryside (lichens, grass, soil and silage) was being affected by emissions from the factory. They were alarmed because it had been intended not to release the report publicly but to incorporate its findings with those of Dr Jamieson. This plan was thwarted by the Hanrahans' vet, Tom de Lacy, who procured a copy of the report, which he produced at a meeting in the Hanrahans' house on 27 September 1982. The county medical officer and Mark Lynch, who were both at the meeting, said they had been unable to get a copy. Later the Irish Times received a copy and it was then decided to release the report. The council wanted changes made in the report. Merck were simply concerned that it had been leaked to the media.

SILENT WHISPERS

These investigations did nothing for the farmers. Each one appeared to exonerate Merck from any responsibility. The strategy of the state, local authorities and the Merck management had been to claim that the problems were confined to one farm (John Hanrahan's), that these problems were caused by his mismanagement and that they had no connection with the Merck factory.

This strategy was undermined by the simple fact that problems existed on other farms near the factory, that John Hanrahan had, until his cattle began to die, been a model farmer and was recognised as such in the locality.

The Trinity study had provided circumstantial evidence to implicate the factory's emissions in the 'chronic levels of pollution' the investigators had found near its boundaries. Yet while that report suggested that the possible cause of the pollution was a toxic combination of chlorine and bromine (and it was hard to see where else such a contaminant could have come from in the local agricultural environment if not from Merck) it too was presented by the local authority as another exoneration of the company.

Earlier in May 1982 the pollution monitors were removed from Hanrahan's farm after the council claimed they had discovered 'acceptable levels of pollution'. (Further monitoring took place on an ad hoc basis for short term surveys. Sources inside the factory claimed that operations inside Merck were cleaned up before each subsequent survey of emissions.) The misrepresentation of the Trinity study angered local farmers who picketed meetings of the council; other farmers came forward to complain about the problems they had been suffering.

Farmer Paddy O'Meara, whose farm is on the opposite side of the road from the Merck factory, told an interesting story, one he has told many times to many people, journalists, county officials, and to officials and politicians from Dublin. Early one Sunday morning in May 1981 O'Meara, in a field with his cattle and sheep, watched as the cows began to sniff the air and the sheep run to the opposite end of the field. The air was thick with a fog that began to burn in his chest. He went home, went to bed and when he awoke he couldn't breath. The doctor was called. 'Your system is rotten with poison,' the doctor said to him. Where, asked the doctor, had he come in contact with poison? O'Meara mentioned the factory.

Paddy O'Meara was ill for several months. The cattle, in the field that day, he claimed faded away. He subsequently sold them to a dealer for half of their value. He also sold the sheep. His story was never investigated. 'Trying to do anything about it is useless. I see Hanrahan across there trying to fight against them all and I say "What's the use?". We got no hearing at any of the meetings. We just want a bit of clean air, that's all we want,' he said in 1983. O'Meara provided a postscript. Between 1981 and 1983 he attempted to keep cattle in a field across from the factory but the cattle would have none of it. 'Whatever it was in the grass the cattle wouldn't stop in field.' He put barbed wire up to keep them in the field. One animal tore its chest open attempting to get out.

Though not as harsh as the Hanrahans' ordeal, O'Meara's accounts were not uncommon. Bertie Kennedy, another local farmer, died in August 1983. He wife claimed that all six doctors her husband visited asked him where he came in contact with chemicals. O'Meara's doctor refused to comment on his patient's case, as the doctors who heard Kennedy have done. There was no inquest into Kennedy's death.

Tommy Rockett, whose farm is opposite the Hanrahans', claimed that his cattle also refused to eat the grass. In 1981, particularly from April onwards, the cattle were seen coughing continuously. None of his animals died on the farm. 'They died in the meat factory, chemicals and all,' was all he would say. Another farmer said imaginatively that the emissions from the factory were 'like a fallout from an atom bomb'. Other farmers have had calving problems. One farmer lost a quarter of the calves born during the spring of 1981. Many farmers reported stampeding, cattle with streaming eyes, their children complaining of chest ailments, everyone feeling tired.

Yet local GPs, vets and the county medical officer were either unable to say what the causes were or, as in the case of the county medical officer, that they were simply 'nuisance' complaints.

This pattern, investigations and allegations of pollution and ill-health around the factory, continued as John Hanrahan began a High Court action against Merck, Sharp and Dohme. More reports were commissioned by the authorities and by several experts on behalf of John Hanrahan. In 1983 the vet, de Lacy, and Hanrahan commissioned a private report on the events at the farm. They refused to release it to either the council or the Department of Agriculture, who later wrote to Hanrahan promising him confidentiality if he released the information he had on the cause of his cattle's death. But de Lacy and Hanrahan had already learned a lesson. 'The first place this information would go,' alleged de Lacy, would be to the Merck, Sharp and Dohme management.' He also stated that the council would have swept it under the table.

On 11 June 1984 ten Ballydine farmers placed a picket outside the council offices before a meeting of the South Tipperary County Council. Among the business that day was a summary report given by the county engineer, summarising two new reports on Merck's alleged pollution completed in May 1984 by the IIRS and Foras Forbatha, which called for comprehensive testing for dioxin on farmlands close to the factory.

Merck denied that dioxins were formed in its incinerator yet the company used it to burn chlorinated solvents – which produce dioxin when incinerated. Testing for phosgene, a toxic chemical originally used as an asphyxiant gas during World War I whose major effect is on the lungs, was also called for.

After the council meeting one farmer, John Joe O'Connell, claimed that the number of unexplained cattle deaths near the Merck factory was much higher than the 200 plus admitted by local farmers. He said many of the farmers sent cattle to meat factories as soon as they began to show disease symptoms.

The council meeting did not resolve the issue; some observers said the obfuscation was apparent particularly as few of the councillors knew or had seen the new reports. One reporter said it was 'extraordinary that South Tipperary County Council have waited so long to test for dioxin, or indeed for phosgene' as the first complaints had been registered six years earlier. One councillor had asked if dioxin was a dangerous substance. 'We're talking about things we know nothing about,' he added.

Despite the concern from some councillors, according to TD Sean Tracey the allegations against Merck were 'casting a shadow over this magnificent industry. No one would have the temerity to say there is anything in the nature of a cover up'.

THE HANRAHANS TAKE MERCK TO COURT

John Hanrahan moved a writ against Merck in February 1982. In March 1983 it was put down for trial. In February 1985 the Hanrahans' High Court suit for damages against Merck, which was to run for 47 days into mid-summer, began before Justice Ronan Keane.

When he entered Dublin's Four Courts, John Hanrahan was convinced that Merck were responsible for the mass grave in his farm that contained 225 dead animals – the result, he claimed, of emissions from their Ballydine factory. Merck, back in 1978, had told him that the emissions and the smells were harmless.

In his evidence to the High Court John Hanrahan presented a death list – a chronology of the manner of deaths of 140 animals, between 1980 and 1984. This high mortality rate was questioned by both the Department of Agriculture (which kept Hanrahan's official herd file – and which was made available to Merck's senior counsel but not to Hanrahan) and the company. The department calculated that only 65 animals had died during the same period and this was accepted by Justice Keane.

In their defence Merck argued that Hanrahan's problems were nothing to do with them, that his ambitions as a farmer were the direct cause. Financial problems, overstocking and underfeeding had led to the deaths of his animals; to justify this mismanagement Hanrahan decided to blame the factory and seek litigation, Merck's defence argued.

Trace levels of dioxin were found in milk samples taken from not only Hanrahan's farm but neighbouring farms as well. Merck continued to insist that dioxins were not formed in their incinerator. At the time so little was known in Ireland about dioxin formation that they were able to confuse people with this propaganda. Yet all the Hanrahans, Mary, John, his wife Seline, their children, were now suffering from symptoms consistent with toxic – significantly dioxin – poisoning.

On 4 July 1985 the High Court case ended. Six weeks later Justice Keane found against the Hanrahan family. Within a month Avonmore Creameries had cut off their credit to John Hanrahan. Livestock and machinery were auctioned. In October the Hanrahan family were ordered to pay legal costs estimated at €1.25 million ($1.46m). The following year Tipperary County Council disconnected the water supply to the Hanrahans' farm. The family had refused to pay water rates until the council guaranteed them clean air.

But the High Court, as far as the Hanrahans were concerned, was only round one. In November and December 1987 an appeal was heard in the Supreme Court. Six months later Justice Henchy ruled in favour of the Hanrahan family.[8] Justice Henchy, in his conclusions, stated that Mary, John and Seline Hanrahan had

> established that the defendants are liable to them in damages for the offensive smells emitted from the factory, that John Hanrahan is entitled to damages for the injurious effect on his health of the factory emissions, and that the defendants are also liable in damages for the cattle ailments to the extent that they were caused by factory emissions.

On several points Justice Henchy disagreed with the High Court decision. Justice Keane had said that the odours 'were never on such a scale or intensity as to justify the award of damages'. Justice Henchy said this 'conclusion was incorrect' and added that it was 'a misinterpretation of the relevant law'. There were three 'possible sources' of atmospheric pollution caused by emissions from the factory, Justice Henchy ruled and referred to the incinerator.

> Because the function of the incinerator is to effect the destruction by combustion of dangerous waste chemicals and solvents and because the incinerator was for significant periods in the years in question running at below its design temperature and therefore at a heat which was not adequate to destroy dangerous and contaminated solvents, it is marked out by the plaintiffs as the primary source of atmospheric pollution on their farm.

Justice Henchy said there was evidence from a variety of witnesses 'of complaints such as a burning sensation in the throat and chest, reddening of the skin, irritation and teaming of the eyes and a smothering feeling in the nose, throat and chest'.

> While complaints of that kind seem to have been experienced by different people in the area, the plaintiffs seem to be the only people who claimed that the atmospheric pollution affected their health. Whether or not the Hanrahan farm vis-a-vis the factory was in a special meteorological position, there was unimpeached independent evidence that the complaints of physical ill-effects in humans on the plaintiffs' farm were matched by observable distress in the animals on the farm.

Justice Henchy questioned whether Justice Keane's 'finding of no causal connection between those complaints and emissions from the factory can be sustained'. He went on to add: 'Even if all the complaints made by or on behalf of the plaintiffs are not accepted, there were uncontroverted items of complaints which suggested that the factory emissions were at the root of the trouble.'

Regarding the nature and extent of the factory emissions Justice Henchy stated that 'it appears to be an unquestionable fact that the defendant's factory is the main source of hydrogen chloride and hydrochloric acid mists in the Suir valley'.

> The possible effects of such emissions have to be considered in terms of factors such as air chemistry, meteorology, the height

of the factory chimneys, the configuration of the Suir Valley, local meteorological features (such as the inversion by which air is trapped in the valley when winds are light) and the effect of prevailing winds.

Readings taken at the point of emission in the factory are therefore not necessarily a sound guide as to the consequences of the emissions in different parts of the valley. For example, some of the emissions take place at levels below that of the valley floor, and the top of the scrubber stack is on a level with the ground floor of the plaintiffs' house. The point has been taken that factory readings and the results shown by computer models do not take account of what actually happens in the Suir Valley.

The criticism has also been made that measurements of airborne concentrations on the plaintiffs' farm give no more than an average daily concentration, thus leaving out short violent emissions and not taking into account the deleterious effect, particularly on grazing animals, of prolonged low-level emissions of gases and mists of unknown degrees of toxicity.

Justice Henchy went on to refer specifically to Ian Jamieson's reports and concluded from his 'consideration of the scientific evidence as a whole' that 'even if accepted in full it only shows what COULD or SHOULD have happened in the way of damage by toxic emissions. In the light of what DID happen in the way of toxic damage, I consider that the defendants' evidence could not be held to rebut the plaintiffs' case'.

Theoretical or inductive evidence cannot be allowed to displace proven facts. It was proven as a matter of probability that John Hanrahan suffered ill-health as a result of toxic emissions from the factory. It was a fact, and so found by the judge, that there was unusual damage to some plant life on the plaintiffs' farm in the relevant period, the only suggested source of this damage being the factory.

And there was a volume of uncontroverted evidence given by eyewitnesses that animals were seen and heard to be ill and in distress at a time when the observer was experiencing foul chemical smells or weeping eyes or irritated skin, which could have been caused only by the factory.

It would be to allow scientific theorising to dethrone fact to dispose of this claim by saying, as was said in the judgement under appeal, that there was 'virtually no evidence in this case of injury to human beings or animals which has been scientifically linked to any chemicals emanating from the defendants' factory'.

Justice Henchy stated that there were many factors that proved that the factory emissions were the cause:

The Causes

1. The plaintiffs' dairy herd was a thriving one up to the time when smells and other factory emissions were noticed.
2. The five veterinary surgeons who regularly saw and treated the animals in the relevant period were all of the firm opinion that what the animals were suffering from was caused by toxic emissions from the factory.
3. The factory incinerator, which was designed to burn, destroy and render harmless seven tons a day of chemical solvents was run for long periods at temperatures which were too low to achieve the desired result, thus breaching one of the conditions of the planning permission for the factory and making damage to humans and animals highly likely.
4. The ailments suffered by the cattle – evidenced by streaming eyes, coughing, a high incidence of abortions, twinning and of calves born deformed, reduced milk yields, sore and cut teats, stampeding, marked lack of thrift, and want of sexual capacity in the bulls – were too pronounced and varied to be accounted for by natural causes (as was suggested by the defendants) or bad farm management. The most credible explanation offered for the ailments and abnormalities in the cattle was the toxic emissions from the factory.

Mary Hanrahan, as resilient as ever, welcomed the judgement with the contentedness of a woman, in her late sixties, who had suffered and watched her family experience great pain and hardship. 'If we never get a shilling damages I am happy that we got our name cleared, that we are not crooks.'[9]

NO MORE INCINERATORS

The Hanrahans' legal victory is an oasis in an otherwise barren desert. Communities and individuals fighting companies who operate toxic waste incinerators have had very little success.

It is clear from what we already know that not enough is known about the toxicity of the majority of synthetic chemicals yet our legal systems appear impervious to this reality, instead focusing on antiquated scientific values to explain away what is known. Toxic pollution from incinerators that burn chlorinated substances is a major health threat to animals and humans. Many scientists, ecologists, environmentalists, medical practitioners and epidemiologists all agree on this. But if it cannot be argued or proven scientifically that pollution is the cause of ill-health it is not a fact!

In British toxic tort legislation it has been made more difficult than ever following Scottish farmer Andrew Graham's failure to prove that the hazardous-waste disposal company ReChem had destroyed his herd with toxic emissions from their Bonnybridge high-temperature incinerator. In its defence, ReChem argued that Graham's problems were not caused by emissions from their incinerator. They alleged it was bad husbandry by Graham.[10]

The Graham case is a classic example of the imbalance in environmental law because the onus was on his legal team to prove that ReChem's incinerator emissions were to blame for the death of his cattle. Unfortunately for the Grahams their solicitors were unable to show 'causation' by ReChem and the judge, Justice Forbes – obviously swayed by the evidence of the defendant's scientists – ruled against them.[11] Desmond Browne, barrister for ReChem, contended that harm or damage cases must be foreseen for liability to be proved. Therefore strict liability only applies if damage can be reasonably foreseen. Browne stated that the emissions 'were not foreseeable consequences of the operation of the incinerator'. Justice Forbes agreed that forseeability 'is indeed a prerequisite of the recovery of damages in private nuisance'.[12] We'll come back to this because this is a crucial element, not only in the Graham case but in how incinerators are supposed to function.

Graham had failed to demonstrate to the court that ReChem and not some other cause had killed his herd – which is proving to be the anvil, Martyn Day has argued, on which modern environmental law is forged.

For those injured by environmental pollution there are two key hurdles. The first is the enormous difficulty in proving causation. They must show that any particular complex cancer has been caused by the environmental pollutant rather than by any of the other possible causes. The second is showing the fault of the defendant. These two hurdles, in most cases, are almost impossible to overcome.[13]

Modern environmental law, as Martyn Day has stressed, is flawed because it favours the polluter not the polluted.

> Those companies that are involved in polluting our environment do so in the pursuit of profit. Where in years to come it is possible to show that a child's cancer has been caused by a particular process, it ill behoves a company to say, 'ah, but we were not clear that the pollution we were pushing out could cause that particular harm and it would be unfair to make us pay'. The child is a totally innocent victim and it should be the polluter, as the party who has profited from the polluting activity, who must take the risk, not the individual.[14]

In the meantime potentially polluting industry is determined it should not be liable and is prepared to devote its enormous resources towards defeating any claim against it. And, as in both the Hanrahan and Graham cases, industry can turn, as Day put it, 'to scientists and lawyers by the score' to make its case that its specific processes are not the cause of illness, despite the accepted scientific fact that certain chemicals are the cause of countless cancers, reproductive and developmental problems, immune and endocrine systems failure and abnormalities in new born children. Day has argued that the 'onus should move to the defendant to show that they are not responsible' – a change in the law that would appear to be highly improbable, given industry's belligerent attitude to pollution claims against it and its determination to continue its present methods of production.

Yet it is obvious that potentially polluting industry has no intention of allowing anyone to make a case against it and frequently attempts to discredit many of the scientific studies that show conclusively that toxic pollution is the cause of ill-health and death among humans and animals. The CanTox report, commissioned by the world's leading chlorine manufacturers to argue a case for a safe level of toxicity in organochlorines, is an example of this. 'The bottom line is that this sort of work, sponsored by industry or otherwise, achieves something for industry,' Tim Barton of the Social Ecology Research Unit argued. 'Once such an article is in the public domain as a scientific paper and in a respected scientific journal, the people that produce the hazardous chemicals involved can refer to it in court' – thus giving legal credibility to their case that 'their' toxic pollution is not to blame for illnesses never seen before the twentieth century.[15]

Legislation in many countries is going a little way towards protecting communities from toxic pollution from incineration but the problem remains – that incineration as a disposal method does not destroy waste, it simply changes its molecular structure while reducing its volume – en route to the food chain via air, land, rivers and sea. The European Community, for example, accepted new standards for dioxin emissions that were thought by the chemical and hazardous waste disposal industries to be technically impossible and financially crippling.[16] Many chemical companies in Europe spent millions of dollars installing new technology, including catalysts, which, they claimed, eliminate 99 per cent of dioxins. BASF in Ludwigshafen in Germany spent DM100 million/€51 million ($59.5 million) on equipment upgrading their eight high-temperature incinerators. It is the industry's argument that the new standards meet what the industry regard as the demands of the anti-incineration lobby. 'We now have a limit – a regulatory 0.1 nanogram per cubic metre and I say that is absolutely agreeable,' Bayer's Gerhard Stolpa said. It is also Stolpa's argument, common among chemical industry executives, that there has to be an acceptable limit of emissions because, 'it makes no sense to ask for zero emissions because zero emissions do not exist'.[17]

The arguments against incineration, specifically incineration processes that include chlorinated substances in the waste stream, have been debated ad nauseam now for several decades, yet still the industry insists that modern incinerators reduce the load of pollution to the environment and reduce the risk to the general health of communities. The chemical industry is, of course, talking about its own burners, which, it has stressed, are manufactured to the highest possible 'state-of-the-art' standards. So who builds the other ones?

Incinerators have been implicated as a huge source of the dioxin that gets into the food chain. Medical waste and municipal waste incinerators (because of the large amounts of PVC in the waste stream) are regarded as the worst culprits.[18] Toxic waste incinerators are seen as less than significant contributors to the dioxin burden in the environment.[19]

All forms of combustion, which contain chlorinated substances, produce dioxin. It does not matter that some incinerators emit less dioxin than others, what matters is that dioxin is formed as a consequence of the combustion of chemicals and waste that contain chlorine molecules. The chemical industry may not want to admit it but as long as chlorine is used in their processes and as long as it is burned the inevitable consequence is the release of dioxins into the environment and ultimately into the food chain. This has been the crucial argument in the green movement's campaign against chlorine. US Greenpeace scientist Pat Costner is unequivocal in her science about dioxin formation.

> Dioxin generation occurs during combustion or other reactions when both organic matter and an available chlorine source are present. Much evidence suggests that the global dioxin burden stems primarily from the life-cycle of chlorine-containing synthetic organic materials (e.g., polyvinyl chloride (PVC) plastic, chlorinated solvents, chlorinated pesticides, chlorine-based bleaching agents, etc.).
>
> For this reason, the elimination of dioxin generation at the source can best be achieved, in many cases, by substituting chlorine-free alternative materials. Indeed, many technically feasible and economically competitive cleaner products and processes already exist. In waste combustion systems, chlorine is the limiting element for dioxin formation. This suggests that the total dioxin output from these systems can be reduced and/or eliminated through a materials policy that curbs chlorine input.[20]

Greenpeace are not isolated in their stance on chlorine and dioxin but the ability of the chemical industry to confuse the issue by presenting conflicting 'scientific reports' means that the debate becomes unfocused again. In 1995 with $150,000 worth of the Vinyl Institute's money the American Society of Mechanical Engineers went about compiling a report on the relationship between chlorine and dioxin in incinerators.[21] As an exercise in risk assessment and damage limitation it is a work of genius, but it is also flawed.[22] The tireless work put in by people like Costner and many like her in the green movement has meant that the chemical industry, in this case the institute that represents the interests of the manufacturers of the plastic PVC, has never been allowed to get away with setting the agenda on this issue. And because honest scientists are able to show the relationship between the combustion of chlorine and the formation of dioxin the issue, essentially, remains political. So despite the power and the wealth that corporations are able to muster the weight of evidence against them grows larger day by day.[23]

The question is: how many more reports have to be written, how many more recommendations have to be made, and how many more communities have to be poisoned before the 'accidental' production of dioxin is ended?[24]

Epilogue
Challenging Power and Money

Almost all PCDDs and PCDFs found in humans from the general population are believed to come from food, especially meat, milk, fish, and their by-products.

Arnold Schecter[1]

Lifetime exposure in a population consuming much Baltic fatty fish can reach the levels of exposures seen in Seveso, Italy, in 1976.

Hannu Kiviranta[2]

The main food sources of PCBs and dioxins after weaning in young children are dairy products, processed foods, and meat and meat products. Strategies should be directed toward reducing PCB and dioxin intake through the food chain at all ages and by lowering the consumption of animal products and processed foods, and not by discouraging breast-feeding.

Svati Patandin[3]

Dioxin is a consequence of chlorine chemistry and it is only now, as we engage another century, that we are beginning to understand the truth about the dioxin family and the technology that created it.

Technology has always had a Jeykll and Hyde effect on humanity. The story about dioxin has only unfolded because some people don't believe everything they are told about technology! While some believe technology is good for us, others argue that it can also be bad. The people who know this understand that ignorance of technology is the reason why it is so impotent.

These are the people who challenge illegitimate authority. These are the people who challenge the lies, who challenge ignorance, who challenge apathy. Without them the secret history of dioxin might never have been told and the consequences of chlorine chemistry known. That the danger to health from dioxin is now a matter of concern among those who are aware of it is, surprisingly, not the issue. It is the difficulty activists and scientists working on toxic pollution and its impact on health are having trying to convince the world that there is really a problem.

THOSE WHO TOLD THE TRUTH

They include people like social ecologist Murray Bookchin. In 1951, in a book-length article entitled 'The Problems of Chemicals in Food',[4] he began to question the unaccountable activities of the chlor-alkali, petrochemical and chemical industries and the impact their organochlorine products were beginning to exert on human health. When he tried to alert America to the consequences to society from the growing dependence on chlorine chemistry his polemic was ignored and is now hardly known.

A decade later biologist Rachel Carson, in her epochal book *Silent Spring*, brought public attention to the insidious impact of chemical products such as aldrin, chlordane, dieldrin, DDT, endrin, lindane, pentachlorophenol, 2,4-D and 2,4,5-T on wildlife and ecosystems in general, predicting that humans were next because of the interdependentness of all species on the health of the biosphere. She described in horrific detail how pesticides, in particular, were infiltrating ecosystems, how they biomagnified in the food chain with devastating effect.[5] Despite the adulation that now surrounds her work, Carson fared little better with her warning in *Silent Spring*: 'Every human being is now subjected to contact with dangerous chemicals, from the moment of conception until death.'[6]

Even Thomas Whiteside's exposé of the health effects of Agent Orange in the late 1960s, which he carried through to the 1970s with concern about the phenoxy herbicides, was allowed to fizzle out. It was his tenacity that made the Bionetics Research Laboratories study on the birth-deforming effects of 2,4,5-T into a political issue, leading Agent Orange use to be suspended.[7]

During the 1970s Carol Van Strum documented the same evidence, in a series of books while embarking on a persistent campaign to get the US authorities to ban 2,4,5-T, 2,4-D, pentachlorophenol and ultimately dioxin.

To those who bear the risk, exposure to poisons is a matter of life and death. Decisions about poisons which disrupt the basic mechanisms of life and the integrity of future generations raise profound moral questions. Society cannot afford to entrust such decisions to corporate or political entities that exempt themselves from the restraints of morality and ethics.[8]

Toxicologist Alastair Hay realised at the end of the 1970s that these decisions would not be taken without a struggle.

For those who have been exposed to (2,4,5-T) or its dioxin contaminant in the past, including the people of Vietnam, the veterans of the Vietnam War, the residents of Seveso, or workers in the chemical industry, no panacea is available. Only further investigations will give any indication of their health prospects in the long term. But even these answers are unlikely to be forthcoming in the immediate future. It is likely to be a long haul.[9]

Ecologist Barry Commoner has been a robust campaigner in the decades since the 1950s on the perils of the chemical industry. In 1994, while the US Environmental Protection Agency procrastinated over its reassessment of dioxin, he told scientists and environmental campaigners that the chemical industry did not want to stop using chlorine in its processes because modern commerce demanded products made from organochlorines.[10]

Peter Montague's Environmental Research Foundation has been the single most effective resource for information on the effects of chlorine chemistry on human health, through his publication *Environment and Health Weekly*. Yet while Montague regularly produces essential ecological, scientific and philosophical texts, his publication has a small circulation and is hardly known outside the green movement.

Zoologist Theo Colborn has presented evidence that synthetic chemicals (including the dioxin family) are threatening the fertility, intelligence and survival of the human species by disrupting the endocrine (hormone producing) system.[11] This hormonal damage, many scientists now believe, is the cause of the 50 per cent drop in the human male sperm count since 1940,[12] the two-fold increase in breast cancer among women since 1960,[13] the three-fold increase in testicular cancer[14] and two-fold increase in prostate cancer since the 1940s,[15] the phenomenal rise in endometriosis (a disease virtually unknown outside the twentieth century – which now affects five million American women)[16] and the increasing number of children born with abnormalities. Human males, Colborn has insisted, will probably become infertile by the middle of the twenty-first century if a ban on the chemicals known to disrupt the endocrine system is not implemented as soon as possible.[17]

These are overwhelming testimonies. They span five decades. Yet they have been ignored. However it's getting harder to ignore the evidence about the health effects of chemicals like dioxin. It has long been known that carcinogenic responses have been detected in every non-human species exposed to dioxin.[18] Between 1989 and 1991 it became clear that dioxin was a human carcinogen as well as a cancer promoter. The Fingerhut and Manz studies on chemical workers proved this. They showed that high exposure to dioxin is a direct cause of cancer and this has since been confirmed by studies of the population exposed to dioxin in Seveso.[19] These include an occupational study by a German scientist in 1989, on-going work by Samuel Epstein – who has stressed that certain cancers are ten times higher among some industrial workers than within the general population – and by studies done by IARC, WHO, USEPA, the Danish EPA and by many others.[20] The WHO have noted that at least 80 per cent of all cancer is attributable to environmental influences, which biologist and cancer researcher Sandra Steingraber calls a 'stunning statistic'.[21]

These figures do not reveal the specific cause of environmental cancers. It is not known how many sprayers and farmers and labourers have died from cancer as a consequence of their exposure to phenoxy herbicides. It is not known how many people have died from cancer because of Agent Orange. It is not known how many workers have died from cancer because they were exposed to chlorophenols. It is not known how many people living in the midst of chemical factories, toxic/medical/municipal incinerators and other installations where the combustion of chlorinated substances take place have succumbed to cancer. But this environmental and occupational exposure to dioxin is only the tip of the iceberg.

There have been many people who were prepared for the long haul and among the scientific community the name Arnold Schecter stands out. Schecter's work is characterised by his unending quest to learn how much damage dioxin does to the human body, specifically by measuring dioxin in human tissue – a quest that has taken him all over the planet. It is a quest that is starting to bring results. 'Compared with the extremely crude and nonspecific biomarkers available to estimate dioxin exposure several decades ago, such as chloracne,' he wrote in 2003, 'chemists, physicians, toxicologists, and epidemiologists have made considerable progress working together in this multidisciplinary field to relate dioxin exposure to human health.'[22]

And then there is Gerson Smoger – attorney, scientist, environmentalist and hero to the Vietnam vets. It is almost 20 years since Smoger, who studied law at the University of California at Berkeley, got involved with dioxin litigation, following an encounter in Atlantic City with Marilyn Leistner, the last mayor of Times Beach. This led him to the Overmann case, contact with Admiral Elmo Zumwalt and his battle to put dioxin back into the courts, confident that he will win. The USEPA's dioxin reassessment, he has argued, is now about politics.

> The dioxin reassessment still hasn't come out. The draft has been approved and they still haven't released it. That's one of the things going on in EPA – stopping everything that's going out. I believe that the reassessment was going to show that dioxin was much less hazardous than it was believed to be. And the reassessment would allow, particularly paper manufacturers supporting bleaching, and others to increase the levels of dioxin. So it was actually [going to be reassessed] as being less dangerous. But by the time they were doing the reassessment, by 1991, it was pretty clear in science and it got clearer all the time that it was actually more dangerous than they thought. The reassessment was initiated by the Republicans. They didn't want that to get out. So it's just a lot of politics. A few years ago, the Republicans put a rider [an addition attached to unrelated legislation], which didn't pass; it said that no public policy should be effected by whatever is said in the dioxin reassessment. That's an interesting rider. That's where it ends … In the meantime, every organisation recognizes dioxin as a Class I carcinogen. The public tends to forget how toxic this substance is. How would you say to the public at large that this is still an important issue for public health that shouldn't be forgotten about? It's an extraordinarily important issue because of what we understand about it. We did some studies on Times Beach kids and now it's generally agreed that the biggest problem is in the immune system and in neuro-cognition, cognitive development from the dangers of exposure. It's ubiquitous in our environment. While in the 1980s, everybody was thinking cancer, cancer, cancer. That's not the same end point. It's a long-term end point with the workers. But in Times Beach particularly we're really worried about the kids.[23]

LIVING IN A TOXIC WORLD

We are all exposed to dioxin and to other pollutants. Pesticides made from organochlorines, phenoxyacetic acids and chlorophenols (all contaminated with dioxin) have exposed millions of people ignorant of the dangers to their health since the late 1940s.[24]

Agricultural workers were being subjected to toxic substances that would impair their health, affect their fertility and offspring and eventually kill them.[25] Those who worked in agriculture, forestry and land use were encouraged to use and then became dependent on weed killers – mainly phenoxy herbicides – for application on monocultures such as soya beans, wheat, barley, corn, sugar beet and on unwanted vegetation. Commercial and financial demands forced farmers to use pesticides on cash crops such as fruit, cereals, grains and legumes (specifically bananas, cocoa, coffee, cotton, maize, rice, soya beans, sugar cane and wheat among many others).[26]

Before the use of pesticides farmers lost as much as a third of their crop. Pesticides would become their salvation, they were told, but it didn't work out like that. Farmers are still losing a third of their crop to nature's predators even though they have increased the volume of pesticide use each year.[27]

The discoveries that dioxin is compromising the health of the planet and its species should have been earth-shattering news, but, because of the complexity of the subject and the ability of industrial scientists, corporate spin-doctors and stonewalling bureaucrats to warp the truth, dioxin still remains a story to be told. Over the past 50 years, this debate about chlorine chemistry and its deadly legacy – dioxin – has continued. Obfuscation by industry scientists, compliant bureaucrats, apologetic academics and dependent family doctors/veterinarians has clouded dioxin's health effects.[28]

Much of the reason for this is ignorance and a belief that science, medicine and technology can provide a solution for everything. This ignorance might explain why it has taken so long for dioxin to become a health issue. But it does not explain why those who did know about the risks from exposure to dioxin chose to deliberately manipulate the truth. An easy answer would be human nature, because there is no evidence that the chemical industry, regulatory authorities and governments collectively sought to deliberately hide their knowledge about dioxin. There is evidence, however, that individual chemical companies decided that the less people knew about dioxin the better it would be for them.

Dioxin is primarily a component of chlorine chemistry. Although some dioxins and furans occur naturally they are not seen as a threat to human health.[29] The dioxins having a serious impact on wildlife and humankind are those that have been identified with chlorine chemistry.[30]

In other words dioxin is a phenomenon of twentieth-century human industrial activity, significantly since the 1939–45 war. Within a decade of the end of the war the products of chlorine chemistry were in common use in agriculture, industry and warfare. As their production increased, the environmental reservoir of dioxin increased. The chemical industry was releasing a potent chemical into the environment and ultimately into the food chain.

WHY CONSUMERISM FUELS THE SYSTEM

To know the dioxin story it is also important to understand how the chemical industry works, how scientists reach their conclusions, how governments and regulatory agencies function, how environmentalists agitate and how we as consumers ultimately fuel the system that is poisoning us.

The chemical industry is in business to sell its products. These products have a market value that is determined by consumerist demand. It is also in business to make profits so that it can continue making new products for the demanding consumer. These are its primary concerns. Anything that effects this process will undermine its ability to keep its shareholders happy.

But the shareholders are society itself. The entire system is funded by society. Every time someone takes out an insurance policy or deposits money in a bank, capitalism benefits. The movement of capital through the system, by financiers, stockbrokers and shareholders, is the stack of cards that hold the corporations up. To stay up the corporations must ensure that their own flow of capital is not impeded. A contaminated product, if prohibited, would bring that house of cards down. So when the chlorophenol producers were faced with bans on their most lucrative products they fought hard to keep them on the market.

By successfully managing to defuse concern about accidental, occupational and environmental exposure of their workers and neighbouring communities and claims that their products were contaminated with deadly poisons, the industry was able to keep making profits. But this also meant convincing themselves that their products were fine. Monsanto took this attitude to the extreme while the industry in general tried to convince themselves that revelations about the explosions at chlorophenol factories and their occupational problems could be easily dismissed.

ASSESSING THE RISKS

The explosion at Seveso in Italy on 10 July 1976 changed that. Hans Paul Bosshardt's delicate warning three years before Seveso, in 1973, had been ignored. 'In the future, to prevent damage, the technical production of chlorinated phenols and formulations will have to be improved so that polychlorinated dibenzo-p-dioxins no longer occur. If this is not possible, the use of these compounds will have to be drastically limited or totally forbidden.'[31] Bosshardt's words were hardly read. If they were, they weren't noted by the industry. Instead industry adopted a different tactic. The propaganda war began. Trouble was brewing for industries involved in chlorine chemistry. And they knew it. There would have to be some serious management and damage limitation. Another war front needed to be established. Risk assessment became a new academic discipline.[32] As Paul Merrell and Carol Van Strum put it, 'government scientists were expected to tailor their risk assessments to support already made management decisions on dioxin.'[33]

The manipulation of dioxin science and scientists became an art form. If the industry could force regulation onto the statute books that would allow them to keep making their profits that would do instead. So despite the mounting evidence about dioxin, in October 1992, officials with the USEPA said they would not draw any conclusions from the work on the reassessment until the agency had drawn up new dioxin risk assessment guidelines.[34] When the USEPA released its 'public review draft' in September 1994, Lynn Goldman, the agency's assistant administrator for Prevention, Pesticides and Toxics, said they needed more information before they could reassess their 1985 reassessment of dioxin's health risks. Greenpeace USA argued they had all the information they needed, calling for a ban on chlorine chemistry that, they insisted, was the source of dioxin.[35]

Others had already been convinced. In the wake of Theo Colborn's report, the International Joint Commission on the North American Great Lakes was reiterating what it had been saying for years about persistent toxic substances like organochlorines. Founded out of the Great Lakes Water Quality Agreement re-signed between the USA and

Canada in 1972, the IJC defined in 1978 toxic substances to mean 'a substance which can cause death, disease, behavioural abnormalities, cancer, genetic mutations, physiological or reproductive malfunctions or physical deformities in any organism or its offspring, or which can become poisonous after concentration in the food chain or in combination with other substances'. By 1994 (at the time of the USEPA draft report), the IJC reinforced its belief that

> persistent toxic substances are too dangerous to the biosphere and to humans to permit their release in any quantity, and all persistent toxic substances are dangerous to the environment, deleterious to the human condition, and can no longer be tolerated in the ecosystem, whether or not unassailable scientific proof of acute or chronic damage is universally accepted.[36]

MATERIAL DEPENDENCY

It has been argued that perhaps half the jobs in the world are dependent on chlorine chemistry in some way or another. So the knowledge we now have that dioxin is damaging organs, altering reproductive patterns, causing infertility and disrupting intelligence in wildlife and humans is not simply a threat to our health, it is also a threat to the social, economic and political fabric of global society. Yet, is not the threat to the health and continued well-being of global communities and the wider disruption of the ecosphere greater in significance than the end of wage-slave, electronic-culture, consumerist society?

Throughout the 1940s, 1950s, 1960s and 1970s the rise in production of organochlorines was regarded as an essential factor in the economic growth and technical progress of western society. At no time did the questions about the consequences of this growth become relevant to everyday lives. The toxic pollution that resulted from this technological progress was never considered a hazard to human health. The post-1939–45 war materialism that was gripping the western world and turning people into apathetic consumers had the force of the *Titanic* on its doomed maiden voyage.

The materialist world was hurtling towards its doom and it didn't know it. The work of scientists in white coats became an aspect of the materialist world – as people took their stories from film and television. The medium as the message had arrived and most people were happy to be brainwashed.[37] The evidence that chemical compounds like dioxin had the ability to disrupt and destroy wildlife was well known to the white-coated laboratory scientists who experimented on small animals – but Hollywood wasn't going to tell you because Hollywood didn't know. The dioxin story, from its beginnings, has never been part of our consumer culture.

DIOXIN DESPAIR

The history of dioxin compares with how we see the universe with its galaxies like grains of sand – each grain an integral aspect of the whole. To understand the dioxin story you must consider the galaxy of information that is present, always mindful that each grain of sand represents a crucial element of the history. Each grain of sand, like a star, is a beacon. But the dioxin story is also like a black hole where those galaxies and their stars disappear into oblivion.

If the dioxin story appears complex it's simply because it is. Every time something has happened to illuminate the story, those who do not want it to be told with truth and honesty have plunged it into darkness with arguments designed to confuse. It now seems remarkable, given the amount of information that is shared every day on this planet, that it has taken so long for the truth about dioxin to emerge and for that truth to be obscured when it appears crystal clear.

Dioxin is only one of a million problems caused by industrial civilisation facing humanity. These problems are not about science, technology, regulation, legislation, reform or empowerment. They are about the way we live. We drive the machine every day as consumers. Dioxin is now part of our lives but so are 500 other synthetic chemicals – which are in our bodies because they are in the food chain via the soil, water and air. Only by changing the way we live will we be able to address these problems.

Once we could blame our ignorance and apathy but we can't any longer. We cannot blame our industrialists, scientists and regulators. We can only blame ourselves. Until we change our everyday habits we will only have ourselves to blame when we come face to face with the reality of living in a world deficient in fossil fuels and laid waste by our greed, ignorance, apathy and consumerism.

Appendix
Bill Gaffey's work

RACHEL'S ENVIRONMENT & HEALTH WEEKLY #494; 16 MAY 1996

Bill Gaffey's work is finished. Bill died suddenly of a heart attack at age 71 on October 6, 1995 in St. Louis. As a result, his libel lawsuit against RACHEL'S ENVIRONMENT & HEALTH WEEKLY and its editor Peter Montague, has been dismissed by a federal judge.

Gaffey, a mathematician who retired in 1989 as director of epidemiology for Monsanto, the St. Louis chemical giant, sued Montague and the Environmental Research Foundation (ERF), publisher of RACHEL'S, for $4 million in 1991. Gaffey said he had been defamed in RACHEL'S #171. The suit was scheduled for a federal jury trial in St. Louis sometime during 1996.

Shortly after he began working for Monsanto in 1979, Gaffey and one Judith Zack studied workers at a Monsanto plant in Nitro, West Virginia, who had been exposed to dioxin while manufacturing Agent Orange for chemical warfare use in Vietnam. In their study, Gaffey and Zack reported finding no evidence of unusual cancers among Monsanto workers who had been exposed to dioxin for many years.[1] In 1980, this was an important finding.

Gaffey's study was important to Monsanto because the company had gotten itself into serious trouble at the time. In the early 1980s, Monsanto was facing hundreds of millions, possibly billions, of dollars in lawsuits by tens of thousands of Vietnam veterans, and by former Monsanto workers, all claiming they had been harmed by exposure to Agent Orange, or to the dioxin that it contains. If all such claims had been sustained in court, it seems likely that Monsanto would have been bankrupted.[2] Bill Gaffey admitted under oath that he knew he had been hired in 1979 partly to help defend Monsanto against lawsuits over dioxin.

Monsanto tacitly acknowledged the importance of the Gaffey/ Zack study when, in October, 1980, three years before the study was published, the company issued a press release headlined, 'Study Fails to Link Agent Orange to Deaths of Industrial Workers.'[3]

No doubt about it, Bill Gaffey's study was important to Monsanto, fighting for its life. With help from Gaffey, Monsanto successfully defended itself against every lawsuit by Vietnam vets and Monsanto workers who felt they had been harmed by dioxin exposures. The company was salvaged, and it went on to pioneer powerful new biocides and genetically-engineered forms of life, thus rounding out a contribution unique in the annals of American industry. (See REHW #144, #295, #327, #381, #382, #383, #384, #434, #454, #483.)

But Gaffey's work was also important to the federal government. The Veterans Administration relied in part on Gaffey's work to deny medical benefits to tens of thousands of Vietnam veterans exposed to Agent Orange. (Not until 1992 did the VA reverse its position on this.) U.S. Environmental Protection Agency (EPA) relied in part on the Gaffey study to set generous limits on dioxin exposures for the American public, thus providing minimal regulation for politically powerful industries such as paper, oil, and chemicals.[4] EPA now acknowledges that dioxin is a devilishly potent growth dysregulator and 'environmental hormone,' but in large measure the agency still regulates dioxin by rules set during the era of Bill Gaffey's work. (See REHW #279, #390, #391, #414.) In the mid-1980s, animal studies were showing dioxin to be breathtakingly toxic, but skeptics (and those sowing doubt for a living) could always point to the Gaffey study (and other work sponsored by Monsanto) as evidence that humans were somehow exempt from harm.

Therefore, it was important news when the veracity of Bill Gaffey's work fell under suspicion. During a worker lawsuit against Monsanto in 1984, plaintiffs' lawyers discovered that Gaffey and Zack had classified four workers as 'unexposed' to dioxin when the very same four workers had been classified as 'exposed' to dioxin in a previous Monsanto study co-authored by Zack.[5] Reluctantly, Zack confirmed this fact under oath.[6] Thus was it discovered that Gaffey's data had been cooked.

When an official of U.S. Environmental Protection Agency (EPA), Cate Jenkins, learned of this in 1990, she immediately sent a memo to her superiors, attaching a portion of a legal brief about the Gaffey study (and other studies sponsored by Monsanto), indicating she believed there was evidence of fraud.[7] Jenkins has since documented that EPA relied upon Monsanto's studies to set national dioxin standards.[4] As an EPA employee, Jenkins is required by federal law to report any evidence of fraud that she encounters in her work. (Monsanto officials complained vigorously to EPA about Jenkins.[8] EPA promptly transferred Jenkins to an unimportant position with nothing to do. She spent the next several years in a legal battle of her own against EPA, finally winning complete exoneration and reinstated to full duty. See REHW #400 and see our new publication by William Sanjour, ANNALS OF THE EPA: PART 4: THE MONSANTO INVESTIGATION [Annapolis, Md.: Environmental Research Foundation, 1996.])

In RACHEL'S #171, we reported on the Jenkins memo and the accompanying legal brief, and were subsequently sued for $4 million by Gaffey, who said his reputation had been tarnished and his consulting business damaged. The ATLANTA CONSTITUTION[9] and the AUSTIN (TEX.) AMERICAN-STATESMAN,[10] among other newspapers,[11] also reported the allegations of fraud, but were not sued.

At the time Jenkins wrote her memo, it was already a matter of debate in the scientific press that Gaffey and Zack had classified workers as 'unexposed' when, in a previous study co-authored by Zack, the same four workers had been classified as 'exposed.' In NATURE (the British equivalent of SCIENCE magazine in this country) in 1985 and 1986, a vigorous debate was conducted over the Gaffey/Zack study and its misclassification of exposed workers.[12] Neither Zack nor Gaffey chose to join in this debate, though they were specifically invited by the editors of NATURE to respond to allegations that they had misclassified workers.

Did Bill Gaffey's creative reclassification of four workers make any difference in the conclusions of the Gaffey/Zack study? It certainly did. By misclassifying workers, Gaffey was able to say that no excessive cancers could be found among Monsanto's Nitro workers – a complete reversal of the truth.

Properly classifying the four workers would have yielded the conclusion that lung cancers were significantly elevated among dioxin-exposed workers at the Monsanto plant – exactly the reverse of Bill Gaffey's widely-publicized finding. Ellen Silbergeld of the Environmental Defense Fund reanalyzed the Gaffey data, after properly classifying the four workers, and she reported statistically significant cancers among the exposed workers. My own analysis of the Gaffey data yielded a similar conclusion.[13]

If Gaffey had not cooked the data, history might have turned out very differently for Monsanto, for the dioxin-exposed Vietnam veterans who had to fight for 15 years for recognition of their troubles, and for the millions of Americans exposed to dioxin as a result of EPA's lax (or non-existent) dioxin regulations. Today the nation is still being poisoned by dioxin regulations set partly on the basis of Bill Gaffey's fraudulent study. Yes, Bill's work was extraordinarily important.

As for his claim that RACHEL #171 cost him $4 million in damaged reputation and lost consulting fees: under oath, Gaffey could not name a single colleague who had read RACHEL #171, and he could not document the loss of a single dollar.

In sum, Bill Gaffey's lawsuit against us was completely without merit, a classic SLAPP suit (strategic lawsuit against public participation) – an entirely frivolous action intended merely to harass and frighten us, and to waste our precious resources.[14] Instead what it did was reveal how many, many good friends we have, willing to sacrifice to come to our defense. Now Bill Gaffey is gone. May the victims of his work grant him forgiveness, and may he rest forever in the coolest spot there is in that unspeakable place that he has surely gone to.

Peter Montague

[1] Judith A. Zack and William R. Gaffey, 'A Mortality Study of Workers Employed at the Monsanto Company Plant in Nitro, West Virginia,' in Richard E. Tucker, Alvin L. Young, and Allan P. Gray, editors, HUMAN AND ENVIRONMENTAL RISKS OF CHLORINATED DIOXINS AND RELATED COMPOUNDS (New York: Plenum Press, 1983) pgs. 575–591.

[2] For example, see: 'More Agent Orange suits filed in Chicago; still others will follow.' CHEMICAL WEEK February 28, 1979, pg. 18.

[3] Dan R. Bishop, 'Study Fails to Link Agent Orange to Deaths of Industrial Workers [press release],' (St. Louis: Monsanto, October 9, 1980).

[4] Cate Jenkins, U.S. Environmental Protection Agency, Characterization and Assessment Division, Regulatory Development Branch (OS-332), memorandum to John West, Special Agent in Charge, and Kevin Guarino, Special Agent, Office of Criminal Investigations, National Enforcement Investigations Center, U.S. Environmental Protection Agency entitled 'Impact of Falsified Monsanto Human Studies on Dioxin Regulations by EPA and Other Agencies – January 24, 1991 NIOSH Study Reverses Monsanto Study Findings and Exposes Certain Fraudulent Methods,' January 24, 1991. And see: Cate Jenkins, U.S. Environmental Protection Agency, Characterization and Assessment Division, Regulatory Development Branch (OS-332), memorandum to John West, Special Agent in Charge, and Kevin Guarino, Special Agent, Office of Criminal Investigations, National Enforcement Investigations Center, U.S. Environmental Protection

Agency, entitled 'Criminal Investigation of Monsanto Corporation – Cover-up of Dioxin Contamination in Products – Falsification of Dioxin Health Studies,' November 15, 1990.

[5] Judith Zack and Raymond R. Suskind, 'The Mortality Experience of Workers Exposed to Tetrachlorodibenzodioxin in a Trichlorophenol Process Accident,' JOURNAL OF OCCUPATIONAL MEDICINE Vol. 22, No. 1 (January, 1980), pgs. 11–14. In this study, the four workers in question can be found in Table 10, cases 1, 2, 5, and 7. In the Gaffey/Zack study the same four workers can be found in Table 11, lines 5, 6, 9 and 22.

[6] James M. Adkins et al v. Monsanto, U.S. District Court, Southern District of West Virginia (Civil Action No. S1–2098). Deposition of Judith Zack, March 1, 1984.

[7] Cate Jenkins, 'Memo to Raymond Loehr: Newly Revealed Fraud by Monsanto in an Epidemiological Study Used by EPA to Assess Human Health Effects from Dioxins,' dated February 23, 1990. At the time she wrote this memo, Dr. Jenkins was a chemist with the Waste Characterization Branch (OS 332), Characterization and Assessment Division, U.S. EPA, 401 M St., SW, Washington, DC 20460. Loehr was Chairperson of the Executive Committee of the Science Advisory Board (A-101), Office of the Administrator, U.S. EPA, 401 M St., SW, Washington, DC 20460. The Jenkins memo had attached to it 25 pages of a brief filed in Case No. 5–88–0420, in the Appellate Court of Illinois, Fifth District. The author of the brief was Rex Carr, 412 Missouri Avenue, East St. Louis, IL 62201.

[8] Richard J. Mahoney, CEO, Monsanto Co., letter to William Reilly, EPA Administrator, March 26, 1990.

[9] Jeff Nesmith and Charles Seabrook, 'Dioxin research altered, EPA says,' ATLANTA CONSTITUTION March 23, 1990, pg A1.

[10] Jeff Nesmith (Cox News Service), 'EPA Memo: Dioxin Study Fraudulent,' AUSTIN AMERICAN-STATESMAN March 23, 1990, pg. A6.

[11] For example, see Jeff Nesmith, 'Key Dioxin Study a Fraud, EPA Says,' THE CHARLESTON GAZETTE March 23, 1990, pg. unknown; and: Jeff Nesmith, 'Monsanto altered dioxin study, EPA memo says.' THE INDIANAPOLIS STAR March 23, 1990, pg. unknown; and: Jeff Nesmith, 'Monsanto Study on Dioxins Called a Fraud by EPA Memo.' THE ORANGE COUNTY [CALIFORNIA] REGISTER March 23, 1990, pg. unknown.

[12] See Alistair Hay and Ellen Silbergeld. 'Assessing the risk of dioxin exposure.' NATURE Vol. 315 (May 9, 1985), pgs. 102–103. And:

Michael Gough, 'Dioxin Exposure at Monsanto,' NATURE Vol. 318 (December 12, 1985), pg. 504. And: Alistair Hay and Ellen Silbergeld. 'Dioxin Exposure at Monsanto,' NATURE Vol. 320 (April 17, 1986), pg. 569.

[13] In NATURE Vol. 320 (April 17, 1986), pg. 569, Silbergeld wrote, 'A reanalysis of the [Gaffey] data, presented by EKS [Ellen K. Silbergeld] at the Dioxin 85 Symposium in Bayreuth in September 1985, indicates an excess mortality due to lung and bladder cancers.' Silbergeld reported her reanalysis in a paper at the Fifth International Conference on Dioxin, September 19, 1985, in Bayreuth, Germany. Unfortunately, this paper was never published and Silbergeld in 1993 did not fulfill a request for a copy. I reanalyzed the data myself in an unpublished paper: Peter Montague, THE EFFECT OF CORRECTING CLASSIFICATION ERRORS IN ZACK/GAFFEY'S STUDY OF THE MORTALITY OF DIOXIN-EXPOSED WORKERS (Annapolis, Md.: Environmental Research Foundation, November 22, 1993.) Properly classifying the four workers in question yields the conclusion that lung cancers and cancers of the respiratory tract were significantly increased ($p < 0.05$) among dioxin-exposed workers, thus reversing the main conclusion of the original Gaffey/Zack paper.

[14] George W. Pring and Penelope Canan, 'Slapp-Happy Companies,' NEW YORK TIMES March 29, 1996, pg. A21. And see the new book by Pring and Canan, SLAPPS: GETTING SUED FOR SPEAKING OUT (Philadelphia: Temple University Press, 1996).

Notes

WHAT IS DIOXIN?

1. Dioxin is made up of two benzene (dibenzo) molecules that are held together by two oxygen (dioxin) atoms in a specific position (para) to each other. Each benzene ring allows the attachment of six atoms. Two are taken up with the oxygen atoms. The other four attract chlorine atoms in the positions filled by hydrogen atoms. Hence the name poly chlorinated dibenzo para dioxins. The most toxic dioxin, 2,3,7,8-tetrachlorodibenzo-p-dioxin (TCDD), has four (tetra) chlorine (chloro) atoms in positions 2, 3, 7 and 8 of the two benzene (dibenzo) rings that are held in place (para) by the two oxygen (dioxin) atoms. Other dioxins have chlorine atoms in other positions, from 1 to 8. All dioxins are called congeners, meaning members of a similar group, and congeners with the same number of chlorine atoms are referred to as isomers. There are, for example, 22 isomers with four chlorine atoms and only one isomer with eight chlorine atoms. Polychlorinated dibenzofurans differ from their dioxin cousins by having only one oxygen atom. So, other chemical compounds are classified as members of the dioxin family if they contain chlorine or bromine atoms and exert dioxin-like toxicity. See the International Agency for Research on Cancer (IARC), Vol 69: *Dioxins and Furans*, Lyon, France, 1997.

2. Unlike dioxins and furans, which are accidental by-products of chemical processes and combustion, PCBs were deliberately synthesised by the chemical industry, by adding chlorine atoms to a biphenyl (two hexagonal benzene rings). Within a few years of their introduction to the marketplace by the Swann Chemical Company in 1929 they could be found in vehicles that store electricity and as lubricants, hydraulic fluids, cutting oils and liquid seals. There are 209 PCB compounds but only 13 are dioxin-like in their biological activity. In her review of PCBs, the EPA's Linda Birnbaum noted that they are also estrogenic, neurotoxic, can alter the levels of thyroid hormones in the blood, and can delay puberty after prenatal exposure.{1,2} By the time Swann had been absorbed into the Monsanto Chemical Company in 1935, regulations – which required the use of nonflammable cooling compounds in transformers – contributed to the commercial success of PCBs. As the commercial value of PCBs became known – they conduct heat but not electricity, do not burn easily and do not change chemically – Monsanto licensed others to manufacture them. As well as their use in transformers and capacitors in the electrical industry they became ingredients in paints, varnishes, inks and pesticides. Because of their nonflammable qualities they were used to treat wood, plastics and rubber.{3} Despite concern among workers exposed to PCBs in the 1930s, documented by Harvard, it wasn't until the 1960s that PCBs were first recognised as an environmental problem when a Danish researcher

reported finding them in 200 pike from all over Sweden, in other fish, and in an eagle.{4} Ten years later, as the environmental damage caused by PCBs became overwhelming, US Congress banned their manufacture, sale and distribution except in 'totally enclosed' systems. Between 1929 and 1989 total world production of PCBs (excluding the Soviet Union) was 3.4 billion pounds, or about 57 million pounds per year; yet even after the US ban world production continued at 36 million pounds per year.{5} – 1. Safe, S., 'PCBs: environmental impact, biochemical and toxic responses and implications for risk assessment', *Crit Rev Toxicol*, 24: 1–63, 1994; 2. Birnbaum, L., 'Endocrine effects of prenatal exposure to PCBs, dioxins and other xenobiotics: implications for policy and future research', *EHP* 102: 676–679, 1994; 3. Robert Risebrough and Virginia Brodine, 'More letters in the wind' in Sheldon Novick and Dorothy Cottrell (eds), *Our World in Peril: an Environment Review*, Fawcett, Greenwich, Con, 1971; 4. Soren Jensen, 'Report of a new chemical hazard', *New Scientist*, 32: 612, 1966; 5. *Rachel's Hazardous Waste News* #327, 4 March 1993.

3. Some other chlorinated and brominated compounds such as polychlorinated naphthalenes (PCNs) and polybrominated biphenyls (PBBs), also have dioxin-like toxicity. See Goldstein, J. A., and Safe, S., 'Mechanism of action and structure activity relationships' in Kimbrough and Jensen (eds), *Halogenated Biphenyls, Terphenyls, Naphthalenes, Dibenzodioxins and Related Products*, Elsevier, 1989. It is also believed there are polybromodibenzo-p-dioxins (PBDDs) and polybromodibenzofurans (PBDFs). According to Linda Birnbaum, director of the Environmental Toxicology Division of the US Environmental Protection Agency (EPA) 'brominated molecules are just about as equally toxic, and we know almost nothing about them, and almost no environmental monitoring has been done to determine whether they are really out there or not'. See Birnbaum, Great Lakes Water Quality Board submission, 1993.

4. In her study of the North American Great Lakes, Theo Colborn showed that the process of biomagnification of dioxin-like PCBs can be 25 million times greater at the top of the food chain than in the surrounding water. She explained this thus: from the sediment micro-organisms take up the PCBs where they accumulate in the body fat of tiny animals such as zoo plankton. Resisting breakdown the PCBs move up the food chain to small fish like smelt, on to the larger trout and finally to the herring gull – where the concentrations in the bird's tissue magnify 25 million times. See Curtis Travis and Holly Hattemer-Frey, 'Human Exposure to 2,3,7,8-TCDD', *Chemosphere* 16, 2331–2342, 1987. They identify dioxins as 'highly lipophilic (fat soluble), extremely persistent compounds that sorb strongly onto air particles, soil and sediment and bioaccumulate in the food chain'. And see Colborn, T., 1996. See Colborn, T., and Clement, C., (eds), *Chemically-Induced Alterations in Sexual and Functional Development: The Wildlife/Human Connection*, Princeton Scientific Publishing Co., 1992 (Colborn, Myers and Dumanoski, *Our Stolen Future*, Little Brown, 1996 is the popular version).

5. See Dewailly, E., 'Inuit exposure to organochlorines through the aquatic food chain in arctic Quebec', *EHP* 101: 618–621, 1993; Dewailly, E., et al, 'Exposure to remote maritime populations to coplanar PCBs', *EHP* 102:

Suppl. 1, 205–209 (1994) and Wania, F. and Mackay, D., 'Tracking the distribution of persistent organic pollutants', *Enviro Sci & Tech*, 30 (9): 390A-396A, 1996.

6. US Environmental Protection Agency, 'Health assessment for 2,3,7,8-TCDD and related compounds'. External Review Draft. EPA/600/BP-92/001a-c (1994) and US Environmental Protection Agency, 'Estimating exposure to dioxin-like compounds'. Prepared by the Office of Health and Environmental Assessment, Office of Research and Development, Washington, DC. External Review Draft, 3 vol. EPA/600/6–88/005Ca, Cb, Cc (1994). Also see Curtis Travis' and Holly Hattemer-Frey's claim that the food chain accounts for 98 per cent of human exposure to TCDD, and Beck, H., et al., 'PCDD and PCDF body burden from food intake in the Federal Republic of Germany', *Chemosphere* 18: 417–424, 1989; Fürst, P., Fürst, C., Groebel, W., 'Levels of PCDDs and PCDFs in food-stuffs from the Federal Republic of Germany', *Chemosphere* 20: 787–792, 1990.

7. Schecter, A., et al., 'Congener-specific levels of dioxins and dibenzofurans in US food and estimated daily dioxin toxic equivalent intake', *EHP* 102: 962–966, 1994.

8. This sets a factor of 1 for 2,3,7,8-TCDD against which all the others are measured. For example 1,2,3,7,8-pentachlorodibenzo-p-dioxin is set at 0.5, 1,2,3,4,6,7,8-heptachlorodibenzo-p-dioxin at 0.01, octachlorodibenzo-p-dioxins at 0.001 and all other polychlorinated dibenzo-p-dioxins at zero. See Committee on the Challenges of Modern Society, International Toxicity Equivalency Factor (I-TEF) Method of Risk Assessment for Complex Mixtures of Dioxins and Related Compounds. Pilot Study on International Exchange on Dioxins and Related Compounds. North Atlantic Treaty Organisation/CCMS. Report no: 176, August 1988, and Bretthauer, E., et al., *Dioxin Perspectives: A Pilot Study on International Exchange on Dioxins and Related Compounds*, Plenum, 1991. See also: Alhborg, U. G., et al., 'Impact of polychlorinated dibenzo-p-dioxins, dibenzofurans and biphenyls on human and environmental health, with special emphasis on application of the toxic equivalency factor concept', *Europ J Pharmacol-environ Toxicol Pharmacol Sect* 228: 179–199, 1992, and Safe, S., 'Polychlorinated biphenyls (PCBs), dibenzo-p-dioxins (PCDDs), dibenzofurans (PCDFs) and related compounds: environmental and mechanistic considerations that support the development of toxic equivalency factors (TEFs)', *CRC crit Rev Toxicol*, 21: 51–88, 1990.

9. USEPA Draft Reassessment of Dioxin, 1994.

10. According to IARC, 1997, 'progress in the analytical chemistry of (dioxins) and (furans) over the past 30 years has been remarkable'. This is because in the 1960s and 1970s the technology (packed column gas chromatography [GC] with electron capture detection [ECD]) allowed detection limits in the parts per million and parts per billion range. Frequently dioxins were not detected using this technology. In the early 1970s the technology advanced to mass spectrometry in conjunction with gas chromatography. Laboratory scientists studying dioxin favoured this GC-MS method. Throughout the 1970s and 1980s it was improved and with other advances it is now possible to identify and quantify individually all of the dioxin family at concentrations in the ppb and

ppt range. Stephens, however, notes that dioxin labs still vary in 'their capabilities and skill in performing these analyses'. There are only 40 WHO-recognised dioxin labs on the entire planet. See Baughmann, R., and Meselson, M., 'An improved analysis for tetrachlorodibenzo-p-dioxins', in Blair, E. H. (ed.), *Chlorodioxins: Origin and Fate* (Advances in Chemistry, Ser 120), American Chemical Society, 1973; Baughmann, R., and Meselson, M., 'An analytical method for detecting TCDD: levels of TCDD in samples from Vietnam', *EHP* 5, 27–35, 1973; Hass and Friesen, 'Qualitative and quantitative methods for dioxin analysis', *Ann NY Acad Sci*, 320, 28–42, 1979; Clement, R. E., and Tosine, H. M., 'The gas chromatographic/mass spectrometry determinations of chlorodibenzo-p-dioxins and furans', *Mass Spect Rev*, 7, 593–636, 1988; Buser, H. R., 'Review of methods of analysis for polychlorinated dibenzodioxins and furans', in, Rappe, C., et al., (eds), *Environmental Carcinogens: Methods of Analysis and Exposure Measurement*. Vol II: *Polychlorinated Dioxins and Furans*, IARC, 1991; Clement, R. E., 'Ultratrace dioxin and dibenzofuran analysis: 30 years of advances', *Analy Chem*, 63, 1130–1137, 1991.

11. Webster, T., *Dioxin and Human Health: A Public Health Assessment of Dioxin Exposure in Canada*, Boston University School of Public Health, 1994.

12. Montague, P., in 'Potent immune system poison: dioxin', *Rachel's Environment and Health Weeky* #414, 3 November 1994.

13. Davies, D., et al., 'International trends in cancer mortality in France, West Germany, Italy, Japan, England and Wales and the USA', *Lancet* 336: 474–481, 1990. See also Davies, D., and Hoel, D., (eds) 'Trends in cancer mortality in industrialised countries', Annals, *New York Acad Sci*, 609: 5–48, 1990.

14. When dioxin enters the body it is stored in our fat cells. Fat loss releases it into our blood stream where it is carried to the various organs, specifically the liver. Attached to the cells of these organs is a mechanism, an enzyme, which deals with contaminants. For reasons scientists are still unsure about dioxin binds very strongly with this mechanism, a cellular protein called the aryl hydrocarbon receptor.{1} Without this bonding to the AH receptor dioxin could not complete its toxic function in the body. Once formed it is then taken on a journey into the heart of the human cell, where the deoxyribonucleic acid (DNA) is located, and begins to play havoc. Dioxins may be broken down and excreted from the body at this stage but many scientists believe this process is very slow.{2} Workers contaminated with TCDD were found to contain abnormal liver enzymes over 20 years after the initial exposure.{3} The Seveso population has now been exposed to dioxin since 1976 and dioxin is still present in their bodies. Once attached to the DNA the dioxin-receptor continues to turn genes on or off, affecting hormones and enzymes, changing their normal biological effect, resulting in a complex disruption of oestrogen, adrenalin, insulin, testosterone and growth hormones. – 1. See McLachlan J. A., Newbold R. R., Teng C. T., and Korach K. S., in: Colborn and Clement, 1992; Giesy J. P., et al., 'Deformities in birds of the Great Lakes region', *Environ Sci Technol* 28 (3): 128–135, 1994; Ovanes, G., et al., 'A QSAR evaluation of Ah receptor binding of halogenated aromatic xenobiotics', *Environ Health Perspect* 104:

1302–1310, 1996; Esser and Welzel, 'Ontogenic development of murine fetal thymocytes is accelerated by 3,3,4,4-Tetrachlorobiphenyl', *Int J Immno*, 15 (8), 841–852, 1993; Esser, 'Dioxins and the immune system: mechanisms of interference', *Int Arch Allergy Immunol*, 104, 126–130, 1994; Kremer et al., 'Thymic stroma exposed to arylhydrocarbon receptor-binding xenobiotics fails to support proliferation of early thymocytes but induces differentiation', *J Immun*, 153, 2778–2786, 1994; Kremer et al., 'Evidence for the promotion of positive selection of thymocytes by ah receptor agonist 2,3,7,8-TCDD', *Euro J Phar*, En Tox & Phar Section 293, 413–427, 1995; Zhi-Wei et al., 'CD8 thymocytes derived from 3,3,4,4-tetrachlorobiphenyl-exposed fetal thymi possess killing activity', *Tox Appl Phar*, 133, 223–232, 1995; Tonn et al., 'Persistence of decreased t-helper cell function in industrial workers 20 years after exposure to 2,3,7,8-TCC', *EHP* 104 (4) 422–426, 1996; Zhi-Wei et al., 'Identification of dioxin-responsive elements (DREs) in the 5 regions of putative dioxin-inducible genes', *Chem-Bio Inter* 100, 97–112, 1996; Zhi-Wei et al., 'Cytokine gene expression during ontogeny in murine thymus on activiation of the aryl hydrocarbon receptor by 2,3,7,8-TCDD', *Mole Phar*, 52, 30–37, 1997; Vogel et al., 'Effect of subcronic 2,3,7,8-TCDD exposure on immune system and target gene responses in mice: calculation of benchmark doses for CYP1A1 and CYP1A2 related enzyme activities', *Arch Tox*, 71, 372–382, 1997. See also *IARC*, 1997. 2. Dioxin has a half life in the human body of no less than seven years. See Pirkle, J. L., Wolfe, W. H., Patterson, D. G., Jr. et al., 'Estimates of the half-life of 2,3,7,8-TCDD in Vietnam veterans of Operation Ranch Hand', *J Toxicol Environ Health* 27: 165–171, 1989 and Wolfe, W. H., Michalek, J. E., Miner, J. C., et al., 'Determinants of TCDD half-life in veterans of Operation Ranch Hand', *J Toxicol Environ Health* 41: 481–488, 1994. 3. Fingerhut, M., et al., 'Cancer mortality in workers exposed to 2,3,7,8-TCDD', *N Eng J Med* 324: 212–218, 1991. A more complete report of this research is available under the title 'Mortality among US workers employed in the production of chemicals contaminated with 2,3,7,8-tetrachlorodibenzo-p-dioxin' from: NTIS, 5285 Port Royal Rd, Springfield, VA 22161. NTIS no: PB91–125971.

PROLOGUE: THE POLITICS OF TRUTH

1. Mumford, L., *The Future of Technics and Civilisation*, Freedom Press, London, 1986.
2. Dement, I., 'The Way I Should', Warner, Songs of Iris ASCAP, 1996.
3. *Washington Post*, 10 June 2003, Final Edition.
4. See Schecter A., et al., 'Dioxin and dibenzofuran levels in food from the United States as compared to levels in food from other industrial countries'. (Paper presented at 12th International Symposium on Dioxins and Related Compounds, Tampere, Finland, August 1992.) Finnish Institute of Occupational Health, Helsinki, Finland, 243–246, 1992.
5. Rex Carr, interview with author, 1998.
6. Gerson Smoger, interview with C. D. Stelzer on behalf of author, 2003.

7. The most significant books on the politics of dioxin start with Thomas Whiteside, a Scot who worked as an investigative reporter for the *New Yorker*. His *Defoliation*, Ballantine/Foe, 1970; *Withering Rain*, Dutton, 1971; and *The Pendulum and the Toxic Cloud*, Yale, 1979 did more to highlight the extreme toxicity and impact of dioxin on human health than anyone. He was followed by Carol Van Strum. Her *A Bitter Fog*, Sierra Club Books, 1983 complimented Alastair Hay's *The Chemical Scythe*, Plenum, 1982, and her two books for Greenpeace, *No Margin of Safety*, 1987, and *The Politics of Penta*, 1989, are essential texts for anyone studying the history of dioxin politics. Other important books around this time include Samuel Epstein's *The Politics of Cancer*, Sierra Club, 1978; Margerison, Wallace and Hallenstein's *The Superpoison*, Macmillan, 1979; Cook and Kaufmann's *Portrait of a Poison: The Story of 2,4,5-T*, Pluto, 1982. Apart from Schuck's *Agent Orange on Trial*, Harvard University Press, 1988, we have to wait until 1994 for another specific book on dioxin, Arnold Schecter's *Dioxins and Health*, Plenum (second edn, Wiley, 2003). Books since have focused on the accumulative effect of synthetic chemicals on human health, notably: Ashford and Millar, *Chemical Exposures: Low Levels, High Stakes*, Van Nostrand Reinhold, London, 1991/98; Colborn and Clement (eds), *Chemically-induced Alterations in Sexual and Functional Development: The Wildlife/Human Connection*, Princeton Sci, 1992 and Colborn, Myers and Dumanoski, *Our Stolen Future*, Little Brown, 1996; Fagin and Lavelle, *Toxic Deception: How the Chemical Industry Manipulates Science, Bends the Law, and Endangers Your Health*, Secaucus, NJ, Carol Publishing Group, 1996; and Steingraber, *Living Downstream*, Addison Wesley/Virago, 1997.

8. Swedish oncologist Lennart Hardell has struggled for many years to get his work on dioxin published. The major scientific journals shied away from the subject, particularly from scientists whose reputations have been deliberately sullied.

9. The contribution of Seveso to the dioxin debate may also disentangle the arguments about bias and confounding. To show that multiple injuries are caused by multiple, systemic chemical substances in a society that pollutes itself, Olav Axelson noted: 'In view of the close association of dioxins and other chemicals it is more relevant to look upon the entire complex of exposures as risky rather than to discuss confounding from various indiscernible component exposures.' See Axelson, O., 'Seveso: Disentangling the dioxin enigma?' *Epidem* 4 (5): 389–392, 1993; Ashford and Millar, 1991/98 and the work of Ana Soto and Carlos Sonnenschein.

10. Plaintiffs-Appellees' Brief in Kemner et al., vs. Monsanto Appeal, Appellate Court of Illinois No 5–88–0420, 1989.

11. Doll, R., letter to The Hon. Mr Justice Philip Evatt, Australian Royal Commission etc, 4 December 1985.

12. See *Agrow*, World Crop Protection News No 165 (7/8/92).

13. Dr Karl Schulz, a dermatologist at the University of Hamburg, and George Sorge, a Boehringer chemist, discovered that heat played a part in the formation of dioxin during the trichlorophenol process. The higher the temperature the more dioxin was produced. BASF, another German chemical manufacturer, had also discovered how to reduce dioxin during

the process. By reducing the amount of solvent, BASF discovered that fewer dioxins would be formed. They alerted other trichlorophenol producers in 1956 and 1957 and sold the technical knowledge to Dow. See Kimmig, J., and Schulz, K., 'Chlorierte aromatische zyklische. Ather Urasche der Sogenannten Chlorakn' (Chloracne caused by chlorinated aromatic cyclic ethers), *Naturwissenschaften*, 44: 337–338, 1957; also *Kemner et al.*, vs. *Monsanto et al.*, Circuit Court, St Clair Co, Illinois, No 80-L-970 and *Kemner et al.* vs. *Monsanto et al.*, Appeal, Appellate Court of Illinois No 5–88–0420, 1989.

14. Bosshardt, H. P., 'Dioxine – Heimtuckische Gifte in unserer Umwelt (Entstehung, Eigenschaften und Verhalten von polychloreierten Dibenzo-p-dioxine)', *Neue Zurcher Zeitung*, Forschung und Technik, 2/12/73.

15. Allsop and colleagues add in their report 'Body of Evidence' that many synthetic chemicals are not needed. 'One of the more notable consequences of technological development in the Twentieth Century is the dispersal throughout the global environment of thousands upon thousands of chemicals that are solely the products of human endeavour. Only a fraction of these are made for commerce; the overwhelming majority are unwanted and often uncharacterized by-products of manufacture, use and disposal.' See Allsop, et al., 'Body of Evidence', Greenpeace International, May 1995.

16. By passing an electrical current via two electrodes – one positive and one negative – through a salt solution of sodium chloride and water, the positively-charged caustic soda and negatively-charged chlorine could be separated into equal quantities.

17. The war between 1914 and 1918 saw elemental chlorine used as a disinfectant and a bleach but also as a chemical weapon.

18. A halogenated aromatic hydrocarbon is a molecular bonding of carbon atoms with any of the following halogen atoms: astatine, bromine, chlorine, fluorine or iodine. An organochlorine is the bonding of chlorine with carbon.

19. In 1874 a German chemist, Dr O. Zeidler, sythesised a chemical called 1,1,1-trichloro-2,2-di-(4-chlorophenyl)ethane, put it in a bottle and placed it on a laboratory shelf where its existence was discovered 65 years later, still stable, by Dr Paul Muller who was working for J. R. Geigy in Switzerland. It was found to be an effective pesticide, against the Colorado beetle, fleas, lice, mosquitoes, flies and numerous other insects. Samples were sent secretly to America and Britain where tests were carried out by volunteers who wore underclothes treated with this chemical that would become known as Dichloro Diphenyl Trichloroethane (DDT). After three weeks the clothes were still lethal to lice and there appeared to be no ill-effects among the volunteers. In 1944 DDT was used to control an outbreak of typhus in Naples. From this discovery until some countries began to ban its use in the 1960s, DDT became one of the most widely used pesticides, even though it wasn't until the 1960s that scientists began to understand how it worked. Muller got a Nobel Prize for his efforts.

20. See Vance Packard's *The Hidden Persuaders*, David McKay Co., 1957.

CHAPTER 1: AWKWARD QUESTIONS

1. Human miscarriages would become linked to the spraying of 2,4,5-T. See Van Strum, C., *A Bitter Fog*, Sierra Club Books, 1983 and USEPA, 'Preliminary report of assessment of a field investigation of six-year spontaneous abortion rates in three Oregon areas in relation to forest 2,4,5-T spray practices', 27 February 1979.
2. It is likely that Melyce Connelly died of breast cancer that metacised as secondary cancers in her lung and brain.
3. Adapted from Carol Van Strum in *Dioxin: The Orange Resource Book*, WD Press/Synthesis/Regeneration, PO Box 24115, St Louis MO 63130, US. The story of what the spraying of toxic herbicides did to western Oregon communities is contained in Van Strum, 1983.
4. Ronnie Dugger is the founder of the Alliance for Democracy, an organisation whose members 'are setting forth to reject the economic and political power of large corporations as illegitimate in a self-governing democracy'. The Alliance can be reached by phone in Cambridge, Massachusetts: (617) 259–9395, or email: peoplesall@aol.com.
5. Hammill, P., 'Chemical World' in *The Quiet Zone, the Pleasure Dome*, Van der Graaf Generator, 1977; lyrics in *Mirrors, Dreams and Miracles*, 1982, Sofa Sound, PO Box 66, Freshford, Bath, England; www.sofasound.com.
6. Plaintiff's exhibit 1363, 10 May 1985 in *Kemner et al.,* vs. *Monsanto et al.,* Circuit Court, St Clair Co, Illinois, No 80-L-970.
7. Located three miles southeast of St Louis, the Krummrich factory began life in 1907 as the Commercial Acid Company when it occupied 30 acres and employed between 70 and 100 people. In 1917 it was purchased by Monsanto to provide a supply of mineral acids. The manufacture of chlorophenols began in 1938. It was renamed the William G. Krummrich Plant in 1951 in honour of a former manager. Krummrich was the sole US producer of PCBs until 1977 when production was discontinued. In 1979 approximately 75 different raw materials (primarily chlorine, phosphorous, benzene, sulphur and salt) were used to produce roughly 20 different intermediate chemical products including chlorophenols, chlorinated benzenes, sulphuric acid, chlorosulfonic acid, chlorine bleaches and stabilisers, detergent materials, feed grade antitoxidants and elastomers. Pentachlorophenol was produced until 1978, mono and di chlorophenols until 1983, and during the 1960s 2,4,5-T and 2,4-D were manufactured there. At the time of the Sturgeon spill, the Krummrich factory occupied 329 acres in east St Louis and employed 1,100 people.
8. Monsanto memo, 24 January 1979. Exhibit in *Kemner et al.,* vs. *Monsanto,* 80-L-970.
9. Monsanto memo, 24 January 1979.
10. Chemical companies provide Chemtrek with informaton about every shipment of chemicals. In turn Chemtrek are able to alert the emergency services about the toxicity of each shipment and what health and safety procedures need to be put in place.
11. Monsanto memo, 24 January 1979.
12. Monsanto's post-trial motion in *Kemner et al.*

13. Rex Carr, interview with author, 1998.
14. *Kemner et al.*, vs. *Monsanto et al.*, Defendant Monsanto co's response to plaintiffs' requests to admit facts, Circuit Court, St Clair Co, Illinois, No 80-L-970.
15. Justice Lewis' opinion (11 June 1991) in *Kemner et al.*, vs. *Monsanto et al.*, Appeal, Appellate Court of Illinois No 5–88–0420, 1989.
16. *Kemner et al.*, vs. *Monsanto et al.*, Defendant Monsanto co's response to plaintiffs' requests to admit facts, Circuit Court, St Clair Co, Illinois, No 80-L-970.
17. *Kemner et al.*, vs. *Monsanto et al.*, Appeal, Appellate Court of Illinois No 5–88–0420, 1989.
18. Carr, interview, 1998.
19. Carr, interview, 1998.
20. Carr, interview, 1998.
21. Carr, interview, 1998.
22. Three reports, two by Raymond Suskind, were produced but all remained unpublished until they were put into the public domain as a result of the discovery of documents by Rex Carr. They had selective circulation and Alastair Hay refers to them in his book, *The Chemical Scythe*, Plenum, 1982.
23. See Hay, 1982 for histories of trichlorophenol factory accidents, from Monsanto in 1949 to Seveso in 1976.
24. See Bettman, S., 'Chlorakne, eine besondere form van professionaller hauterkrankung', *Deutsche Med Wochenschrift*, 27: 437, 1901 and Herxheimer, K., 'Weitere mitteilungen uber chlorackne', in VII Dermatological Kongress Breslau, 152, 1901.
25. Hay, 1982.
26. The rabbit ear test is described in Adams, E. M., et al., 'The response of rabbit skin to compounds reported to have caused acne from dermatitis', *Ind Med Ind Hyg* Section 2: 1–4, 1941. See also Hambrick, G. and Blank H., 'Whole mounts for the study of the skin and its appendages', *J Invest Derm*, 23: 437, 1954 and Hambrick, G., 'The effect of substituted naphthalenes on the pilosebaceous apparatus of rabbit and man', *J Invest Derm*, 28: 89–103, 1957.
27. In 1995 a study of 1,189 workers employed for three months or more at the Boehringer factory and exposed to dioxin between 1952 and 1984 revealed an increase in death from cancer and heart disease. The scientists who conducted the study measured dioxin levels in the blood of the most heavily exposed group of workers and concluded that the results 'support the hypothesis of a dose-related effect of dioxins and furans on cancer and ischemic heart disease mortality'. See Dieter Flesch-Janys, et al., 'Exposure to polychlorinated dioxins and furans (PCDD/F) and mortality in a cohort of workers from a herbicide-producing plant in Hamburg, Federal Republic of Germany', *Am J Epidem* 142 (11): 1165–1175, 1995.
28. Kimmig, J. and Schulz, K., 'Chlorierte aromatische zyklische. Ather also Urasche der Sogenannten Chlorakn' (Chloracne caused by chlorinated aromatic cyclic ethers), *Naturwissenschaften*, 44: 337–338, 1957.
29. Holmstedt, B., 'Prolegomena to Seveso', *Arch Toxicol* 44: 211–230, 1980.

30. Suskind, R., testimony in *Boggess et al.*, vs. *Monsanto Co.* Civil no: 81–2098–265, 1986.
31. Suskind, 1986.
32. Zack, J. A., and Suskind, R. R., 'The mortality experience of workers exposed to tetrachlorodibenzodioxin in a trichlorophenol process accident', *J Occup Med* 22: 11–14, 1980.
33. Zack J. A., and Gaffey W, A., 'Mortality study of workers employed at the Monsanto Company plant in Nitro, West Virginia', *Environmental Sci Res*, 26 (6): 575–591, 1983.
34. Suskind, R., and Hertzberg, V., 'Human health effects of 2,4,5-T and its toxic contaminants', *J Am Med Ass*, 251 (18): 2372–2380, 1984.
35. Costner, P., *Science for Sale*, Greenpeace USA, 1990.
36. See Hay, A., and Silbergeld, E., 'Assessing the risk of dioxin exposure', *Nature* 315: 102–103, 9 May 1985; Gough, M., 'Dioxin exposure at Monsanto', *Nature* 318: 504, 12 December 1985; Hay A., and Silbergeld, E., 'Dioxin exposure at Monsanto', *Nature* 320: 569, 17 April 1986.
37. Raymond Suskind examined by Rex Carr, *Kemner et al.*, vs. *Monsanto*, 80-L-970, 19 February 1986.
38. Suskind, 19 February 1986.
39. Raymond Suskind examined by Rex Carr, *Kemner et al.*, vs. *Monsanto*, 80-L-970, 7 March 1986.
40. Paraphrased from Plaintiffs-Appellees' Brief in *Kemner et al.*, vs. *Monsanto* Appeal, Appellate Court of Illinois No 5–88–0420, 1989.
41. Carr, interview, 1998.

CHAPTER 2: HEART OF DARKNESS

1. Cook, J. and Kaufman, C., *Portrait of a Poison: The Story of 2,4,5-T*, Pluto, 1982.
2. Cook and Kaufman, 1982.
3. *Rachel's Hazardous Waste News* #377, 17 February 1994.
4. In a letter to *Tampa Tribune*, Florida, 23 March 2003.
5. Quoted in Whiteside, T., *Defoliation*, Ballantine/FoE, 1970.
6. Whiteside, 1970.
7. Whiteside, 1970.
8. Whiteside, 1970.
9. See Zumwalt, Admiral E. R., 'Report to the secretary of the department of veterans affairs on the association between adverse health effects and exposure to Agent Orange', 5 May 1990 citing Myers, B., 'Soldier of Orange: The administrative, diplomatic, legislative and litigatory impact of herbicide Agent Orange in south Vietnam', BC Enviro Aff L Rev 159–162, 1979.
10. Stellman J. M., et al., 'The extent and patterns of usage of Agent Orange and other herbicides in Vietnam', *Nature* 422, 681–687, 17 April 2003. See also Mydans S., 'Researchers raise estimate on defoliant use in Vietnam War', the *New York Times*, 17 April 2003 and Cauchi S., 'Vietnam vets' double dose of chemicals', *Sydney Morning Herald*, 17 April 2003 in which Brian McKenzie, national president of the Vietnam Veterans' Association

of Australia, said: 'The whole thing [Agent Orange] has been a series of cover-ups during the war and ever since.'

11. It is hard to identify literature on the Vietnam War that does not have a bias. Though the literature is also vast. For the story of Agent Orange the reader could start with Whiteside, 1970; Whiteside, *Withering Rain*, Dutton, 1971; Hay, A., *The Chemical Scythe*, Plenum, 1982; Westing, A., *Herbicides in War: the Long Term Ecological and Human Consequences*, Taylor and Francis, 1984. The majority of the best material was published in the 1970s and early 1980s.

12. Chlorophenols are produced by hydrolysis and direct chlorination. Hydrolysis: Starts with the direct chlorination of benzene, which creates chlorobenzene. Specific chlorophenols are then made by reacting the chlorobenzene with caustic in a solvent at a specific controlled temperature and pressure. The solvent is usually methanol but ethylene glycol is also used by some manufacturers. Another process uses water as the solvent in hydrolysis of dichloro- and trichlorobenzenes. Yet another uses a combined methanol–water solvent. Another uses the solvent, dimethylsulfoxide. According to the USEPA, 'the high-temperature, high-pressure, and strongly alkaline conditions of the hydrolysis process are conductive to the formation of dioxin compounds'. The commercial hydrolysis method is known to produce 2,3,7,8-TCDD from 1,2,4,5-tetracholorobenzene.

    Direct Chlorination: Starts with the addition of a hydroxyl group to benzene to form hydroxybenzene or phenol. The phenol is then passed along with chlorine gas through a reaction vessel. Unless the mixture is further distilled dioxin will contaminate the product. Pentachlorophenol made by this method will produce dioxins. All penta production in the USA is done this way.

13. Sweden, for example, banned all chlorophenols in 1978.

14. Sandra Steingraber, interview with author, 1998.

15. It was the 2,4,5-T spraying of her four children that set Carol Van Strum on the campaign road. Her story has been mirrored all over the planet. See Van Strum, C., *A Bitter Fog*, Sierra Club Books, 1983.

16. In 1963 a trade union representing the forestry workers requested health information from the manufacturers of Hormoslyr®. The reply stated that this 'chemical cannot in any way be considered to be carcinogenic. The chemical is characterised by low toxicity and no cases of intoxication of human beings or animals have been reported to us'. Cited in Hardell, L., 'Pesticides and soft-tissue sarcoma' in Mehlman, M., and Upton, A., (eds) 'The indentification and control of environmental and occupational diseases', *Princeton Sci* 23: 461–472, 1994.

17. Lennart Hardell, interview with author, 1998.

18. Hardell, interview, 1998.

19. Phenoxy herbicides have been in use in Sweden since 1947 when about a ton was used. Within three decades this increased to 2,700 tonnes when the chemical was in constant use against weeds and brush, hardwoods and brush and to control vegetation along railway lines, road verges, power lanes, parks and lawns. The Forestry Service began using phenoxy

herbicides in the early 1950s to irradicate hardwoods that impeded the growth of conifers.

20. Soft tissue sarcoma is a disease of the muscle tissues. EPA employee Cate Jenkins in her paper 'Recent scientific evidence developed after 1984 supporting a causal relationship between dioxin and human health effects' states: 'Soft-tissue sarcomas include a wide range of cancers arising from tissue of mesenchymal origin (primordial embryonic tissue), including smooth and striated muscle, fat, blood or lymph vessels, synovial structures (cavities between the joints) or fibrous and adipose connective tissue.'

21. See Axelson, O., and Sundell, L., 'Herbicide exposure, mortality and tumour incidence: an epidemiological investigation on Swedish railroad workers', *Work Enviro Health*, 11: 21–28, 1974; Axelson and Sundell, 'Phenoxy acids and cancer', *Läkartidningen* 74: 2887–2888, 1974.

22. Olav Axelson, interview with author, 1998.

23. Hardell, L., and Sandström, A., 'Case-control study: Soft tissue sarcomas and exposure to the phenoxyacetic acids or chlorophenols', *Br J Cancer*, 39: 711–717, 1979.

24. Hardell, interview, 1998.

25. Eriksson, M., Hardell, L., Berg N. O., Möller, T., and Axelson O., 'Soft-tissue sarcomas and exposure to chemical substances: a case reference study', *Br J Ind Med* 38, 27–33, 1981.

26. See also Axelson, et al., 'Herbicide exposure and tumour mortality: an updated epidemiological investigation on Swedish railroad workers', *Scand J Work Enviro Health*, 6: 73–79, 1980; Barthel, E., 'Gehäufes Vorkommen von Bronchialkrebs bei beruflicher Pestizidexposition in der Landwirshaft', *Zeitschrift fur Erkrankungen der Atmungsorgane* 146: 266–274, 1976; Edling C. and Granstam S., 'Causes of death among lumberjacks – a pilot study', *J Occ Med* 22: 403–406, 1980; Hogstedt C. and Westerlund, B., 'Kohortstudie av dödsorsaker för skogsarbetare med och utan exposition för fenoxisyrepreparat', *Läkartidningen*, 77: 1828–1831, 1980; Riihimäki, V, et al., 'Symptomatology, morbidity and mortality experience of chlorinated phenoxyacid herbicide (2,4-D and 2,4,5-T) sprayers in Finland. A clinical and epidemiological study'. Working paper for the IARC Working Group meeting on Co-ordination of epidemiological studies on the long-term hazards of chlorinated dibenzodioxins and chlorinated dibenzofurans, Lyon, France, 10–11 January 1978 in *Chemosphere* 12: 799, 1983.

27. Hardell, interview, 1998.

28. Hardell, interview, 1998.

29. Hardell, interview, 1998.

30. For media reports on the legacy of Agent Orange in Vietnam today see Scott-Clark, C., and Levy, A., 'Spectre Orange', *Guardian*, 29 March 2003; Bensinger, G., 'Vietnam echoes with horrors of war', *The Gazette*, Montreal, 26 March 2003; Arnold Schecter, a dioxin specialist who has tested the blood of Vietnamese communities where Agent Orange was stored, believes several million people are living in contaminated areas. See 'Vietnamese exposed to Agent Orange', p 649, in Schecter A., and Gasiewicz T., *Dioxins and Health*, second edition, Wiley, 2003;

Schecter A., et al., 'A Follow up: high levels of dioxin contamination in Vietnamese from Agent Orange three decades after the end of spraying', *J Occup Environ Med* 44, 218–220, 2002; Schecter A., et al., 'Recent dioxin contamination from Agent Orange in residents of a southern Vietnam city', *J Occup Environ Med* 43, 435–443, 2001; Schecter A., et al., 'Agent Orange and the Vietnamese: the persistence of elevated dioxin levels in human tissues', *Am J Public Health* 85: 516–522, 1995; also Verger P., et al., 'Correlation between dioxin levels in adipose tissue and estimated exposure to Agent Orange in South Vietnamese residents', *Environ Res* 65: 226–242, 1994; Kramárová, E., 'Exposure to Agent Orange and occurrence of soft-tissue sarcomas or non-hodgkin lymphomas: an ongoing study in Vietnam' in 'Dioxins and furans: epidemiologic assessment of cancer risks and other human health effects', *Environmental Health Perspectives*, Volume 106, Supplement 2, April 1998.

31. This study was funded by Dow as part of a grant to the state of Michigan.

32. 'Dow Chemicals, dioxin, Agent Orange and human health', 1984.

33. Anonymous, 'Swedish studies discounted in 2,4,5-T risk assessment', *Am Ind Hyg Assoc J*, 42: A-32, March 1981.

34. Hardell, interview, 1998.

35. Bayliss, D., letter to Hardell, L., 20 February 1986.

36. Hardell, interview, 1998.

37. Evidence that was also starting to accumulate in Vietnam. See Sterling, T. D. and Arundel, A., 'Review of recent Vietnamese studies on the carcinogenic and teratogenic effects of phenoxy herbicide exposure', *Int J Health Services*, 16(2): 265–279, 1986.

38. Doll, R., letter to The Hon. Mr Justice Philip Evatt, Australian Royal Commission etc, 4 December 1985.

39. Hardell, interview, 1998.

40. Hardell, L., (Axelson, O., ed), 'Rebuttals of the final report on cancer by the Royal Commission on the use and effects of chemical agents on Australian personnel in Vietnam', Department of Occupational Medicine and Industrial Ergonomics, University Hospital, Linkoping, 21 January 1986.

41. Armstrong, B., 'Storm in a cup of 2,4,5-T', *Med J Aust*, 144: 284–285, 1986.

42. Saracci, R., 'Storm in a cup of 2,4,5-T', *Med J Aust*, 144: 611–613, 1986. See also Christophers, A., 'Storm in a cup of 2,4,5-T', *Med J Aust*, 145: 298–299, 1986 and Hardell, L., and Axelson, O., 'The boring story of Agent Orange and the Australian Royal Commission', *Med J Aust*, 150: 602, 1989.

43. Axelson, O., and Hardell, L., 'Australian epidemiology – on Royal misruling the realm of epidemiology', Paper presented at the 5th Int Symp, Epidemiology in Occupational Health, Los Angeles, USA, 9–11 September 1986. See also Axelson, O., 'Pesticides and health: some problems in risk assessment', public lecture, Huckley Lecture Theatre, Australian National University, Sydney, 18 April 1989.

44. Hardell, L., 'Serious errors in new volume on Agent Orange and dioxin', *Am J Ind Med*, 17: 261–267, 1990.

45. Hardell, L., 'Re: Agent Orange controversy: a response', *Am J Ind Med*, 19: 403–405, 1991.

46. See Barthel, E., 1976; Edling, C., and Granstam, S., 1980; Hogstedt, C., and Westerlund, B., 1980; Riihimäki, V, et al., 1978/83 (all in Note 26).

47. Hardell, L., 'Pesticides and soft tissue sarcoma', 461–472 in Mehlman, M., and Upton, A., *The Identification and Control of Environmental and Occupational Diseases*, Princeton Sci, 1994.

48. Axelson, O., and Sundell, L., 'Herbicide exposure, mortality and tumour incidence: an epidemiological investigation on Swedish railroad workers', *Work Environ Health* 11, 21–28, 1974; Axelson, O., and Sundell, L., 'Phenoxy acids and cancer', *Läkartidningen* 74, 2887–2888, 1977; Axelson, O., 'Pesticides and cancer risks in agriculture', *Med Oncol Tumor Pharmacolther* 4, 207–217, 1987; Axelson, O., et al., 'Herbicide exposure and tumour mortality: an updated epidemiological investigation on Swedish railroad workers', *Scand J Work Environ Health* 6, 73–79, 1980; Axelson, O., (1994) 'Exposure to phenoxy herbicides and chlorinated dioxins and cancer risks: an inconsistent pattern of facts and frauds?' in Renzoni, et al., *Contaminants in the Environment*, Lewis, Boca Raton 23, 213–220, 1994; Axelson, O., 'Dynamics of management and labor in dealing with occupational risks' in Mehlman and Upton (eds), *The Identification and Control of Environmental and Occupational Diseases*, Vol. 23, Princeton Sci Pub, New Jersey, 1994; Erickson, J. D., et al., 'Vietnam veterans' risk of fathering babies with birth defects', *J Am Med Assoc* 252: 903–912, 1984; Eriksson, M, Hardell, L, Berg, N. O., Möller, T and Axelson, O., 'Soft-tissue sarcomas and exposure to chemical substances: a case reference study', *Br J Ind Med* 38, 27–33, 1981; Eriksson, M., and L., Hardell, 'Employment in pulp mills as a possible risk factor for soft tissue sarcoma: a case report', *Br J Ind Med* 48: 288, 1991; Eriksson, M., Hardell, L., and Adami, H. O., 'Exposure to dioxins as a risk factor for soft-tissue sarcoma: a population based case-control study', *J Nat Can Inst*, 82(6): 486–490, 1990; Hardell, L., 'Soft-tissue sarcomas and exposure to phenoxy acids: a clinical observation', *Läkartidningen* 74, 2753–2754, 1977; Hardell, L., 'Malignant lymphoma of histiocytic type and exposure to phenoxyacetic acids or chlorophenols', *Lancet* 1, 55–56, 1979; Hardell, L., and Sandström, A., 'Case control study: soft-tissue sarcomas and exposure to phenoxyacetic acids or chlorophenols', *Br J Cancer* 39, 711–717, 1979; Hardell, L., Eriksson, M., Lenner, P., and Lundgren, E., 'Malignant lymphoma and exposure to chemicals, especially organic solvents, chlorophenols and phenoxy acids: a case-control study', *Br J Cancer* 43, 169–176, 1981; Hardell, L., and Bengtsson, N. O., 'Epidemiological study of socioeconomic factors and clinical findings in Hodgkin's disease, and reanalysis on previous data regarding chemical exposure', *Br J Cancer* 48, 217–225, 1984; Hardell, L., and Eriksson, M., 'The association between soft-tissue sarcomas and exposure to phenoxyacetic acids: a new case-referent study', *Cancer* 62, 652–656, 1988; Hardell, L., Johansson, B., and Axelson, O., 'Epidemiological study on nasal and nasopharyngeal cancer and their relation to phenoxy acid or chlorophenol exposure', *Am J Ind Med* 3, 247, 1982; Hardell, L., Eriksson, M., Fredriksson, M., and Axelson, O., 'Dioxin and mortality from cancer', *N Eng J Med* 324, 1810, 1991;

Hardell, L., 'The boring story of Agent Orange and the Australian Royal Commission', *Med J Aus* 150: 602, 1989; Hardell, L., 'Relation of soft-tissue sarcoma, malignant lymphoma and colon cancer to phenoxy acids, chlorophenols and others agents', *Scand J Work Environ Health* 7, 119–130, 1981; Hardell, L., and Eriksson, M., 'The association between cancer mortality and dioxin exposure: a comment on the hazard of repetition of epidemiological misinterpretation', *Am J Ind Med* 19, 547–549, 1991; Hardell, L., 'Human exposure to 2,3,7,8-TCDD and risk of cancer', *CRC Crit Rev Toxicol* 23, 337–339, 1993; Hardell, L., 'Phenoxy herbicides, chlorophenols, soft-tissue sarcoma and malignant lymphoma', *Br J Cancer* 67, 1154–1155, 1993; Hardell, L., Eriksson, M., and Axelson, O., 'On the misinterpretation of epidemiological evidence relating to dioxin-containing phenoxyacetic acids, chlorophenols and cancer effects', *New Solutions* 4, 49–56, 1994; Hardell, L., 'TCDD carcinogenicity in humans', *Environ Health Per* 102, 814, 1994; Hardell, L., Eriksson, M., and Degerman, A., 'Exposure to phenoxyacetic acids, chlorophenols or organic solvents in relation to histopathology, stage, and anatomical localization on non-Hodgkin's lymphoma', *Cancer Research* 54, 2386–2389, 1994; Hardell, L., Eriksson, M., Axelson, O., and Zahm, S. H., 'Cancer epidemiology' in Schecter (ed.), *Dioxins and Health*, Plenum Press, New York, 1994; Hardell, L., 'Pesticides and soft-tissue sarcoma' in Mehlman and Upton (eds), *The Identification and Control of Environmental and Occupational Diseases*, Vol. 23, Princeton Sci Pub, New Jersey, 1994; Hardell, L., 'Chlorophenols, phenoxyacetic acids, and dioxins' in Zenz, Dickerson and Horvath (eds), *Occupational Medicine*, 3rd edn, Mosby, St Louis, 1994; Hardell, L., Eriksson, M., and Degerman, A., 'Meta-analysis of four Swedish case-control studies on exposure to pesticides as risk-factor for soft-tissue sarcoma including the relation to tumour localization and histopathological type', *Int J Oncology* 6, 847–851, 1995; Hardell, L., Eriksson, M., Athlin, L., Hansson, M., and Rappe, C., 'Adipose tissue concentrations of dioxins and dibenzofurans in potentially exposed patients with malignant lymphoma or sarcoma', *Oncology Reports* 2, 749–753, 1995; Hardell, L., Frediksson, M., Eriksson, M., Hansson, C., and Rappe, C., 'Adipose tissue concentrations of dioxins and dibenzofurans in patients with malignant lymphoproliferative diseases and in patients without a malignant disease', *Euro J Cancer Prevention* 4, 225–229, 1995; Hardell, L., Bavel, B. V., Lindström, G., Fredriksson, M., Hagberg, H., Lilijegren, G., Nordström, M., and Johansson, B., 'Higher concentrations of specific polychlorinated biphenyl congeners in adipose tissue from non-Hodgkin's lymphoma patients compared with controls without a malignant disease', *Int J Oncology* 9, 603–608, 1996; Persson, B., et al., 'Malignant lymphomas and occupational exposures', *Br J Ind Med*, 46, 516–520, 1989; Wiklund, K., et al., 'Risk of malignant lymphoma in Swedish agricultural and forestry workers', *Br J Ind Med* 45, 19–24, 1988; Wingren, G., et al., 'Soft-tissue sarcoma and occupational exposures', *Cancer* 66, 806–811, 1990; Wingren, G., et al., 'Mortality pattern among pulp and paper mill workers in Sweden: a case-referent study', *Am J Ind Med* 20, 769–774, 1991.

49. 'Regarding specific types of malignant tumours, STS as well as NHL, by now seem to be fairly clearly associated with exposure to phenoxy herbicides and related chlorinated phenols.' STS, they declared without fanfare, is associated with exposure to TCDD – significantly among industrial populations, while the epidemiological evidence is unclear about the link between TCDD and NHL.

50. See O'Keefe, B., 'Soft tissue sarcoma: law, science and logic: an Australian perspective' in Young/Reggiani, *Agent Orange*, Elsevier, 1988. Barry O'Keefe was the lawyer who represented Monsanto at the Royal Commission.

51. Hardell, interview, 1998.

52. Hardell, L., Eriksson, M., Axelson, O., and Zahm, S. H., 'Cancer epidemiology' in Schecter (ed.), *Dioxins and Health*, Plenum Press, New York, 1994.

53. The Swedish doctors had also identified non-Hodgkin's lymphoma – a member of the hematologic family of cancers and includes leukemias, myelomas and lymphomas (which are cancers of the blood and blood-forming tissues).

54. Axelson, O., 'Exposure to phenoxy herbicides and chlorinated dioxins and cancer risks: an inconsistent pattern of facts and frauds?' in Renzoni, Mattei, Lari and Fossi (eds) *Contaminants in the Environment*, Lewis, Boca Raton 23, 213–220 (1994).

55. The struggle to defend their reputations hadn't ended. In 1994 another book *Medicine at War: Medical Aspects of Australia's Involvement in Southeast Asia 1950–72* by Brendan O'Keefe with F. B. Smith repeated the prejudices about their work. Again they wrote a paper, 'Agent Orange in war medicine: an aftermath myth'. They sent it to the *Medical Journal of Australia*, *Journal of Australian and New Zealand Medicine*, *Journal of Medical Ethics* and the *Australian Journal of Public Health*. None would take it. One reviewer said the paper was 'not a balanced scientific report' and stressed, 'the review of the literature is one-sided. Positive studies are quoted and negative studies are under-emphasised or not mentioned'. The reviewer agreed with Richard Doll that the evidence about the phenoxy herbicides 'is weak and contradictory'. The *AJPH* said they could not print the paper because the statements in it 'could be subject to legal action under Australian defamation laws'. By spring 1998 the Swedish doctors were still sending the paper out.

56. Carson, R., *Silent Spring*, 1962.

57. Whiteside, 1970. See also Sterling, T. D., 'Problems in determining if a commonly used herbicide (2,4,5-T) has an effect on human health', 6th Berkeley Symposium, 1971.

58. On 15 April 1970 the Deputy Secretary of Defense, David Packard, announced that the US military would stop using phenoxy herbicides in Vietnam. Coincidentally, but perhaps not, on the same day Dr Jesse Steinfeld, the Surgeon General of the USA, appeared before a hearing of the Senate Subcommittee on Energy, Natural Resources and the Environment, headed by Philip Hart, on the human health effects of 2,4,5-T. This was the beginning of a battle that would last 13 years to have 2,4,5-T banned in the USA. Steinfeld announced actions that would restrict the use of 2,4,5-T but not ban it completely.

59. See US Inst of Medicine, *Veterans and Agent Orange*, Nat Acad Publishers 1994, 2nd edn 1996 and IARC, 1997.
60. Hardell, interview, 1998.
61. Hardell, interview, 1998.

CHAPTER 3: IGNORANCE IS BLISS

1. Quoted in Stelzer, C. D., 'Terrified in Times Beach', *Riverfront Times*, St Louis, 26 April 1995.
2. This is taken from 'Overview: The Dioxin Debate' in Schecter, A. and Gasiewicz, T., *Dioxins and Health*, 2nd edn. Wiley Interscience, 2003.
3. Russell Bliss, interview with author, 1998
4. Bliss also used tanks kept on his Strecker Road property. In the late summer of 1972 he rented two 100,000-gallon tanks from an oil company.
5. Bliss, interview, 1998. See also memorandum to the Director, CDC, and US Public Health Service from Dr Robert Koehler 14 August 1972 and see also memorandum to Chief, Bacterial Diseases Branch from Renate D. Kimbrough, HEW Public Health Service, Centers for Disease Control, Atlanta, Georgia, 30 July 1974. Cited in Hay, A., *The Chemical Scythe*, Plenum, 1982.
6. See Linda James, 'Missouri's dioxin contamination, 1968–1988: The politics and administration of a hazardous waste catastrophe'. A dissertation, University of Missouri-Columbia, August 1988. Available from UMI Dissertation Services, 300 N Zeeb Road, Ann Arbor, Michigan 48106 (313–761–4700).
7. Russell Bliss deposition, *Hampel and Piatt* vs. *Russell Bliss, Evelyn Bliss, Signet Graphic Products Inc., Syntex Agribusiness Inc., Hoffman Taff Inc., Northern Eastern Pharmaceutical and Chemical Co. Inc., and Independent Petrochemicals Corporation* in the Circuit Court of Pike County, Missouri, 11 April 1975.
8. Missouri Hazardous Waste Management Commission Hearing. *Jerry Russell Bliss* vs. *Department of Natural Resources*, 1983.
9. Bliss, deposition, 1975.
10. Bliss, interview, 1998.
11. Bliss, interview, 1998.
12. Bliss, interview, 1998.
13. There is a discrepancy about the amount of waste Bliss hauled from NEPACCO. IPC invoiced NEPACCO for six loads of waste and a figure of 18,500 gallons is mentioned. So at least one trip must have featured a load of 3,500 gallons. This would explain why, on the 20 May trip, Bliss' driver was given a ticket for being overweight. Bliss has also admitted that on one occasion he took two trucks on one trip, indicating that at least 6,000 gallons were hauled. And the last trip, on 25 October, is not mentioned in the IPC invoices, presumably because Bliss agreed with Bill Ray, the NEPACCO plant foreman, to haul directly for the company. This would mean that Bliss hauled 21,500 gallons. See also James, 1988.
14. Bliss, interview, 1998.
15. Bliss, interview, 1998.

16. As a result of this indiscriminate dumping Bliss lost 70 chickens. See Kimbrough, R., et al., 'Epidemiology and pathology of a tetrachlorodibenzodioxin poisoning episode', *Arch Environ Health*, 32, 77–86, 1977. See also Russell Bliss deposition in *Hampel and Piatt* vs. *Russell Bliss and Evelyn Bliss* in the Circuit Court of Lincoln County, Missouri, 20 November 1972; and Bliss deposition, 1975. Confirmed 1998.

17. Bliss, deposition, 1975.

18. David Covert, in an interview with Stephen P. Krchma of the Missouri Attorney General's office.

19. Quoted in Stelzer, C. D., 'Wasted in West County', *Riverfront Times*, St Louis, 9 July 1997.

20. Bliss, deposition, 1972.

21. James, 1988.

22. Bob Feild, EPA project manager for the clean-up of Missouri's dioxin sites, quoted by Stelzer, C. D., in 'Deja vu on Lemar Drive', *Riverfront Times*, St Louis, 13 August 1997.

23. Bliss, interview, 1998.

24. Russell Bliss deposition in *State of Missouri, et al.*, vs. *Bliss*, in the circuit court of Jefferson, state of Missouri, 21 April 1977 and Bliss, interview, 1998.

25. Bliss, deposition, 1977.

26. Bliss, deposition, 1977.

27. Dioxin was an issue in the USA in 1971. Following a meeting between producers of phenolic compounds and the federal government on 5 March 1971 Dow Chemicals noted that 'the subject of dioxins is pretty explosive and could blow up at any time'. The producers set out to detoxify dioxin. Exhibit in *Kemner et al.*, vs. *Monsanto et al.*, No 80-L-970.

28. Bliss, deposition, 1972.

29. Russell Bliss deposition in *Piatt et al.*, vs. *Bliss et al.*, in the circuit court of the city of St Louis, state of Missouri, 4 February 1983, reaffirmed 1998.

30. Bliss, deposition, 1983.

31. Little, J., 'Hauler says he was tricked into spraying dioxin', *St Louis Post Dispatch*, 2 November 1982.

32. Bliss, interview, 1998.

33. Patrick McCarthy, of the Illinois EPA, told the Missouri Hazardous Waste Management Commission in 1983 that he had followed one of Bliss' drivers, Jay Covert, and watched him spray waste oil containing high levels of trichloroethylene on the Illinois Central Gulf Railroad yard in Madison County. See also Bliss, deposition, 1977.

34. Bliss, interview, 1998.

35. Missouri Department of Natural Resources, Anonymous interview, 27 August 1980 quoted in James, 1988.

36. David Covert deposition, 16 November 1982.

37. Anonymous, 27 August 1980.

38. Bliss, interview, 1998.

39. Bliss, 1998.

40. James, 1988; Bliss, interview, 1998.
41. Dr Patrick E. Phillips, a veterinarian with the Missouri Division of Health, quoted in the media. See 'Death of animals laid to chemical', *New York Times*, 28 August 1974.
42. Coleman D. Carter et al., 'Tetrachlorodibenzodioxin: an accidental poisoning episode in horse arenas', *Science*, 88 (4189), 738–740, 1975. See also Commoner et al., 'Accidential contamination of soil with dioxin in Missouri: effects and countermeasures, a contribution to the Dioxin Information Project', Scientists Institute for Public Information, New York, 29 September 1976.
43. Commoner et al., 1976.
44. See Memorandum from Roger Feldman and John Bennett, CDC, to the Director, CDC, 24 August 1971 and Koehler, 14 August 1971.
45. Patrick Phillips, quoted in Larry Katzenstin, 'Dioxin pollution most tragic in Missouri history', *Columbia Missourian*, 31 July 1977.
46. All Case could say about the poisoning of Shenandoah was the recommendation: 'do not use discarded motor oil on enclosed areas where man or his animals work or live'. Case, A. A., and Coffman, J. R., 'Waste oil: toxic for horses', *Vet Clinics of N Am*, May 1973.
47. See Kimbrough, R., et al., 'Tetrachlorodibenzodioxin: an accidental poisoning episode in horse arenas', *Science*, 188, 738–740, 16 May 1975.
48. Kimbrough, R., et al., 'Epidemiology and pathology of a tetrachloro-dibenzodioxin poisoning episode', *Arch Environ Health*, 32, (2), 77–86, 1977. See Beale, M., et al., 'Long-term effects of dioxin exposures', *Lancet* 1, (8014), 748, 2 April 1977. And see Coleman Carter deposition in *Hampel and Piatt* vs. *Bliss et al.*, 28 February 1975.
49. Piatt and Hampel Dossier, 1972. See James, 1988.
50. Judy Piatt deposition, in *Hampel and Piatt* in the circuit court of Lincoln County, state of Missouri, November 1972. See also Missouri Hazardous Waste Management Commission Hearing. *Jerry Russell Bliss* vs. *Department of Natural Resources*, 1983.
51. Piatt and Hampel, 1972. See also Missouri DNR and Department of Social Services, Missouri Dioxin Report, 22 December 1982.
52. Missouri Dioxin Report, 1982.
53. Mandel, M., 'Setback by Bliss in dioxin quest', official asserts', *St Louis Post Dispatch*, 26 January 1983.
54. Stelzer, C. D. 'Dangerous ground', *Riverfront Times*, St Louis, 14 February 1996.
55. James, 1988.
56. Times Beach began as a river resort in the mid-1920s, when the now-defunct *St. Louis Star Times* sold property along the Meramec River to increase circulation. A six-month subscription qualified a reader to purchase a lot for $67.50.
57. Quoted in 'Times Beach: image of a clean-up or clean-up of an image', *Three River Confluence*, Fall 1997, PO Box 63232, St Louis, MO 63163.
58. When Enviro-Dyne reported back on 13 December 1982 they told Leistner that their analysis had revealed another toxic substance – PCBs.

59. Uhlenbrock, T., 'Times Beach. Images of a town that was', *St Louis Post Dispatch*, 14 January 1996.

60. Fred Striley, interview with author, 1998.

61. Striley, F, A., 'Citizens' report on the Times Beach Superfund Site', 25 June 1997 available from 231 Walden Court, Eureka, Missouri 63025, USA.

62. Stelzer, C. D., 'Keeping a safe distance', *Riverfront Times*, St Louis, 11 September 1996.

63. The American Security Council is an extreme right wing organisation formed in the 1950s to ferret out communists in the labour unions. It compiled more than a million dossiers on radicals and anti-war protesters in the Vietnam War, moved onto international issues and supported death squad activities in central America in the 1980s. Shaw was involved in a spin-off of the ASC called the the Coalition for Peace Through Strength, during the first Reagan administration, circa 1981. Peace Through Strength was rabidly anti-communist.

64. Bliss, interview, 1998.

65. Quoted in Thornton, J., 'Dioxin deception', *Greenpeace Magazine*, May/June 1991.

66. In her affidavit 'Recent scientific evidence developed after 1984 supporting a casual relationship between dioxin and human health effects' in *Ivy et al.*, vs. *Diamond Shamrock Chemicals, et al.*, 3 September 1991, Cate Jenkins wrote: 'Since 1984, numerous new studies using refined statistical methods have shown significantly elevated rates of birth defects and other reproductive abnormalities among Vietnam veterans and other dioxin-exposed populations, including two studies by the Air Force. Furthermore, numerous new studies are now available that show male-mediated reproductive abnormalities due to pre-conception paternal exposures to other toxic substances. The eventuality of male-mediated birth defects was denied as ever being demonstrated in any human population by the CDC in 1984. Many Vietnam veterans have experienced more than one of the adverse health effects associated with dioxin. Such a coincidence of injuries increases the probability that the common casual factor of the multiple injuries was dioxin rather than two or more coincidental factors. In addition, a variety of human population exposed to dioxin have experienced these health effects (Vietnam veterans, farmers, forestry workers, residential populations in Missouri and Italy, and chemical production workers in the U.S. and other countries), thus establishing a firm basis for concluding that dioxin, and not some other unique factor related to service in Vietnam, was responsible for these health effects. Further, many Vietnam veterans and other populations exposed to dioxin have experienced dose-related increased rates of these adverse health effects, proving strong epidemiologic evidence that the effects were caused by, not merely associated with, dioxin. In all cases, animals have experienced these same health effects when dioxin is administered in a controlled laboratory setting, thus providing a plausible biological basis for the health effects observed in humans. The effects demonstrated by these new studies to be significantly associated with dioxin exposures include elevated cancers of all sites combined (representing a general carcinogenic effect of dioxin), as well as cancers of specific sites, namely:

soft tissue sarcomas; non-Hodgkin's lymphoma; Hodgkin's disease; leukemias, lymphomas, and other hematologic cancers; respiratory system cancer; skin cancer; testicular cancer; and cancers of the brain, stomach, colon, rectum, prostate, hepatobiliary tract, pancreas, and kidney. One adverse effect in addition to cancer significantly associated with dioxin is organic nerve damage, including peripheral as well as central nervous system damage, and the severe consequences of central nervous system damage, such as suicide and fatal accidents, depression, anxiety, and other neuropsychological problems. Other adverse effects significantly associated with dioxin include reproductive abnormalities; immunological abnormalities; dermatologic abnormalities; hepatoxic effects; gastrointestinal ulcer; cardiovascular disorders; metabolic disorders such as porphyria cutanea tarda, thyroid dysfunction, diabetes, and altered lipid metabolism; and lung and thorax abnormalities. Data contained in some recent studies do not always support a statistically significant association between dioxin and adverse health effects. The reasons for a lack of such an association may be poor classification of the exposed population (for example, including Vietnam veterans who did not have significant exposures), or other variations in the population under study. The preponderance of the evidence from all recent studies, however, supports the conclusion that dioxin is significantly associated with these health effects.' See also US Committee on Government Operations, 'The Agent Orange cover-up: a case of flawed science and political manipulation', Report 101–672, 9 August 1990.

67. Quoted in *Confluence*.
68. Stelzer, C. D., 'Terrified in Times Beach', *Riverfront Times*, St Louis, 26 April 1995.
69. Quoted in *Confluence*.
70. Steve Taylor, interview with author, 1998.
71. Monsanto memorandum, St Louis to Nitro, 22 September 1952; Monsanto memorandum, Nitro to St Louis, 7 November 1952; Letter Russell Jenkins, Director of Research, Monsanto, St Louis, to Lt Colonel Loyd E. Harris, Chemical Corps Medical Laboratories, Army Chemical Center, Maryland, 26 November 1952; Letter from Jenkins to Harris, 16 January 1953. The Times Beach Action Group obtained this correspondence from Peter Sills, a former attorney for the Vietnam Veterans of America, who acquired the evidence after the 1984 settlement of the Vietnam veterans' class-action suit against Monsanto and other manufacturers of 2,4,5-T, the dioxin-contaminated component found in Agent Orange.
72. C. D. Stelzer, interview with author, 1998.
73. Schmitt, T., *Confluence*.
74. Sanjour, W., 'What's wrong with EPA', *In These Times*, 28 July 1997, 2040 N Milwaukee, Chicago, IL 60647.
75. Quoted in *Confluence*.
76. Striley, F., 1997.
77. Bliss, interview, 1998.
78. Gooden deposition.
79. See US Committee on Government Operations, 'The Agent Orange cover-up: a case of flawed science and political manipulation', Report

101–672, 9 August 1990; Zumwalt, Admiral E. R., 'Report to the secretary of the department of veterans affairs on the association between adverse health effects and exposure to Agent Orange', 5 May 1990 citing Myers, B., 'Soldier of Orange: the administrative, diplomatic, legislative and litigatory impact of herbicide Agent Orange in south Vietnam', BC Enviro Aff L Rev 159–162, 1979.
80. Bliss, interview, 1998.
81. Bliss, interview, 1998.
82. Rex Carr, interview with author, 1998.
83. Bliss, interview, 1998.
84. Bliss, interview, 1998.
85. Bliss, interview, 1998.

CHAPTER 4: TOXIC SHOCK

1. Hamburg Court of Social Security and Related Matters, ruling of Judges Horn, Landmann and Leven, Case no: 26 U 245/84. See also Kimmig, J. and Schulz, K., 'Chloriete aromtische zyklische. Ather Urasche der Sogenannten Chlorakn' (Chloracne caused by chlorinated aromatic cyclic ethers), *Naturwissenschaften*, 44: 337–338, 1957; and see Dieter Flesch-Janys, et al., 'Exposure to polychlorinated dioxins and furans (PCDD/F) and mortality in a cohort of workers from a herbicide-producing plant in Hamburg, Federal Republic of Germany', *Am J Epidem* 142 (11): 1165–1175, 1995; Manz, A., et al., 'Cancer mortality in workers of the Hamburg-Moorfleet plant of the Boehringer Ingelheim Company. A retrospective cohort study. Methodology and preliminary results'. Paper presented at conference: 'Dioxin '90', Bayreuth, Germany, September, 1990 and Manz, A., et al., 'Cancer mortality among workers in a chemical plant contaminated with dioxin', *Lancet* 338: 959–964, 1991.
2. Greenpeace Italy's Fabrizio Fabbri in a press release, 8 July 1997.
3. Gerhard Stolpa, interview with author, 1993.
4. Dylan, B., 'Subterranean Homesick Blues' in *Bringing It All Back Home*, Warner Bros Music, 1967.
5. Dennis Goss, interview with author, 1994, 1995. See also *Sheffield Star*, 24 April 1968, *Derbyshire Times*, 26 April 1968.
6. *Derbyshire Times*, 26 April 1968.
7. *Derbyshire Times*, 26 April 1968.
8. Hexachlorophrene, an anti-bacterial agent used in soaps, deodorants, toothpastes, talcum powder, perfumes and cosmetics, has since been banned in many countries. In 1972 36 children died and 145 were hospitalised with nerve damage following exposure to talcum powder that contained 6 per cent hexacholophrene. Subsequent tests showed that hexachlorophrene was neurotoxic. In Sweden 11 out of 65 children born to mothers who had been exposed to hexachlorophrene soap in early pregnancy were malformed. NEPACCO had started production of hexachlorophrene in the spring of 1970 after entering into an agreement with Hoffman Taff (one of four companies in Missouri producing 2,4,5-T in the 1960s) on 18 November 1969. Following the death of the

French children the market for hexachlorophrene collapsed. The US FDA banned the commercial sale of hexachlorophrene and NEPACCO ceased production in February 1972.

9. Orthochlorobenzene is known to produce dioxin when heated.

10. Cook, J., and Kaufman, C., *Portrait of a Poison: The Story of 2,4,5-T*, Pluto, 1982.

11. The disasters at Bolsover and Seveso are chronicled in detail in Margerison, T., Wallace, M., and Hallenstein, D., *The Superpoison*, Macmillan, 1979; Whiteside, T., *The Pendulum and the Toxic Cloud*, Yale University Press, 1979 (based on articles published in the *New Yorker* magazine, 1977 and 1978); Hay, A., *The Chemical Scythe*, Plenum, 1982 and Cook and Kaufman, 1982.

12. See May, G., 'Chloracne from the accidental production of tetrachloro-dibenzodioxin', *Br J Ind Med* 30, 276–283, 1973 and Milnes, M. H., 'Formation of 2,3,7,8-tetrachlorodibenzodioxin by thermal decomposition of sodium trichlorophenate', *Nature*, 232, 395–396, 1971.

13. Bertazzi, P. A., and di Domenico, A., 'Chemical, environmental and health aspects of the Seveso, Italy, accident' in *Dioxins and Health*, Schecter (ed.), Plenum, 1994.

14. Hay, A., 'Tetrachlorodibenzo-p-dioxin release at Seveso', *Disasters* 1, 289–308, 1977; Peterson, J., 'Seveso; the event', *Ambio*, 7, 232–233, 1978; Sambeth, J., 'What really happened at Seveso', *Chem Eng*, 90, 44–47, 1983; Fortunati, G. U., 'The Seveso accident', *Chemosphere*, 14, 729–737, 1985; di Domenico, A., et al., 'A report of NATO/CCMS working group on management of accidents involving the release of dioxins and related compounds' in *ISTISAN 88/8*, di Domenico, A., and Radwan, A., (eds), Istituto Superiore di Sanita, 1988; Reggiani, G., in *Agent Orange and its Associated Dioxin: Assessment of a Controversy*, Young, A., and Reggiani, G., (eds), Elsevier, 1988.

15. Ferrara, M., 1977, Le Donne di Seveso, Rome. Editori Riuniti.

16. Whiteside, 1979.

17. ICMESA letter to F. Uberti, 12 July 1976.

18. In 1976 ICMESA reported annual sales of four billion lire ($2.4m) and employed 163 workers.

19. Margerison, et al., 1979.

20. Fanelli, C., et al., 'Presence of 2,3,7,8-tetrachlorodibenzo-p-dioxin in wildlife living near Seveso, Italy: a preliminary study', *Bull Environ Contam Tox*, 24, 460–462, 1980; Fanelli, C., et al., '2,3,7,8-tetrachlorodibenzo-p-dioxin levels in cow's milk from the contaminated area of Seveso, Italy', *Bull Environ Contam Tox*, 24, 634–639; Fanelli, C., et al., '2,3,7,8-tetrachlorodibenzo-p-dioxin toxic effects and toxic levels in animals from the contaminated areas of Seveso, Italy', *Arch Environ Contam Tox*, 9, 569–577, 1980, Fanelli, C., et al., 'TCDD contamination in the Seveso incident', *Drug Metab Rev*, 13, 407–422, 1982.

21. Whiteside, 1979.

22. Bertazzi, P. A., 'Industrial disasters and epidemiology: a review of recent experiences', *Scand J Work Environ Health*, 15, 85–100, 1989. Also given as a lecture at the Sixth International Symposium on Epidemiology in Occupational Health, Stockholm, 16–19 August 1988.

23. Mayor of Seveso, Stampa, 28 July 1976.
24. See Hay, 1982, Margerison, et al., 1979, Whiteside, 1979.
25. Italian law required the company to inform their workers about occupational hazards and risks to their health. For some reason they never bothered. See also Whiteside, 1979.
26. Bertazzi, P. A., 'Long term effects of chemical disasters: lessons and results from Seveso', *Science Total Environ* 106, 5–2, 1991.
27. Bertazzi, 1991.
28. Caramaschi, R., et al., 'Chloracne following environmental contamination by TCDD in Seveso, Italy', *Int J Epi* 10, 135–143, 1981.
29. Fillippini, G., et al., 'Relationships between clinical and electrophysiological findings and indicators of heavy exposure to 2,3,7,8-tetrachlorodibenzo dioxin', *Sand J Work Environ Health*, 7, 257–262, 1981.
30. Tenchini, M. L., et al., 'A comparative cytogenetic study on cases of induced abortion in TCCD-exposed and nonexposed women', *Environ Mutagen*, 5, 78–85, 1983.
31. Seveso offical quoted in Margerison, et al., 1979.
32. Mastroiacovo, P., et al., 'Birth defects in the Seveso area after TCCD contamination', *JAMA*, 259, 1668–1672, 1988.
33. See Cook and Kaufman, 1982 and Margerison, et al., 1979.
34. Moracrelli, A., et al., 'Clinical laboratory manifestations of exposure to dioxin in children: a six-year study of the effects of an environmental disaster near Seveso, Italy', *JAMA*, 256, 2687–2695, 1986.
35. Assennato, G., et al., 'Follow-up of subjects who developed chloracne following TCDD exposure at Seveso', *Am J Ind Med*, 16, 119–125, 1989.
36. Caramaschi et al., 1981.
37. Margerison, et al., 1979.
38. Bertazzi, 1989.
39. Bertazzi, 1991.
40. Bertazzi, 1991.
41. Bertazzi, 1991.
42. Bertazzi and di Domenico, 1994.
43. Bertazzi and di Domenico, 1994.
44. Bertazzi and di Domenico, 1994.
45. Council of the European Communities, 'Council Directive of 24 June 1982 on the major accident hazards of certain industrial activities', *Off J Eur Communities* XX, L230/1–27, 1982.
46. Now the Czech Republic and Slovakia.
47. See IARC 1997 for a list of industrial accidents involving the manufacture of chlorinated phenols.
48. In an interview with Alastair Hay, 1968. See Hay, 1982.
49. See Schecter, A., and Gasiewicz, T., (eds), *Dioxins and Health*, 2nd edn, Wiley Interscience, 2003.
50. Blank, C., 'Bolsover project 1977–1978, Genetic damage' (unpublished); Martin, J., 'Report on a biochemical study carried out on workers at Coalite and Chemical Products Ltd, Chesterfield, Derbyshire' (unpublished); Ward, A., 'Investigation of the immune capability of workers previously exposed to 2,3,7,8-tetrachlorodibenzo-p-dioxin' (unpublished).

51. Walker, A., and Martin, J., 'Lipid profiles in dioxin exposed workers', *Lancet*, 1, 446, 1979.
52. Jenny Martin, interview with author, 1994, 1995, 1997.
53. Hay, A., 'Chemical company suppresses dioxin report', *Nature*, 284, 2, 1980.
54. Goss, interview, 1994, 1995.
55. See also *Sheffield Star* 24 April 1968, 30 July 1976, 2, 11 August 1976, 23 October 1976, 23, 31 December 1976; *Sheffield Telegraph* 17 May 1968, 7 August 1976, 10 September 1976, 8, 15 October 1976; *Derbyshire Times* 25 April 1968.
56. HSE, Coalite report, 1995.
57. The company were then known as Hoffman LaRoche.
58. Martin, interview, 1994, 1995, 1997.
59. Martin, interview, 1994, 1995, 1997.
60. When Mary Shelly wrote Frankenstein in the early years of the nineteenth century she wanted to show the inherent dangers in humanity's belief that science has the solution to everything, including the creation of life. See also Midgley M., *Science as Salvation: A Modern Myth and its Meaning*, Routledge, 1992.
61. Ken Sheldon, Coalite Head of Environment, Safety and Quality, interview with author, 1994.
62. Joe Holland, interview with author, 1994.
63. See Allen, R., 'Doctor I'm in trouble', *New Statesman & Society*, 6 May 1994.
64. Ann Link, interview with author, 1994.
65. Martin, interview, 1994.
66. Holland, interview, 1994.
67. Howard, V., Fetal and Infant Pathology, University of Liverpool, England.
68. Bertazzi, P. A., et al., 'Ten-year mortality study of the population involved in the Seveso incident in 1976', *Am J Epidemiol* 129: 1187–1200, 1989.
69. In the USA alone breast cancer kills 46,000 women each year. See *Rachel's Environment and Health Weekly* #571 to #575.
70. Bertazzi, P. A., and di Domenico, A., 'Health consequences of the Seveso, Italy, accident' in Schecter, 2003.
71. Crump, K., et al., 'Meta-analysis of dioxin cancer dose response for three occupational cohorts', *EHP*, 111, 5, May 2003; Fingerhut, M., et al., 'Cancer mortality in workers exposed to 2,3,7,8-TCDD', *N Eng J Med* 324: 212–218, 1991. A more complete report of this research is available under the title 'Mortality among US workers employed in the production of chemicals contaminated with 2,3,7,8-tetrachlorodibenzo-p-dioxin' from: NTIS, 5285 Port Royal Rd, Springfield, VA 22161 NTIS no: PB91-125971; Flesch-Janys, D., et al., 'Estimation of the cumulated exposure to polychlorinated dibenzo-p-dioxins/furans and standardized mortality ratio analysis of cancer mortality by dose in an occupationally exposed cohort', *EHP* 106 (suppl 2): 665–662, 1998; Ott, M. G., and Zober, A., 'Cause specific mortality and cancer incidence among employees exposed to 2,3,7,8-TCDD after a 1953 reactor accident', *Occup Environ Med* 53: 606–612, 1996; Steenland, K., et al., 'Cancer, heart disease, and diabetes

in workers exposed to 2,3,7,8-tetrachlorodibenzo-p-dioxin', *J Natl Cancer Inst* 91: 779–786, 1999; see also Becher, H., and Flesch-Janys, D., 'Dioxins and furans: epidemiologic assessment of cancer risks and other human health effects', *EHP Perspectives*, 106 (Suppl 2), 1998

72. Starr, T. B., 'Significant shortcomings of the U.S. Environmental Protection Agency's latest draft risk characterization for dioxin-like compounds', *Toxicol Sci* 64: 7–13, 2001.

73. Warner, M., 'Serum dioxin concentrations and breast cancer risk in the Seveso women's health study', *EHP*, 110, 7, 2002.

74. Mocarelli, P., 'Clinical and laboratory follow-up of TCDD exposed people: results and future studies'. Paper given at 'Chemistry, Man and Environment', University of Milan, 21 October 1996.

75. Caporase, N., and Landi, M. T., 'Elevated TCDD levels in females 20 years after an industrial accident in Seveso'. Paper given at 'Chemistry, Man and Environment', University of Milan, 21 October 1996.

76. The dioxin levels in the Missouri horse arenas were higher.

77. Serum levels of TCDD measured by Centers for Disease Control (CDC), Atlanta, USA.

78. Axelson, O., 'Seveso: disentangling the dioxin enigma?' *Epidem* 4 (5): 389–392, 1993.

79. Axelson, 1993.

CHAPTER 5: THE EPA

1. Armstrong, R., et al., 'Pentachlorophenol poisoning in a nursery for newborn infants', *J Ped* 75: 317–325, 1969.

2. Quoted in Thornton, J., 'Dioxin deception', *Greenpeace Magazine*, May/June 1991.

3. Birnbaum, L., 'Re-evaluation of dioxin: a presentation to the 102nd Meeting of the Great Lakes Water Quality Board', Chicago, Illinois, 15 July 1993.

4. See *Kemner et al.*, vs. *Monsanto*, 80-L-970 and *Kemner et al.*, vs. *Monsanto* Appeal, Appellate Court of Illinois No 5–88–0420, 1989.

5. Quoted in Van Strum/Merrell, *The Politics of Penta*, Greenpeace, 1989.

6. For a comprehensive account of the scandal surrounding alar see *Rachel's Environment & Health Weekly*, 'The true story of alar', #530–533, 23 January–13 February 1997.

7. Van Strum/Merrell, 1989.

8. USEPA, 'Dioxins', EPA 600/2–80–197, 1980.

9. Centre for Disease Control, NIOSH, Health hazard evaluation determination report no. 74–117–251, 1975.

10. USEPA, 'Dioxins', 1980.

11. USEPA, Notice of Rebuttable Presumption Against Registration of Pesticide Products Containing Pentachlorophenol, 43 Fed Reg 48443, 18 October 1978; see also Van Strum/Merrell, 1989.

12. Van Strum/Merrell, 1989.

13. See *NRDC* vs. *USEPA*, Civil no. 83–1509, Washington DC District Court.

14. Van Strum/Merrell, 1989.
15. The Great Lakes contain 18 per cent of the planet's fresh surface water. About 16 million people in the USA and Canada draw their drinking water from the lakes.
16. See USEPA Office of Inspector General, Report on Conflict of Interest Investigation of Deputy Administrator John Hernandez, File no 1–83–036, 14 July 1983.
17. See US House Hearing Report 98–81, EPA Investigation of Superfund and Agency Abuses, 1983.
18. See US House Hearing Report 98073, Hazardous Waste Contamination of Water Resources, Subcommittee on investigations and oversight, Committee on public works and transportation, US House, 98th Congress, 1st sesssion, 16–24 March 1983
19. For a more detailed account of the 2,4,5-T and pentachlorophenol campaigns see Van Strum/Merrell, *A Bitter Fog*, Sierra Club Books, 1983, Van Strum/Merrell, *No Margin of Safety*, Greenpeace 1987 and Van Strum/Merrell, 1989. See also EPA: 2,4,5-T and Silvex Products: Intent to cancel registrations, revocation of notices of intent to hold a hearing and statement of enforcement policy, Federal Register, 48 (202): 48434–37.
20. Dow had learned that when dioxin exceeded production specifications in the manufacture of the phenoxy herbicides birth defects would occur. See Zumwalt, Admiral E. R., 'Report to the secretary of the department of veterans affairs on the association between adverse health effects and exposure to Agent Orange', 5 May 1990.
21. In October 1988 at an industry conference, Dennis Lindsay, project manager of the organic chemicals division of Vulcan Chemicals boasted about their lobbying efforts that had led to the reassignment of Jenkins, noting that the EPA official's draft regulation if it had been accepted 'would have meant a certain end for the use of Penta, if not elimination of the entire wood preserving industry as we know it'. Speech to the Wood Pole Conference, 20–21 October 1988, Portland, Oregon. See Van Strum/Merrell, 1989.
22. Quoted in Van Strum/Merrell, 1989.
23. Jenkins, C., Memo to Raymond Loehr: Newly Revealed Fraud by Monsanto in an Epidemiological Study Used by EPA to Assess Human Health Effects from Dioxins, 23 February 1990.
24. Hay, A., to Rex Carr, 19 March 1990.
25. William Gaffey, who knew exactly how the Nitro studies had been put together, wasn't impressed by the coverage of Monsanto's alleged fraud and his role in it. But instead of suing for libel against someone like the *Washington Post* he picked on Peter Montague's publication. Gaffey wrote to Montague on 23 April demanding a retraction. 'You have repeated an accusation of fraud that you had better be able to prove. If Carr's brief has said that my methods were wrong or that my conclusions were in error, then by quoting it you would be citing someone's opinion, which is entirely proper. What you actually did was to print that "Zack and Gaffey deliberately and knowingly omitted 5 deaths from ..." which is quite another matter in my mind and that of an attorney with whom I discussed the issue.' Montague replied on 29 April requesting clarification

on the points in Gaffey's letter, concluding: 'I am sure you can appreciate that it is a journalist's responsibility to report such unpleasant facts as that one person has accused another person of scientific misdeeds in a matter that has great impact on public health and safety. I can only hope you will help me understand better the nature of the dispute(s) in this present matter. I assure you that, if I become convinced that Mr Carr has misrepresented you or your work in the court documents I quoted in *Rachel's Hazardous Waste News* #171, I will tell my readers about it and set the record straight.' Gaffey subsequently issued a lawsuit against Montague, which Gerson Smoger agreed to settle. Smoger: 'Peter had this law firm that was defending him on the First Amendment (free speech as guaranteed under the First Amendment of the U.S. Constitution). They lost the summary judgment. They then told Peter it was going to cost a couple hundred thousand dollars to represent him. And I said, "Peter I'll do it for free. But I want you to know that I don't want to defend this on First Amendment grounds, I want to defend this on you being right and it was a fraud." I deposed Gaffey, and Gaffey testified that they had no study protocol before doing the study. It was the only study that he was aware of that was ever done without a study protocol. If you don't have a study protocol and you're doing epidemiology and you're figuring out the protocol after you get all the statistics you can manipulate the things to find whatever you want. I think [Monsanto] were using that in a way to get this quick verdict against Peter and then they can come out with this public relations thing that their studies had been exonerated. When [Gaffey] passed away there was nothing further we were going to do even though it cost Peter a lot of time and a lot of money.' See 'Bill Gaffeys' Work' in the Appendix.

26. During the Kemner trial Monsanto's George Roush was questioned about a press release issued by the company on 9 October 1980 while facing litigation from the Sturgeon residents, workers at its Nitro, West Virginia factory, Vietnam vets and others in relation to dioxin exposure. The release referred to a study, which failed to link 'TCDD, the toxic dioxin contaminant in Agent Orange, and the cause of death of 58 employees potentially exposed to it during 2,4,5-T herbicide production at the company's Nitro, W. Va., plant'. Roush was asked whether this study left out half of the cancer deaths. He replied: 'Yes.' The press release also stated that the study was authored by Judith Zack and Raymond Suskind. But Suskind had refused to be listed as a co-author. It eventually came out under the names of Zack and Gaffey. Roush admitted that Gaffey had nothing to do with it but said he didn't know why Suskind had refused to be listed as co-author. See George Roush examined by Rex Carr, *Kemner et al.*, vs. *Monsanto*, 7, 8, 9 July, 1985. See also Monsanto news release from D. R., Bishop, Public Relations Department, 800 N Lindbergh Boulevard, St Louis, Missouri, 63166, 9 October 1980.

27. Memo, EPA Office of Criminal Investigation (OCI) 16 August 1990 (names blanked out).

28. Jenkins, C., Affidavit, *Ivy* vs. *Diamond Shamrock*, 3 September 1991.

29. Jenkins, C, Memo to West, J., and Guarino, K., OCI, 15 November 1990.

30. Jenkins, memo, 15 November 1990.
31. Greenpeace USA, 'Fraudulent and/or invalid human studies on effects of TCDD'. Petition before the USEPA, November 1990.
32. Thornton, J., and Costner, P., 'Science for sale: critique of Monsanto studies on worker health effects due to exposure to 2,3,7,8-TCDD', Greenpeace USA, 1990.
33. Roberts, L., 'Monsanto studies under fire', *Science* 261: 626.
34. Jenkins, C., Memo to West, J., and Guarino, K., OCI, 24 January 1991.
35. Bertazzi, et al., 1989.
36. Clapp, R. W., et al., 'Human Health Effects Associated with Exposure to Herbicides and/or Their Associated Contaminants (Chlorinated Dioxins) – A Review of the Scientific Literature', available from John Minnick, Public Relations Division, The American legion, 1608 K Street, NW, Washington, DC 20006, tel: 00 1 202 681 2790.
37. Rohleder, F., 'Dioxins and cancer mortality: reanalysis of the BASF cohort' (paper given at the 9th international dioxin symposium, Toronto, Canada, 1989).
38. Fingerhut, M., et al., 'Cancer mortality in workers exposed to 2,3,7,8-TCDD', *N Eng J Med* 324: 212–218, 1991. A more complete report of this research is available under the title 'Mortality among US workers employed in the production of chemicals contaminated with 2,3,7,8-tetrachlorodibenzo-p-dioxin' from NTIS, 5285 Port Royal Rd, Springfield, VA 22161 NTIS no: PB91-125971.
39. Manz, et al., 'Cancer mortality among workers in a chemical plant contaminated with dioxin', *Lancet* 338: 959–964, 1991.
40. See US Committee on Government Operations, 'The Agent Orange cover-up: a case of flawed science and political manipulation', Report 101–672, 9 August 1990.
41. Roberts, L., 'Flap erupts over dioxin meeting', *Science*, 251: 866, 1991.
42. This letter was entered into the public domain by Greenpeace at a public hearing on the dioxin reassessment that EPA held in Washington, DC, 15 November 1991.
43. Addendum, American Paper Institute in letter to William Reilly, EPA Administrator, 25 January 1991.
44. Silbergeld, E., letter to Witkowski, J., 29 January 1991.
45. Roberts, 1991.
46. Uhlenbrock, T., 'Dioxin scare now called a mistake', *St Louis Post Dispatch*, 23 May 1991. See also Uhlenbrock interview in *The Three River Confluence*, Fall 1997, PO Box 63232, St Louis, Missouri, MO 63163 and *In These Times*, 25 September 1992, which reported that Houk 'admitted copying virtually verbatim from paper industry documents in proposing relaxed standards for dioxin'; Schneider, K., 'US officials say dangers of dioxin were exaggerated', *New York Times*, 12 August 1991; and Monk, V., 'See No Evil', *American Journalism Review*, June 1993.
47. *New York Times*, 15 August 1991.
48. *Rachel's Environment and Health Weekly* #457, 31 August 1995.
49. Sanjour, W., memo to David Bussard, Characterisation and Assessment Division, EPA, 20 July 1994.
50. Montague, P., *Rachel's Hazardous Waste News* #400, 28 July 1994.

51. Sanjour, memo, 20 July 1994.
52. Bretthauer, E., et al., *Dioxin Perspectives*, Plenum, 1991.
53. See *Wall Street Journal*, 16 October 1992.
54. Paul Raeburn, 'Dioxin dangers', Associated Press (AP), 29 August 1993, and see *Rachel's Hazardous Waste News* #353, 2 September 1993.
55. *Rachel's Environment & Health Weekly* #463, 12 October 1995.

CHAPTER 6: TEARS IN THE VALLEYS

1. Macken, W., *Brown Lord of the Mountain*, Macmillan, 1968.
2. Mary Hanrahan, interview with author, 1990.
3. Johnson K. L., et al., 'Promotion of endometriosis in mice by polychlorinated dibenzo-p-dioxins, dibenzofurans, and biphenyls', *EHP*, 105 (7), 750–755, 1997; Mayani A., Barel S., Soback S., Almagor M., 'Dioxin concentrations in women with endometriosis', *Hum Reprod*, 12 (2), 373–375, 1997; Ringvold S., Rottingen J. A., 'Environmental pollutants with hormonal effects. Is estrogen theory a good model?', *Tidsskr Nor Laegeforen*, 117 (1), 66–70, 1997; Yang J. Z., Foster W. G., 'Continuous exposure to 2,3,7,8-tetrachlorodibenzo-p-dioxin inhibits the growth of surgically induced endometriosis in the ovariectomized mouse treated with high dose estradiol', *Toxicol Ind Health*, 13 (1), 15–25, 1997; Mann P. C., 'Selected lesions of dioxin in laboratory rodents', *Toxicol Pathol*, (1), 72–79, 1997; Cummings A. M., Metcalf J. L., Birnbaum L., 'Promotion of endometriosis by 2,3,7,8-tetrachlorodibenzo-p-dioxin in rats and mice: time-dose dependence and species comparison', *Toxicol Appl Pharmacol*, 38 (1), 131–139, 1996; Rier S. E., Martin D. C., Bowman R. E., Becker J. L., 'Immunoresponsiveness in endometriosis: implications of estrogenic toxicants', *EHP*, 103 Suppl 7: 151–156, 1995; Cummings A. M., Metcalf J. L., 'Induction of endometriosis in mice: a new model sensitive to estrogen', *Reprod Toxicol*, 9 (3), 233–238, 1995; Eskenazi B., Kimmel G., 'Workshop on perinatal exposure to dioxin-like compounds. II. Reproductive effects', *EHP*, 103 Suppl 2: 143–145, 1995; Koninckx P. R., Martin D., 'Treatment of deeply infiltrating endometriosis', *Curr Opin Obstet Gynecol*, 6 (3), 231–241, 1994; Koninckx P. R., Braet P., Kennedy S. H., Barlow D. H., 'Dioxin pollution and endometriosis in Belgium', *Hum Reprod*, 9 (6), 1001–1002, 1994; Bois F. Y., Eskenazi B., 'Possible risk of endometriosis for Seveso, Italy, residents: an assessment of exposure to dioxin', *EHP*, 102 (5), 476–477, 1994 (plus erratum in *EHP*, 102 (8), 627, 1994); Holloway M., 'An epidemic ignored. Endometriosis linked to dioxin and immunologic dysfunction', *Sci Am*, 270 (4), 24–26, 1994; 'Dioxin and endometriosis', *EHP*, 101 (7), 571–572, 1993; Gibbons A., 'Dioxin tied to endometriosis', *Science*, 262 (5138), 1373, 1993; Rier S. E., Martin D. C., Bowman R. E., Dmowski W. P., Becker J. L., 'Endometriosis in rhesus monkeys (Macaca mulatta) following chronic exposure to 2,3,7,8-tetrachlorodibenzo-p-dioxin', *Fundam Appl Toxicol*, 21 (4), 433–441, 1993.
4. This was the rumour that went around the Irish Four Courts Law Library in the aftermath of the decision.

5. For a fuller account of what happened to the Hanrahans see Allen, R., *No Global*, Pluto, 2004.
6. *Magill*, August 1988.
7. Byron L. Rowe, General Manager MSD, letter to James O'Callaghan, County Engineer, Tipperary (South Riding) County Council, 6 November 1981.
8. (Irish) Supreme Court judgement of Justice Henchy, 5 July 1988; *Mary Hanrahan, John Hanrahan and Seline Hanrahan* vs. *Merck Sharp & Dohme (Ireland) Limited* 1982 No 2138P and 1985 No 316.
9. Quoted in *The Clonmel Nationalist*, 9 July 1988.
10. *Andrew Graham* vs. *ReChem International Ltd*, 1996, Env LR D11.
11. Interview with Graham's solicitor, 1995.
12. Browne in *Graham* vs. *ReChem*.
13. Martyn Day, interview with author, 1994.
14. Day, interview, 1994.
15. Tim Barton, interview with author, 1995.
16. Directive 2000/76/EC. See also http://europa.eu.int/comm/environment/wasteinc/.
17. Gerhard Stolpa, interview with author, 1993.
18. This was the view during the 1990s but it was not always the case. In 1987 a report on experiments at an incinerator in Pittsfield, Massachusetts into the relationships between combustion conditions, garbage constituents, and dioxin production found no evidence that the amount of PVC plastic in the garbage affects the amount of dioxin produced. See 'Results of the combustion and emissions research project at the Vicon incinerator facility in Pittsfield, Massachusetts', NYSERDA Report 87–16, June 1987, available from Department of Communications, NY State Energy R&D Authority, Two Rockefeller Plaza, Albany, NY 12223.
19. The USEPA noted in 1994 that dioxin is produced in combustion processes as a result of three activities that are not mutually exclusive. '(1) The feed material to the combustor contains CDDs and CDFs and some portion survives the thermal stress imposed by the heat of the incineration or combustion process, and is subsequently emitted from the stack. While this explanation is not thought to be the principal explanation for dioxin and furan emissions from combustor sources (explanations 2 and 3 below are thought to be the predominant cause of these emissions), in fact it is the single theory best thought to explain the release of the dioxin-like, coplanar PCBs. (2) CDDs/CDFs are ultimately formed from the thermal breakdown and molecular rearrangement of precursor compounds. Precursor compounds are chlorinated aromatic hydrocarbons having a structural resemblance to the CDD/CDF molecule. Among the precursors that have been identified are polychlorinated biphenyls (PCBs), chlorinated phenols (CPs), and chlorinated benzenes (CBs). The formation of CDDs/CDFs is believed to occur after the precursor has condensed and adsorbed onto the binding sites on the surface of fly ash particles. The active sites of the surface of fly ash particles promote the chemical reactions forming CDDs/CDFs. These reactions have been observed to be catalysed by the presence of inorganic chlorides sorbed to the particulate. Temperature in a range

of 250–450°C has been identified as a necessary condition for these reactions to occur, with either lower or higher temperatures inhibiting the process. Therefore, the precursor theory focuses on the region of the combustor that is downstream and away from the high temperature zone of the furnace or combustion chamber. This is a location where the gases and smoke derived from combustion of the organic materials have cooled during conduction through flue ducts, heat exchanger and boiler tubes, air pollution control equipment or the stack. (3) CDDs/CDFs are synthesized *de novo* in the same region of the combustion process as described in (2), e.g. the so-called cool zone. In this theory, CDDs/CDFs are formed from moieties bearing little resemblance to the molecular structure of CDDs and CDFs. In broad terms, these are non-precursors and include such diverse substances as petroleum products, chlorinated plastics (PVC), non-chlorinated plastics (polystyrene), cellulose, lignin, coke, coal, particulate carbon, and hydrogen chloride gas. Formation of CDDs/CDFs requires the presence of a chlorine donor (a molecule that provides a chlorine atom to the pre-dioxin molecule) and the formation and chlorination of a chemical intermediate that is a precursor. The primary distinction between theories (2) and (3) is that theory (2) requires the presence of precursor compounds in the feed material whereas theory (3) begins with the combustion of diverse substances that are not defined as precursors, which eventually react to form precursors and eventually, dioxin-like molecules.'

20. Costner, P., 'PVC – The Poison Plastic, The Burning Question, Chlorine & Dioxin', Greenpeace International, April 1997.
21. Rigo, H. G., et al., *The Relationship Between Chlorine in Waste Streams and Dioxin Emissions from Waste Combustor Stacks*, American Society of Mechanical Engineers, 1995.
22. Costner, 1997.
23. On Monday 24 November 1997 in response to a debate about incineration and recycling Jon Campbell posted the following to dioxin list subscribers on the internet. 1. Incineration does not eliminate landfilling. Up to one-third of the original weight and volume of waste is left behind as toxic ash, which must be landfilled. 2. Incineration creates substances far more toxic than the original landfill material, which contaminate the rest. The combustion of PVC produces massive amounts of chlorinated aromatics, among them the most toxic organic chemicals on earth, the polychlorinated dibenzo dioxins and dibenzo furans (collectively called 'dioxin'). A large percentage of dioxin ends up in the fly ash, making it an incredibly hazardous material. Heavy metals from ordinary batteries (such as cadmium and mercury) and other products also heavily contaminate the ash. (Note that the U.S. Supreme Court ruled that incinerator ash was to be classified as hazardous waste. The U.S. EPA, in a huge giveaway to save the incinerator industry, offered an alternative ash handling and testing scheme, thereby making the ash non-hazardous by political rather than technical means. The EPA allowed the mixing of bottom ash with fly ash, which, through the addition of lime, temporarily binds heavy metals. The EPA then went on to specify a non-acidic leaching test … .) 3. Incinerators are the largest sources of dioxin and mercury

in the air. 4. Because of the nature of trash hauling, incinerators divert public money to private companies. Because incinerator operators are perceived of doing a public service (trash 'disposal') they are paid handsomely (and, in some cases, royally) from the public coffers. The amount typically spent to build and run an incinerator is an order of magnitude larger than a similar collection of facilities built to accomplish comprehensive (near-100 per cent) recycling. 5. 'Current' pollution control techniques merely divert some of the dioxin and heavy metals from the air to the ash. Taken together: 1. Incinerators do not accomplish what the municipalities intend – to stop the landfilling of trash. Instead, incinerators turn municipal trash into toxic ash. (sort of catchy, isn't it?) 2. Incinerators divert public funds to private corporations and bond-holders. 3. Incinerators create an environmental nightmare, both in requiring toxic ash landfills that require monitoring for eternity, and in creating massive air pollution.

24. Throughout the 1990s several institutions, government agencies and departments recommended the reduction or elimination of chlorine from incineration and combustion waste streams. See also, Air Pollution Abatement Review Group, Report on the Abatement of Toxic Organic Micropollutants (TOMPS) from Stationary Sources 1995, Prepared at the request of Air Quality Division, Department of the Environment, AEA Technology, National Technology Centre, Abingdon, Oxfordshire, England, 1995; Intergovernmental Forum on Chemical Safety, IFCS Ad Hoc Working Group on Persistent Organic Pollutants Meeting: Final Report, Geneva: IFCS Secretariat, c/o World Health Organization, 21–22 June 1996; United Nations Environmental Programme, International Action to Protect Human Health and the Environment Through Measures Which Will Reduce and/or Eliminate Emissions and Discharges of Persistent Organic Pollutants, Including the Development of an International, Legally-Binding Instrument, Decision Taken By Nineteenth Session of the UNEP Governing Council, Nairobi, 7 February, 1997, Geneva: United Nations Environmental Programme, February 1997; American Public Health Association, Resolution Adopted at the 124th Annual Meeting, New York City, New York, 20 November 1996; Central Pollution Control Board, Ministry of Environment and Forests, Government of India, Environmental Standards and Guidelines for Management of Hazardous Waste, New Delhi, India, 12 July 1996; International Joint Commission, Seventh Biennial Report on Great Lakes Water Quality, 1994.

EPILOGUE: CHALLENGING POWER AND MONEY

1. Schecter, A., et al., 'Congener-specific levels of dioxins and dibenzofurans in US food and estimated daily dioxin toxic equivalent intake', *EHP*, 102: 962–966, 1994.
2. Kiviranta, H., et al., 'Polychlorinated dibenzo-p-dioxins, dibenzofurans, and biphenyls in fishermen in Finland', *EHP*, 110, 4, 2002.
3. Patandin, S., et al., 'Dietary exposure to polychlorinated biphenyls and dioxins from infancy until adulthood: a comparison between breast-feeding, toddler, and long-term exposure', *EHP*, 107, 1, 1999.

4. Bookchin, M., (writing as Lewis Herber), 'The problems of chemicals in food', *Contemporary Issues*, vol 3, no12, 1952 and 'A follow-up on the problem of chemicals', *CI*, vol 6, no21, 1955. See also: *Our Synthetic Environment* (Knopf 62, Cape 63).

5. Biomagnification occurs when each dose is increased every time it is absorbed into a new body. For example, during the mid-1950s to counteract pests, Dutch Elms in the USA were sprayed with DDT. Earthworms ate the DDT-contaminated leaves. Robins unwarily ate the poisoned earthworms and suffered the consequences. By the time the pesticide had reached the bodies of the birds it had magnified hundreds of times. Over a period of three years more than 1,000 dead birds were reported.

6. Carson, 1962.

7. See Whiteside, T., *Defoliation*, Ballantine/Foe, 1970; *Withering Rain*, Dutton, 1971; *The Pendulum and the Toxic Cloud*, Yale, 1979. Also see Bionetics Research Laboratories, 'Evaluation of the carcinogenic, teratogenic and mutagenic activity of selected pesticides and industrial chemicals', 1969. And see Van Strum, C., *A Bitter Fog*, Sierra Clum Books, 1983.

8. See Van Strum, 1983, Van Strum/Merrell, *The Politics of Penta*, Greenpeace, 1989.

9. Hay, A., *The Chemical Scythe*, 1982.

10. Commoner, B., Keynote address at 2nd Citizens Dioxin Conference, St Louis. Published in *Dioxin: The Orange Resource Book* or from Center for the Biology of Natural Systems, CUNY.

11. The endocrine system consists of specialised cells, tissues and organs that create and secrete, usually into the blood, biological chemicals known as hormones – the body's chemical messengers – which in turn regulate the bodily functions necessary for life. It is the endocrine system that starts the female menstrual cycle and in a developing foetus it is the endocrine system that regulates cell division and organ differentiation. When synthetic chemicals enter the bodies of humans, animals and wildlife, largely through the food chain, they mimic hormones. What Colborn and her colleagues discovered is that the body mistakes these environmental hormones for natural hormones. The body's natural hormones carry a specific biological message and are then dispatched from the blood steam. However these environmental hormones remain in the body for long periods, causing continual biological destruction.

12. Wyrobek, A., et al., 'An evaluation of human sperm as indicators of chemically induced alterations of spermatogenic function', *Mutation Res* 115: 73–148, 1983; Carlsen, E., et al., 'Evidence for decreasing quality of semen during the past 50 years', *British Medical Journal*, 305: 609–613, 1992; Sharpe, R., and Skakkebaek, N., 'Are oestrogens involved in falling sperm counts and disorders of the male reproductive tract?' *Lancet*, 341: 1392–1395, 29 May, 1993; Sharpe, R., 'Declining sperm counts in men – is there an endocrine cause?' *Journal of Endocrinology*, 136: 357–360, 1993; Swan, S., et al., 'Have sperm densities declined? A reanalysis of global trend data', *Environ Health Per*, 105: 1228–1232, 1997; Sharpe, R., et al., 'Gestational and lactational exposure of rats to xenoestrogens results in reduced testicular size and sperm production', *Environ Health*

Per, 103 (12): 1136–1143, 1995. In Europe it is falling 1 per cent a year, in the USA 1.5 per cent a year.

13. Harris, J. R., et al., 'Breast cancer', *N Eng J Med*, 327 (5): 319–328, 1992; El-Bayoumy, K., 'Environmental carcinogens that may be involved in human breast cancer etiology', *Chem Res Tox*, 5 (5): 585–590, 1992.

14. Danish Environmental Protection Agency, 'Male reproductive health and environmental chemicals with estrogenic effects'. Miljo-Kopenhawn, Denmark (April 1995); Giwercman, A., and Skakkebaek, N., 'The human testis – an organ at risk?' *International Journal of Andrology*, 15: 373–375.

15. Of all the scientists associated with Colborn, it is the research of Richard Peterson and Robert Moore that is the most alarming. See Peterson, R., et al., 'Male reproductive system ontogeny; effects of perinatal exposure to 2,3,7,8-TCDD' in Colborn, T. and Clement, C., (eds), *Chemically-induced Alterations in Sexual and Functional Development: The Wildlife/Human Connection*, Princeton Sci, 1992. Operating out of the School of Pharmacy and the Environmental Toxicology Center at the University of Wisconsin, these two toxicologists, through their exhaustive research, discovered that dioxin does not just cause cancer. From their research they learned that it acts like a persistent hormone at very low levels – levels similar to those presently being found in humans. Linda Birnbaum, one of the scientists who led the EPA's 1991 reassessment of dioxin, said she was also concerned about the chemical compound's impact on the human immune system, 'that much lower exposure to dioxin may result in adverse health effects that are very subtle and difficult to detect'. Quoted in *Science News*, 24–27, 11 January 1992.

16. Eaton, S. B., et al., 'Women's reproductive cancers in evolutionary context', *Q Rev Bio*, 69 (3): 353–367, 1994; Whitten, P. L., 'Chemical revolution to sexual revolution: historical changes in human reproductive development' in Colborn and Clement, 1992; Rier, S. E., et al., 'Endometriosis in rhesus monkeys following chronic exposure to TCDD', *Fund App Tox*, 21: 433–441, 1993.

17. Colborn and Clement, 1992; see also Colborn, vom Saal and Soto, 'Developmental effects of endocrine-disrupting chemicals in wildlife and humans', *Environmental Health Perspectives*, 101 (5): 378–384, Oct 1993; and Colborn and others, 'Great Lakes, Great Legacy?', Conservation Foundation, Washington DC, 1990. Chemicals known to disrupt the endocrine system, Dr Colborn and her colleagues agreed, include: '2,4-D, 2,4,5-T, alachlor, amitrole, atrazine, metribuzin, nitrofen, trifluralin, benomyl, hexachlorobenzene, mancozeb, maneb, metiram-complex, tributyl tin, zinab, ziram, beta-HCH, carbaryl, chlordane, dicofol, diedrin, DDT and metabolites, endosulfan, heptachlor and heptachlor epoxide, lindane (gamma-HCH), methomyl, methoxychlor, mirex, oxychlordane, parathion, synthetic pyrethriods, toxaphene, transmonachlor, aldicarb, DBCP, cadmium, dioxin (TCDD), lead, mercury, PBBs, PCBs, pentachlorophenol (PCP), penta- to nonylphenols, phthalates, styrenes.'

18. See Schecter, A., (ed.), *Dioxins and Health*, Plenum, 1994.

19. Bertazzi, P. A. et al., 'Mortality in an area contaminated by TCDD following an industrial accident', *Med Lav* 80 (4), 316–329, 1989; Bertazzi, et al., 'Ten-year mortality study of population involved in the Seveso incident

in 1976', *Am J Epidemiol* 6: 507, 1989; Bertazzi, 'Industrial disasters and epidemiology', *Scand J Work Environ Health*, 15, 85–100, 1989; Bertazzi, 'Long term effects of chemical disasters. Lessons and results from Seveso', *Sci T Environ*, 106, 5–20, 1991; Bertazzi et al., 'Mortality of a young population after accidental exposure to 2,3,7,8-TCDD', *Int J Epi*, 21 (1), 118–123, 1992; Pesatori et al., 'Cancer in a young population in a dioxin-contaminated area', *Int J Epi*, 22 (6), 1010–1013, 1993; Bertazzi, et al., 'Cancer incidence in a population accidently exposed to 2,3,7,8 TCDD', *Epidemiology* 4 (5): 398–406, 1993; Bertazzi and di Domenico, 'Chemical, environmental, and health aspects of the Seveso, Italy, accident' in Schecter, 1994; Pesatori, 'Dioxin contamination in Seveso: the social tragedy and the scientific challenge', *Med Lav*, 86 (2), 111–124, 1995; Landi et al., 'Concentrations of dioxin 20 years after Seveso', *Lancet*, 349, 21 June 1997; Bertazzi et al., 'Dioxin exposure and cancer risk: a 15-year mortality study after the Seveso accident', *Epidemiology*, 8 (1), 1997; Pesatori et al., 'Dioxin exposure and non-malignant health effects: a mortality study', *OEM*, 1997; See also IARC, Vol 69, *PCDDs and PCDFs*, Lyon, France. And see Hay, 1982, Whiteside, 1979; Margerison, et al., *The Superpoison*, Macmillan, 1979; Cook and Kaufman, 1982.

20.   Rohleder, F., 'Dioxins and cancer mortality: reanalysis of the BASF cohort' (paper given at the 9th international dioxin symposium, Toronto, Canada, 1989) 1989; Epstein, S., 'Problems of causality, burdens of proof and restitution: Agent Orange diseases', Trial, November 1983, 91–99/137–138. Epstein noted that 'the symptomatology and effects induced by TCDD reflect a wide range of factors including dosage or exposure levels, duration of exposure, presence of other toxic chemicals and contaminants, and age, sex and reproductive status of exposed populations'; Epstein, S. S., Moss, R. W., and Wiewel, F. D., 1991, 'People Against Cancer: New Directions in Cancer', Monograph, Otho; IARC publish regular statistics and reports from Lyon, France.

21.   It's all the more stunning because it is not new, as Steingraber discovered. 'Cancers of all types and all causes display even under already existing conditions, all the characteristics of an epidemic in slow motion,' wrote Hueper and Conway, two senior scientists at the National Cancer Institute in the USA, in 1964. The reason for this epidemic? 'Increasing contamination of the human environment with chemical and physical carcinogens and with chemicals supporting and potentiating their action.' See Hueper, W., and Conway, C., *Chemical Carcinogenesis and Cancers*, Charles Thomas, 1964 quoted in Steingraber, S., *Living Downstream*, Addison-Wesley, 1997.

22.   Schecter, A., et al., 'Exposure assessment: measurement of dioxins and related chemicals in human tissues', in Schecter, A., and Gasiewicz, T. (eds), *Dioxins and Health*, 2nd edn, Wiley Interscience, 2003.

23.   Gerson Smoger, interview with C. D. Stelzer on behalf of author, 2003.

24.   The World Health Organisation has estimated that there are a minimum of three million acute severe cases of pesticide poisonings and 20,000 unintentional deaths each year. This excludes chronic pesticide poisoning – which, according to one report, may affect up to 25 million agricultural workers in the so-called developing world.{1} Workers regularly exposed

to pesticides have reported symptoms such as anxiety, sleep disturbance, depression and severe headaches while the increase in various cancers among communities exposed to pesticides has alarmed GPs. Dr K. T. Shenoy of the Thiruvanathapuram Medical College in India noted cancers of the lip, stomach, skin and brain, leukaemia, lymphoma and multiple myeloma among the farmers in Kuttanad – an area that has seen an increase of pesticide consumption from 1,200 tonnes in 1972 to 13,400 tonnes in 1980. – 1. Jeyaratnam, J., 'Acute pesticide poisoning: a major problem', *World Health Statistics Quarterly*, 43: 139–144, 1990.

25. Within 25 years from the end of the 1939–45 war more than 500 pesticides were introduced to the market, for use as weed killers on crops, trees and brush land and as pest and fungi control in commercial and domestic agriculture – in 1991 cotton crops accounted for 11 per cent of all pesticide use. See *Agrow*, World Crop Protection News No 161 (10/7/92), No 165 (7/8/92).

26. Farm workers are not stupid. They know that if they are employed by someone else and make a fuss about protective clothing, it's up the road for them, but they also know how difficult it is to work with sprays. The chemical has to be diluted, an action that is virtually impossible to achieve without splashing, It then has to be carried over awkward terrain. It's easy to imagine the sealed containers of today but in the decades when phenoxy herbicide sprays like 2,4,5-T, 2,4-D and silvex were first used, leaking canisters were common. Sprayers often walked through areas that had already been sprayed. And the spraying itself was fraught with danger. Users were advised not to spray during windy conditions but as one farm worker noted, 'find me anyone who has stood in a 60 acre field and found there was no wind'. As Cook and Kaufman stress, 'there is no way of anticipating wind changes, gusts, circular motions and changes in direction' and add that users are often simply unaware of the directions for use or, if they are aware of them, find that they are working under so much pressure that it is easier to ignore them. 'The experts may know the risks of 2,4,5-T. They may handle the stuff properly. So they tell us we'll be alright if we use the spray "normally", but have they any idea what "normally" means in the field,' is the farm worker's response. 'My experience is that nobody really knows what the dangers are, what is relatively okay.' See Cook and Kaufman, 1982 for the account of the campaign to ban 2,4,5-T in Britain.

27. See among other sources Lester Brown's *State of the World*, Norton, 1998 and subsequent editions.

28. Among the arguments that would be made include the assertion that organochlorines are also created naturally. Allsop and colleagues in the Greenpeace report *Body of Evidence* made this counter-argument. 'Approximately 1,200 compounds which contain chlorine or its related elements bromine or fluorine (which are known collectively as organohalogens) are created by some living organisms and other natural processes. These compounds have been isolated from bacteria, fungi, marine algae and a few have been found in higher plants and animals. Naturally produced organochlorines are not persistent, and nearly all are produced in very small quantities. One exception, chloromethane, the

simplest of the organochlorines, is primarily produced by marine algae at the rate of 5 million tons per year. It is thought that this organochlorine may play a part in regulating the ozone layer.' See Allsop, et al., 'Body of Evidence', Greenpeace International, May 1995.

29. Arnold Schecter gathered data on dioxin levels in human tissue from nine diverse geographical locations – from the USA, Germany, Vietnam, the former Soviet Union, Thailand, Cambodia, China, South Africa and the south Pacific island of Guam. Commenting on the Dow Chemical company's 1980 paper, 'Trace chemistries of fire: a source of chlorinated dioxins' (Bumb, *Science* 210: 385–390 (1980)) – which claimed that dioxins have always been ubiquitous in the environment because of natural phenomena – Schecter stated: 'The question as to whether chlorinated dioxin and dibenzofurans existed before industrialisation and formation is addressed in two ways by human tissue data. The higher levels of PCDD/Fs found in tissue from industrial countries and lower levels in samples from less industrialised countries suggests industrial origins for most PCDD/Fs. Compared to present adult levels, the finding of quite low levels of PCDD/Fs in frozen ancient Eskimo tissue from the United States, similiar to levels found in stillborns at the present time, is also consistent with an anthropological (human-made) origin of almost all dioxins and dibenzofurans in the environment' (Schecter, A. et al., 'Chlorinated dioxins and dibenzofurans in human tissue from general populations: a selective review', *EHP* 102, Suppl 1: 159–171, 1994). Schecter was simply confirming what the Indiana University researchers Jean Czuczwa and Ronald Hites had shown in 1985 with their study of Lake Huron sediments, that 'the high levels of PCDD and PCDF presently accumulating in the sedimentary environment can reflect only anthropogenic combustion ... of chlorinated precursors present in combustion fuels'.

30. Czuczwa, J. M., McVeety, B. D., and Hites, R. A., 'Polychlorinated dibenzo-p-dioxins and dibenzofurans in sediments from Siskiwit Lake, Isle Royale', *Science* 226, 1984; Czuczwa, J. M., and Hites, R. A., 'Environmental fate of combustion-generated polychlorinated dioxins and furans', *Environ Sci Techol*, 18:6: 444–450, 1984; Czuczwa, J. M., and Hites, R. A., 'Historical record of polychlorinated dioxins and furans in Lake Huron sediments', in: Keith, L. H., Rappe, C., and Choudhary, G., (eds) *Chlorinated Dioxins and Dibenzofurans in the Total Environment*. Butterworth Publishers, Boston, MA. 59–63, 1985; Czuczwa, J. M., and Hites, R. A., 'Sources and fate of PCDD and PCDF', *Chem* 15: 1417–1420, 1986; Schecter, A., et al, 'Chlorinated dioxin and dibenzofuran levels in sediments collected from rivers in Vietnam', *Chem* 18: 831–834, 1989; Schecter, A., et al., 'Levels of 2,3,7,8-TCDD in silt samples collected between 1985–86 from rivers in the north and south Vietnam', *Chem* 19 (1/6): 547–550, 1989; Schecter, A., et al., 'Sources of dioxin in the environment: a study of PCDDs and PCDFs in ancient, frozen Eskimo tissue', *Chem* 17: 627–631, 1987 and Tong, H. Y., et al., 'Sources of dioxin in the environment: second stage study of PCDD/Fs in ancient human tissue and environmental samples', *Chem* 20 (7/9): 987–992, 1990.

31. Bosshardt, H. P., 'Dioxine – Heimtuckische Gifte in unserer Umwelt (Entstehung, Eigenschaften und Verhalten von polychloreierten Dibenzo-p-dioxine)', *Neue Zurcher Zeitung*, Forschung und Technik, 2/12/73.

32. Allsop and colleagues describe risk assessment as 'at its core, a series of mathematical equations which are used to estimate the emissions of a chemical, human exposure to the chemical and finally the health effects from such exposure'. Allsop, et al., 1995.

33. See Van Strum/Merrell, 1989 and Thornton, J., 'Dioxin deception', *Greenpeace Magazine*, May/June 1991.

34. USEPA memo, from Erich Bretthauer, assistant administrator for research and development, to EPA chief administrator William Reilly (9 October 1992). See also *Wall St Journal*, 'Dioxin's health risks may be greater than believed, EPA memo indicates', 16 October 1992.

35. Thornton, J., 'Comments on USEPA dioxin reassessment', Greenpeace USA, Washington, DC, 13 January 1995.

36. International Joint Commission on the Great Lakes, Seventh Biennial Report, IJC, 1994. See also the Sixth and Eighth reports.

37. See Marshall McLuhan's *Understanding Media*, Routledge, London, 1963 (1993).

Further Reading

This book can never be anything more than a glance at the history of dioxin. A serious history of dioxin would run to many volumes so any serious student of dioxin and its toxicological, epidemiological and social political history would need a spare year or more to read the vast library of scientific literature on the subject. If you are such a person you will need to start with the following books. Despite the obvious perspective I have taken with the complex history of dioxin, this list is not based on subjective choice. It includes a selection of documents from many perspectives with clear biases, but it also embraces the key objective reports from scientists, epidemiologists, researchers and activists.

Ashford, N. A. and Millar, C. S., *Chemical Exposures: Low Levels, High Stakes*, Van Nostrand Reinhold, London, 1991/1998.

Bretthauer, E. W. (ed), *Dioxin Perspectives*, Plenum, 1991.

Colborn, T. and Clement, C. (eds), *Chemically-induced Alterations in Sexual and Functional Development: the Wildlife/Human Connection*, Princeton Sci, 1992.

Colborn, T., Myers, D. and Dumanoski, J. P., *Our Stolen Future*, Little Brown, 1996.

Cook, J. and Kaufman, C., *Portrait of a Poison: The story of 2,4,5-T*, Pluto, 1982.

Epstein, S., *The Politics of Cancer*, Sierra Club, 1978/98.

Esser, C. and Gleichmann, E. (eds), *Dioxins and the Immune System*, Karger, 1994.

Fagin, D. and Lavelle, M., *Toxic Deception: How the Chemical Industry Manipulates Science, Bends the Law, and Endangers your Health*, Carol Publishing Group, Secaucus, NJ, 1996.

Hay, A., *The Chemical Scythe*, Plenum, 1982.

US Inst of Medicine, *Veterans and Agent Orange*, Nat Acad Publishers, 1994/1996.

Keith, L., *Chlorinated Dioxins and Dibenzofurans in the Total Environment*, Ann Arbor Science, 1983.

Kimbrough, R. D., (ed.), *Halogenated Biphenyls, Terphenyls, Naphtalenes, Dibenzodioxins and Related Products*, Elsevier 1980.

Margerison, T., Wallace, M. and Hallenstein, D. *The Superpoison*, Macmillan, 1979.

Mellanby, K., *DDT Story*, British Crop Protection Soc, 1992.

Rappe, C. (ed.), *Environmental Carcinogens, vII Dioxins and Furans*, IARC, 1991.

Schecter, A. (ed.), *Dioxins and Health*, Plenum, 1994.

Schecter, A. and Gasiewicz, T. (eds), *Dioxins and Health*, second edition, Wiley Interscience, 2003.

Schuck, P. H., *Agent Orange on Trial*, Harvard UP, 1988.

Steingraber, S., *Living Downstream*, Addison Wesley, 1997.
Van Strum, C., *A Bitter Fog*, Sierra Club Books, 1983.
Van Strum, C., *No Margin of Safety*, Greenpeace, 1987.
Van Strum, C., *The Politics of Penta*, Greenpeace, 1989.
Whiteside, T., *Defoliation*, Ballantine/Foe, 1970.
Whiteside, T., *Withering Rain*, Dutton, 1971.
Whiteside, T., *The Pendulum and the Toxic Cloud*, Yale, 1979.
World Health Organisation, *Dioxins and Furans*, WHO, 1990.
Young, A. and Reggiani, G., (eds), *Agent Orange*, Elsevier, 1988.

A companion bibliography, regularly updated, on dioxin is available from the author: atgrallen@yahoo.com

Index

Compiled by Sarah Chambers